Waterbirds in the UK 2010/11
The Wetland Bird Survey

Chas Holt, Graham Austin, Neil Calbrade,
Heidi Mellan, Richard Hearn, David Stroud,
Simon Wotton & Andy Musgrove

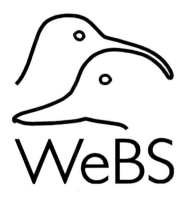

WeBS

Published by

British Trust for Ornithology,
Royal Society for the Protection of Birds
and Joint Nature Conservation Committee
in association with
Wildfowl & Wetlands Trust

September 2012

ISBN 978-1-906204-33-4
ISSN 1755-6384

This publication should be cited as:
Holt, C.A., Austin, G.E., Calbrade, N.A., Mellan, H.J., Hearn, R.D., Stroud, D.A., Wotton, S.R. & Musgrove, A.J. 2012. *Waterbirds in the UK 2010/11: The Wetland Bird Survey*. BTO/RSPB/JNCC, Thetford.

Published by: BTO, RSPB and JNCC in association with WWT. **www.bto.org/webs**

Cover: *Winter Trio: Pintails* - Thelma Sykes.
Thelma was born in Yorkshire and now lives in Cheshire close to the Dee Estuary – a source of both inspiration and subject matter. She came to print-making without formal training, but has become one of the most respected artists in that medium. Elected to the Society of Wildlife Artists (in the Federaton of British Artists) in 1999, her prints are now held in many collections including the Mall Galleries in London. Some of Thelma's prints have also been used on BTO merchandise.

Photos: Dawn Balmer, John Bowers, Neil Calbrade, Edmund Fellowes, gray-images.co.uk, John Harding, Tommy Holden, Howard Lacey, Amy Lewis, Jill Pakenham, Rob Robinson, Glyn Sellors, Howard Vaughan

Artwork: Jack Ashton-Booth, C.J.F. Coombs, Thelma Sykes

Produced by: BTO

Printed by: Swallowtail Print, Drayton Industrial Park, Taverham Road, Norwich NR8 6RL. www.swallowtailprint.co.uk

Available from: BTO, The Nunnery, Thetford, Norfolk IP24 2PU, UK.

This report is provided free to all WeBS counters and those who participate in the other national waterbird surveys, none of whom receive financial reward for their invaluable work. Additional feedback is provided to counters through the annual WeBS Newsletter. For further information please contact the WeBS Office at the BTO: **webs@bto.org**

ACKNOWLEDGEMENTS

This book represents the twenty-ninth report of the Wetland Bird Survey and comprises information from WeBS and complementary national and local surveys, *e.g.* goose censuses. It is entirely dependent on the many thousands of dedicated volunteer ornithologists who supply the data, and to whom we are extremely grateful. The Local Organisers who coordinate these counts deserve special thanks for their contribution.

We are also grateful to the following individuals and groups for providing technical assistance, supplementary information and additional data, or comments on draft texts:

Niall Burton, Lee Cadwell, Nigel Clark, Mark Collier, Aonghais Cook, COWRIE, Olivia Crowe, Diana de Palacio, Iain Downie, Simon Gillings, Matthew Guillemain, Colette Hall, Mark Hammond, Paul Harrup, Paul Harvey, Martin Heubeck, Maria Knight, John Marchant, Carl Mitchell, Nick Moran, Deborah Procter, Warren Read, Jim Reid, Marcia Sayer, John Shillitoe, Judith Smith, Ron Summers, Richard Thewlis, Rick Vonk, Chris Waltho, Colin Wells, Linda Wilson, Ilka Win, and Karen Wright. Many amateur observers also provide reports of their studies; these are acknowledged within the text.

Grateful thanks to all and apologies to anyone who has inadvertently been missed.

Any maps partially based on Ordnance Survey products have been reproduced with the permission of the controller of HMSO. © Crown copyright. All rights reserved. Licence Number 100021787.

THE WETLAND BIRD SURVEY
Organised and funded by:

British Trust for Ornithology
The Nunnery, Thetford, Norfolk IP24 2PU
www.bto.org

Royal Society for the Protection of Birds
The Lodge, Sandy, Bedfordshire SG19 2DL
www.rspb.org.uk

Joint Nature Conservation Committee
Monkstone House, City Road, Peterborough
PE1 1JY
www.jncc.org.uk

in association with
Wildfowl & Wetlands Trust
Slimbridge, Gloucestershire GL2 7BT
www.wwt.org.uk

WETLAND BIRD SURVEY CONTACTS

WeBS Counter Network: Heidi Mellan
WeBS Core Counts: Chas Holt
WeBS Low Tide Counts: Neil Calbrade
General queries: webs@bto.org

WeBS Office
British Trust for Ornithology
The Nunnery
Thetford
Norfolk IP24 2PU, UK
Tel: 01842 750050
Fax: 01842 750030
E-mail: firstname.surname@bto.org
or webs@bto.org
www.bto.org/webs

GOOSE & SWAN CENSUSES
Organised and funded by: Wildfowl & Wetlands Trust, Joint Nature Conservation Committee and Scottish Natural Heritage.

Contact: Carl Mitchell
E-mail: Carl.Mitchell@wwt.org.uk
or monitoring@wwt.org.uk

Wildfowl & Wetlands Trust
Slimbridge
Gloucestershire GL2 7BT, UK
Tel: 01453 891225
Fax: 01453 891901
www.wwt.org.uk/speciesmonitoring

OTHER NATIONAL WATERBIRD SURVEYS

Details of, and contacts for, many of the other waterbird surveys used in this report and of forthcoming surveys, can be obtained via the websites of the WeBS partner organisations.

ERRATA TO PREVIOUS REPORTS

Please note the following corrections to data presented in previous reports:

Kingsbridge Estuary: The peak count of Little Egret in 2009/10 was 90 (not 13).
Langstone Harbour: Incorrect totals for Dark-bellied Brent Goose and Black-necked Grebe in 2009/10 were used in the sites tables.
Ribble Estuary: The peak count of Wigeon in 2008/09 was 97,512 (not 101,594).
Stour Estuary: Incorrect totals for Dunlin in 2008/09 and 2009/10 were used in the sites table.

CONTENTS

*Details of WeBS survey methods, analysis, data presentation, interpretation of waterbird counts, and historical reports, are available via the WeBS website:
www.bto.org/volunteer-surveys/webs/publications/annual-reports

Summary

WeBS AND 'WATERBIRDS IN THE UK'

The Wetland Bird Survey (WeBS) is a joint scheme of the British Trust for Ornithology (BTO), Royal Society for the Protection of Birds (RSPB) and Joint Nature Conservation Committee (JNCC), in association with Wildfowl & Wetlands Trust (WWT).

The principal aims of the scheme are to identify population sizes, determine trends in numbers and distribution, and identify important sites for non-breeding waterbirds in the UK. WeBS Core Counts are made annually at approximately 2,000 wetland sites of all habitats; estuaries and large still waters predominate. Monthly coordinated counts are made mostly by volunteers, principally from September to March, with fewer observations during summer months. Data from other sources, *e.g.* roost counts of geese, are included where relevant.

This report presents total numbers counted for all species in the most recent year in Great Britain and Northern Ireland. Annual indices are provided for the more numerous species, as are monthly indices showing relative abundance during the winter. Following publication of latest waterbird population estimates (Wetlands International 2012), revised thresholds for listing sites of international importance are used in this report. Where applicable, interpretation of WeBS results is placed in the context of trends from other countries in the East Atlantic flyway.

2010/11 WeBS COVERAGE

This report summarises counts during 2010/11 and previous years (since 1960 for wildfowl, 1969 for waders, and the early 1980s/1990s for other species). In 2010/11, WeBS counters covered 4,476 count sectors at 2,422 count sites. A total of 4,409 sectors were counted at least once during the core 'winter' period of September to March, and over 2,000 were covered in all twelve months.

This represents a fantastic effort by everyone involved. A huge THANK YOU goes to all!

WeBS HEADLINES FROM 2010/11

The coldest winter for 35 years... resulted in frozen conditions across northwest Europe. Many wetlands in the UK were frozen during November 2010 to January 2011.

Responses to cold weather... The number of European White-fronted Geese was the highest in the UK for several years, and bucks a recent 'short stopping' trend. Following a record peak of 5,600+ Svalbard Light-bellied Brent Geese at Lindisfarne in autumn, an influx was noted on the east coast of Britain in response to the cold midwinter conditions in Denmark and adjacent areas. Species such as Lapwing, Grey Plover and Smew also reached notable peaks in the UK during the cold period (including a record count of 72,319 Lapwings at Somerset Levels in January). In contrast, the frozen conditions resulted in marked net decreases of some wildfowl and waders at WeBS sites; species such as Shoveler and Golden Plover probably departed the UK in search of milder areas, perhaps further south in the flyway.

Ducks declining or shifting range? Northern Ireland's wintering populations of most ducks, both dabbling and diving species, continue to decline. Reasons are not fully understood, but it may be in response to recent climate change. In Britain, Pochard and Goldeneye also declined further, despite frozen midwinter conditions across northwest Europe which, all else being equal, might have been expected to lead to an arrival of waterfowl to the UK.

Seaducks... particularly Long-tailed Duck and Velvet Scoter, appear to be in serious decline in the UK. This is in line with the situation elsewhere, including the Baltic Sea.

Ringed Plovers... have reached lowest ever wintering numbers across the UK.

Little Egrets... Following the rapid increase in the England since the mid-1990s, numbers at WeBS sites are now stable (but may be continuing to increase within the wider countryside).

Swans & Geese

Numbers of **Bewick's Swan** rose slightly compared to recent winters, while **Whooper Swan** numbers were in keeping with the species' upward trend. Whereas the estimated number of **Pink-footed Geese** fell compared to the last two years, all-time peaks in terms of national index values were once again attained by both the **Svalbard** and **Canadian** populations of **Light-bellied Brent Goose, Svalbard Barnacle Goose**, as well as **Egyptian Goose** and **naturalised Barnacle Goose**. During the cold midwinter period, **European White-fronted Goose** showed a marked rise compared to recent years. There was further evidence that a drop in numbers of **Greenland White-fronted Goose** has bottomed out. **Canada** and **Greylag Geese** (both the **Icelandic** and **British** populations) were present in typically high numbers.

Ducks

Dabbling ducks responded to freezing conditions during the midwinter period; influxes of **Wigeon**, **Teal** and **Mallard** contrasted with an exodus of **Shoveler** and another poor showing by **Pintail**. These events occurred within the context of probable longer-term shifts in core wintering range of species such as **Mallard**, **Pochard**, **Goldeneye** and **Red-breasted Merganser**, that may be at least partly in response to the longer-term trend of relatively mild winters. **Gadwall** and **Tufted Duck** both remained at high levels in 2010/11 in Britain, and **Smew** numbers were notably greater than recent years. **Eider** continue to decline slowly in Britain. In general, monitoring of seaducks through WeBS is notoriously difficult; species such as **Long-tailed Duck** and **Velvet Scoter** require more targeted surveys of favoured sites, so it is difficult to draw conclusions about the current status of these species.

Divers, Grebes, Herons & Rails

The divers and scarcer sea grebes were present in similar numbers to recent years; the assessment of which relies heavily on submission of supplementary data from sites not counted routinely through Core counts. Both **Little** and **Great Crested Grebes** decreased during the frozen conditions in December and January, and the former appears to have struggled to recover in subsequent months. Although **Little Egret** continued to expand both north and westward in England, the overall trend at WeBS sites is no longer one of increase. Also stable in Britain is **Coot**, but a recent marked decline is apparent in Northern Ireland. **Moorhen** shows signs of a slight drop in Britain, perhaps in response to increased mortality after two cold winters.

Waders

Golden Plover and **Lapwing**, whose numbers typically fluctuate more than other waders, have both shown recent declines; the former showed a particularly marked drop in response to the cold weather. The long-term decline of **Ringed Plover** continues, although **Dunlin** is showing some signs of stability and both **Curlew** and **Redshank** bucked recent downward trends. **Turnstone** remained close to the all-time low reached in 2009/10. There were further improved fortunes for **Grey Plover** and **Sanderling**, and **Bar-tailed Godwit** also appears to be recovering from a slump six years ago. Numbers of wintering **Black-tailed Godwit** and **Avocet** remained high and the populations of both continue to rise. **Knot** and **Purple Sandpiper** have remained stable in the last decade, but **Oystercatcher** are showing signs of a recent decline particularly in Scotland. Numbers of **Snipe** recorded were lower than normal, in response to the cold winter; the WeBS trend for this species is included for the first time.

Gulls & Terns

Gulls and terns recorded by WeBS reflect coverage as much as abundance of birds *per se*. WeBS trends for the six most regular gull species are again published in this report. The increase in **Mediterranean Gull** is again evident. Numbers of **Black-headed, Herring** and **Great Black-backed Gulls** appear to be relatively stable at WeBS sites in Britain, whereas **Common** and **Lesser Black-backed Gulls** are both showing signs of decline.

Introduction

The UK is of outstanding international importance for waterbirds. Lying on some of the major flyways for Arctic-nesting species, large numbers of waterbirds are attracted, especially during winter, by the relatively mild climate and extensive areas of wetland, notably estuaries. The UK thus has both moral and legal obligations to conserve both these waterbirds and the wetlands upon which they depend.

As a signatory to a number of international conservation conventions, and as a member of the EU, the UK is bound by international law. In particular, the 'Ramsar' Convention on Wetlands of International Importance especially as Waterfowl Habitat, the EU Birds Directive and the EU Habitats and Species Directive, between them, require the UK to identify important examples of wetland and other habitats and sites important for birds and designate them for protection. Implicit in these obligations is the need for regular monitoring to identify and manage such sites. These instruments also lay particular significance on the need to conserve migratory populations, and consequently most of the waterbird populations in the UK.

The UK has ratified the Agreement on the Conservation of African-Eurasian Migratory Waterbirds (AEWA) of the Bonn Convention on the Conservation of Migratory Species of Wild Animals. AEWA entered into force in 1999. It is a specific Agreement requiring nations to take coordinated measures to conserve migratory waterbirds given their particular vulnerability due to their migration over long distances and their dependence on networks that are decreasing in extent and becoming degraded through non-sustainable human activities. Article three of the Agreement requires, among other things, that sites and habitats for migratory waterbirds are identified, protected and managed appropriately, that parties initiate or support research into the ecology of these species, and exchange information and results. Explicit in this Agreement is that adequate monitoring programmes are set in place to fulfil these objectives and the Action Plan to the Agreement specifically requires that nations endeavour to monitor waterbird populations.

The Wetland Bird Survey (WeBS) aims to monitor all non-breeding waterbirds in the UK in order to provide the principal data on which the conservation of their populations is based. To this end, WeBS has three main objectives:

- to assess the size of non-breeding waterbird populations in the UK;
- to assess trends in their numbers and distribution; and
- to assess the importance of individual sites for waterbirds.

These results also form the basis for informed decision-making by conservation bodies, planners and developers and contribute to the sustainable and wise use and management of wetlands and their dependent waterbirds. The data and the WeBS report also fulfil some of the objectives of the Conventions and Directives listed above. WeBS also provides UK data to Wetlands International to assist their function of coordinating and reporting upon waterbird status at an international flyway scale.

Structure and organisation of WeBS

WeBS is a partnership scheme of the British Trust for Ornithology (BTO), Royal Society for the Protection of Birds (RSPB) and the Joint Nature Conservation Committee (JNCC) (on behalf of the Council for Nature Conservation and the Countryside), the Countryside Council for Wales (CCW), Natural England (NE) and Scottish Natural Heritage (SNH)), in association with Wildfowl & Wetlands Trust.

WeBS continues the traditions of two, long-running count schemes which formed the mainstay of UK waterbird monitoring since 1947 (Cranswick et al. 1997). WeBS Core Counts are carried out at a wide variety of wetlands throughout the UK. Synchronised counts are conducted once per month, particularly from September to March, to fulfil all three main objectives. In addition, WeBS Low Tide Counts are undertaken on selected estuaries with the aim of identifying key areas used during the low tide period, principally by feeding birds; areas not otherwise noted for their importance by Core Counts which are normally conducted at high tide. The success and growth of these count schemes accurately reflects the enthusiasm and dedication of the several thousands of volunteer ornithologists who participate. It is largely due to their efforts that waterbird monitoring in the UK is held in such high regard internationally.

Aim of this report

This report presents syntheses of data collected between July 2010 and June 2011 (see *The WeBS Year*), and in previous years, in line with the WeBS objectives. Data from other national and local waterbird monitoring schemes, notably the WWT/JNCC/SNH Goose & Swan Monitoring Programme, are included where WeBS data alone are insufficient to fulfil this aim, so that the report provides a single, comprehensive source of information on waterbird status and distribution in the UK.

Species accounts provide yearly maxima for all sites supporting internationally and nationally important numbers. Sites with changed status are highlighted and significant counts are discussed. Wherever possible, counts are placed in an international context and relevant research is summarised. Waterbird totals are provided for all sites meeting criteria for international importance and species occurring in internationally important numbers on each are identified.

WeBS Low Tide Counts are carried out on selected estuaries to determine the distribution of birds during low tide, and to identify important feeding areas that may not be recognised during Core Counts that are made mostly at high tide. A summary of results for these estuaries, and distribution maps for selected species, are provided.

Waterbird totals recorded by the Irish Wetland Bird Survey (I-WeBS), a similar scheme operating in the Republic of Ireland, are also included.

Methods

Details of WeBS methodologies, included in the Introduction of the annual WeBS report until Holt *et al.* (2009), are available via the WeBS website: **www.bto.org/webs**.

WEATHER IN 2010/11

This summary of UK weather is drawn from the Meteorological Office web site at www.metoffice.gov.uk. Bracketed figures following the month refer to the Core Count priority date for the month in question.

United Kingdom

July (18) saw a west-east split in terms of weather. Temperatures and rainfall were typical across much of Scotland, Northern Ireland, Wales and western England, but it was warmer and drier than expected elsewhere particularly East Anglia.

August (15) was characterised by cool and rather cloudy weather, with showers and longer spells of rain. It was the coolest August since 1993, while in East Anglia it was the second wettest August on record.

September (19) proved to be an extremely changeable month with plenty of rain, especially across the northern half of the UK, but also some more settled spells. Overall, over the course of the month, average temperatures and rainfall levels were close to normal.

October (10) saw an opening period of unsettled weather across the UK, with copious rainfall. Colder, settled conditions mid-month were followed by the return of frontal systems and associated unsettled weather. Overall, rainfall amounts were close to normal in most areas, and it proved to be the equal-sunniest October on record in Wales.

November (14) saw temperatures well below average across most of the UK, typically by 1.5-2.0°C. Consequently, it proved to be the coldest November since 1993. The lowest temperature registered was -18°C in Powys; new November minima were set for Wales and Northern Ireland. Rainfall was generally close to normal in most areas.

Cold conditions intensified in **December** (19) and mean temperatures proved to approximately 5°C lower than normal. This rendered it the coldest December in over 100 years. There was significant snowfall in many areas and a minimum temperature of -21.3°C was recorded in Highland. Although it was cold throughout, a period of exceptionally frozen conditions occurred for ten days from mid-month, which therefore impacted WeBS coverage for the month.

In **January** (16), the very cold conditions from the previous month slowly moderated during the open fortnight. Overall, temperatures remained below average, and Scotland continued to experience snow and frozen conditions beyond mid-month. Despite a gradual thaw, some freshwater wetlands remained frozen at the time of the mid-month WeBS Core count date.

February (13) proved to be a more typical month with Atlantic depressions bringing unsettled conditions to much of the UK. Average temperature was about 2°C higher than the recent thirty-year average; the ninth mildest February in the last 100 years and a stark contrast to the preceding two months.

March (13) proved to be largely dry and settled thorough the first half of the month, although there was a period of snowfall in Scotland during the second week. Rainfall was very low across much of England; East Anglia experienced its second driest March in 100 years.

April (17) was dominated by high pressure and most of the UK experienced warm, dry conditions. Overall, England recorded less than 10 % of expected rainfall. It was the sunniest April since 1929, and a maximum temperature of 28°C was noted in Surrey.

May (15) proved to be relatively unsettled with more rainfall than expected in the north and west, but relatively dry conditions persisted in the east. Mean temperatures were slightly above average.

After a dry start, **June** (12) proved to be wetter than expected across many parts, particularly central and southern England where it was 150% wetter than normal.

Table 1. The percentage of inland count units (lakes, reservoirs, gravel pits, rivers and canals) in the UK with any ice and with 75% or more of their surface covered by ice during WeBS counts in winter 2010/11 (England divided by a line drawn roughly between the Humber and the Mersey Estuaries).

Region	Ice	S	O	N	D	J	F	M
Northern Ireland	>0%	0	0	0	86	35	0	0
	>74%	0	0	0	66	22	0	0
Scotland	>0%	0	<1	13	75	54	10	3
	>74%	0	0	6	68	40	5	<1
N England	>0%	0	0	3	81	22	<1	<1
	>74%	0	0	<1	73	7	0	0
S England	>0%	0	<1	2	82	9	1	<1
	>74%	0	0	<1	70	4	<1	0
Wales	>0%	0	0	<1	81	7	2	0
	>74%	0	0	0	60	5	0	0

Arctic Breeding Conditions 2010

Arctic breeding conditions for birds that winter within the UK are summarised from information available from the website www.arcticbirds.ru having been collated by Soloviev & Tomkovich (2011).

Typically, there was considerable variation in summer temperatures across the Arctic region in 2010, but generally the figures were above average. This was particularly the case across most of arctic Russia, eastern Siberia, arctic Canada and Greenland – where recorded temperatures were up to 5.5°C higher than usual. An exception to this was northern Scandinavia where it was cooler than expected, particularly during the early stages of the summer.

Rodent abundance was generally low across most arctic regions in 2010, although high densities were recorded at a scattering of regularly monitored sites in arctic Russia.

Indications from sites across the Arctic were of good avian breeding success across the majority of regions in 2010. Typically however, some stations did not conform to this trend; for example, results from the small number of monitoring stations located in Greenland and northern Canada were more mixed, and in some cases there success was considered to be poor.

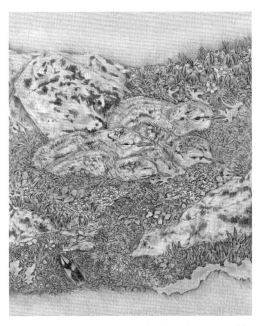

Turnstone chicks *(Jack Ashton-Booth)*

COVERAGE

WeBS Core Counts

Coordinated, synchronous counts are advocated to prevent double-counting or birds being missed. Priority dates are recommended nationally (Table 2). Due to differences in tidal regimes around the country, counts at some estuaries were made on other dates to match the most suitable conditions. Weather and counter availability also result in some counts being made on alternative dates.

Standard Core counts were received from 2,422 sites for July 2010 to June 2011 (5% increase compared to previous year), comprising 4,476 count sectors (sub-divisions of large sites for which separate counts are provided).

Figure 1. Position of all locations counted for standard WeBS and I-WeBS counts between July 2010 and June 2011.

WeBS and I-WeBS coverage in 2010/11 is shown in Figure 1. The location of each count sector is shown using only its central grid reference. The grid references of principal WeBS count sites mentioned in the Principal Sites table (Table 6.) are given in Table A2, Appendix 2 and are shown in Figure A1, Appendix 2.

Table 2. WeBS Core Count priority dates in 2010/11

18 July	16 January
15 August	13 February
19 September	13 March
10 October	17 April
14 November	15 May
19 December	12 June

Areas with few wetlands (*e.g.* inland Essex/ Suffolk) or low population density (*e.g.* much of Scotland) are apparent on the map as areas with little coverage. Although poorly covered compared to most areas, Northwest Scotland was again covered by the RAF Ornithological Society in 2010/11. Northern Ireland remains relatively poorly covered away from the major sites, and further volunteers from there or indeed anywhere in the UK are always welcome.

Goose censuses

In 2010/11, counts of Taiga Bean Geese were submitted by the Bean Goose Action Group (Slamannan Plateau) and the RSPB (Middle Yare Marshes). Surveys of Pink-footed and Icelandic Greylag Geese were undertaken at, primarily, roost sites in October to December 2010 as part of the Icelandic-breeding Goose Census. A census of Greylag Geese at key sites in Northwest Scotland was carried out in August 2010 and February 2011 by the Uist Greylag Goose Management Committee and other groups. Counts of Greenland White-fronted Geese were undertaken by the Greenland White-fronted Goose Study. Greenland Barnacle Geese were counted regularly by SNH and others on Islay and other key locations, while Svalbard Barnacle Geese on the Solway were counted regularly by WWT staff and volunteers. Data were also provided by the International Light-bellied Brent Goose census.

Seaduck surveys

Monthly aerial and/or land-based counts of Common Scoter in Carmarthen Bay were carried out in January to March 2010 (CCW/APEM 2012).

TOTAL NUMBERS

Total numbers of waterbirds recorded through WeBS in 2010/11 are given in Tables 3 & 4, for Great Britain (including Isle of Man but excluding Channel Islands) and Northern Ireland, respectively. Site coverage for gulls and terns is given separately since recording of these species was optional.

I-WeBS counts of waterbirds in Ireland are available from a link on the WeBS website at www.bto.org/webs.

Grey Plovers *(John Bowers)*

Introduced and escaped waterbirds

Many species of waterbird occur in the UK as a result of introductions, particularly through escapes from collections. Several species have become established, *e.g.* Canada Goose. The British Ornithologists' Union Records Committee categorises each species occurring in Britain according to its likely origin. The categories are explained at www.bou.org.uk. Species that have been recorded as 'introductions, human-assisted transportees or escapes from captivity, and whose breeding populations (if any) are not thought to be self-sustaining' are included in the BOURC's category E. WeBS records of these species are included in this report both for the sake of completeness and in order to assess their status and monitor any changes in numbers, a key requirement given the need, under the African-Eurasian Waterbird Agreement of the Bonn Convention '...to prevent the unintentional release of such species...' and once introduced, the need '...to prevent these species from becoming a threat to indigenous species' (Holmes *et al.* 1998).

Numbers of established populations (*e.g.* Canada Goose and Ruddy Duck, which are placed in category C) are excluded from Figure 2.

Additionally, species that occur both naturally (category A) and as introductions or escapes (category E), *e.g.* Pink-footed Goose, are also excluded since separation of introduced and escaped birds from wild ones is not readily possible. However, Ruddy Shelduck (categories B/E) is included; the BOURC does not consider any recent records to have been of wild origin. Additionally, a small number of species not yet assigned to category by BOURC (e.g. Coscoroba Swan) are included.

A total of 22 category E species were recorded in 2010/11, at 182 sites. This is an increase of 2% in terms of sites compared to 2009/10. The summed site maximum of 417 birds is the same total as that registered in 2009/10.

Typically, the majority of the total (53%) was made up of Black Swans and Muscovy Ducks. These were followed in abundance by Bar-headed Goose, Ruddy Shelduck, Chinese Goose, Emperor Goose, Lesser Canada Goose, Wood Duck; all of which were recorded in at least double-figures.

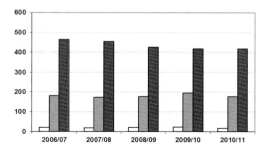

Figure 2. Number of species (white bars), number of sites at which birds were recorded (grey bars) and summed site maxima (black bars) for waterbirds in the BOURC's category E.

Wood Duck *(Neil Calbrade)*

Table 3. Total numbers of waterbirds recorded by WeBS Core Counts in Great Britain in 2010/11. Census totals are indicated by '*'.

	Species	Jul	Aug	Sep	Oct	Nov
	Number of sites visited	*944*	*1,011*	*1,554*	*1,794*	*1,822*
YU	Lesser Whistling Duck	0	0	0	1	0
MS	Mute Swan	13,768	16,101	20,293	22,852	23,440
AS	Black Swan	33	44	46	44	41
BS	Bewick's Swan	0	0	0	0	99
WS	Whooper Swan	24	16	165	1,358	6,160
HN	Chinese Goose	0	0	3	6	7
XF	Taiga Bean Goose	0	0	210*	250*	265*
XR	Tundra Bean Goose	0	0	0	0	8
PG	Pink-footed Goose	18	27	24,340	288,798*	271,394*
EW	European White-fronted Goose	0	0	0	58	94
NW	Greenland White-fronted Goose	1	1	10	3	1,049
LC	Lesser White-fronted Goose	1	0	1	3	3
JI	Icelandic Greylag Goose	3,944	5,232	7,903	23,948	101,506*
JE	British Greylag Goose	18,624	30,439	37,428	39,448	37,207
ZM	Hybrid goose	32	32	33	44	28
HD	Bar-headed Goose	10	9	18	30	8
SJ	Snow Goose	1	2	4	6	4
RJ	Ross's Goose	1	1	0	5	4
EM	Emperor Goose	5	14	12	13	12
CG	Canada Goose	39,561	46,073	62,515	65,548	58,936
LQ	Lesser Canada Goose	0	0	2	3	1
NE	Hawaiian Goose	0	0	0	0	0
YN	Greenland Barnacle Goose	1	0	218	317	1,924
YS	Svalbard Barnacle Goose	28	24	33	35,640*	23,180
YE	Naturalised Barnacle Goose	331	454	895	1,100	1,324
DB	Dark-bellied Brent Goose	41	13	264	59,676	58,916
QN	Canadian Light-bellied Brent Goose	0	1	42	480	844
QS	Svalbard Light-bellied Brent Goose	1	1	2,837	5,637	5,385
BB	Black Brant	0	0	0	0	4
EB	Red-breasted Goose	1	1	5	0	5
EG	Egyptian Goose	492	620	724	602	371
UB	Paradise Shelduck	0	0	0	0	0
UA	Australian Shelduck	0	0	0	0	0
UD	Ruddy Shelduck	1	7	3	3	6
SU	Shelduck	18,197	14,000	25,314	37,673	46,806
MY	Muscovy Duck	27	18	31	44	58
DC	Wood Duck	3	2	3	6	5
MN	Mandarin	215	231	370	400	703
MQ	Maned Duck	0	0	1	1	0
WN	Wigeon	470	1,122	34,818	183,569	289,502
AW	American Wigeon	0	0	0	0	0
HL	Chiloe Wigeon	2	0	6	1	1
GA	Gadwall	3,728	7,986	13,291	15,478	16,826
IK	Baikal Teal	0	0	0	0	0
T.	Teal	1,447	13,960	58,320	114,774	118,361
TA	Green-winged Teal	0	0	0	0	2
MA	Mallard	55,234	76,805	112,076	127,198	126,619
ZF	Feral/hybrid mallard type	477	470	540	690	726
QB	Chestnut Teal	0	1	0	0	1
PT	Pintail	8	109	3,296	9,592	15,561
YL	Yellow-billed Pintail	0	0	0	0	0
PN	White-cheeked Pintail	0	1	1	1	0
GY	Garganey	6	32	16	6	3

Table 3. continued

	Dec	Jan	Feb	Mar	Apr	May	Jun
sites	1,525	1,965	1,959	1,804	1,151	986	973
YU	0	0	0	0	0	0	0
MS	17,002	20,080	18,479	17,839	11,336	9,467	12,000
AS	38	21	19	27	22	21	21
BS	1,023	1,939	1,565	67	0	0	0
WS	4,135	4,795	5,843	5,214	162	47	20
HN	4	10	6	7	1	2	1
XF	126	82	80	0	0	0	0
XR	5	26	21	3	1	0	0
PG	225,221*	152,916	67,956	71,459	48,958	1,973	69
EW	1,153	3,087	1,788	118	11	0	0
NW	12,435*	553	208	13,255*	10	0	0
LC	1	2	1	1	1	0	0
JI	98,078*	21,671	19,798	20,975	1,546	889	4,064
JE	28,335	31,975	21,775	20,347	10,362	10,957	22,989
ZM	29	33	19	25	68	17	34
HD	7	14	9	3	5	7	12
SJ	26	0	2	8	1	3	0
RJ	2	4	1	1	1	0	1
EM	10	9	8	7	7	9	8
CG	44,184	60,044	41,590	30,661	16,593	14,119	30,240
LQ	0	0	1	0	0	0	0
NE	0	0	0	1	0	1	0
YN	44,844*	618	1,476	35,661*	655	13	0
YS	11,076	23,953	5,362	16,759	15,718	244	8
YE	891	1,802	1,014	1,297	408	467	569
DB	49,236	68,483	71,550	47,694	14,330	4,688	65
QN	907	1,018	564	736	22	0	1
QS	1,869	4,498	1,993	855	19	4	0
BB	3	5	5	2	0	0	0
EB	4	2	3	6	0	3	2
EG	304	429	412	358	385	304	443
UB	0	0	0	1	0	0	0
UA	0	1	0	1	0	0	0
UD	2	2	3	5	1	1	0
SU	28,060	52,041	45,398	37,776	20,145	13,956	15,471
MY	36	65	46	48	30	37	33
DC	3	4	5	7	2	1	0
MN	326	442	325	265	207	210	215
MQ	0	0	0	0	0	0	0
WN	265,219	391,660	245,046	127,978	2,747	277	279
AW	0	2	1	0	1	0	0
HL	1	0	0	0	0	0	1
GA	17,457	20,526	16,719	10,395	4,395	3,466	3,909
IK	0	0	0	1	0	1	0
T.	105,769	162,401	142,773	63,934	7,260	383	536
TA	3	4	2	3	1	0	0
MA	121,279	133,775	93,313	62,340	31,168	30,983	43,759
ZF	597	700	659	575	343	332	410
QB	0	0	0	0	0	0	0
PT	12,340	19,655	15,592	4,923	174	32	12
YL	0	0	0	0	1	0	0
PN	0	0	1	0	0	0	0
GY	0	0	0	2	39	45	11

Table 3. continued

	Species	Jul	Aug	Sep	Oct	Nov
	Number of sites visited	*944*	*1,011*	*1,554*	*1,794*	*1,822*
TB	Blue-winged Teal	0	0	0	0	0
SV	Shoveler	549	2,337	8,107	11,104	10,469
IE	Ringed Teal	2	0	1	0	0
RQ	Red-crested Pochard	46	133	397	348	470
PO	Pochard	2,876	5,567	7,415	9,574	16,846
NG	Ring-necked Duck	1	0	1	2	2
FD	Ferruginous Duck	1	2	3	4	2
TU	Tufted Duck	25,068	38,279	51,368	53,699	55,626
SP	Scaup	7	9	15	928	1,299
AY	Lesser Scaup	0	0	0	0	0
ZD	Aythya hybrid	1	0	1	8	7
EE	Eider (Except Shetland)	14,295	15,342	15,022	16,506	16,420
EF	Eider (Shetland)	28	20	0	0	1
KE	King Eider	0	0	1	0	1
LN	Long-tailed Duck	0	0	2	1,011	481
CX	Common Scoter	441	1,957	2466	2,859	5,354
FS	Surf Scoter	0	0	0	0	1
VS	Velvet Scoter	133	173	285	72	102
UX	Unidentified scoter	0	0	0	70	0
DX	Black Scoter	0	0	0	0	0
GN	Goldeneye	295	254	317	881	7,144
HO	Hooded Merganser	0	0	0	0	0
SY	Smew	0	1	1	3	15
RM	Red-breasted Merganser	704	930	1,038	1,622	2,712
GD	Goosander	889	1,215	1,331	1,824	2,622
RY	Ruddy Duck	62	71	118	121	111
UM	Unidentified duck	9	4	9	165	25
RH	Red-throated Diver	40	74	285	283	357
BV	Black-throated Diver	2	4	9	31	33
ND	Great Northern Diver	2	2	3	42	215
UL	Unidentified diver	0	0	1	0	0
PJ	Pied-billed Grebe	0	0	0	0	1
LG	Little Grebe	1,867	3,343	5,276	5,260	4,908
GG	Great Crested Grebe	4,555	6,548	9,312	8,719	8,555
RX	Red-necked Grebe	0	0	5	2	7
SZ	Slavonian Grebe	2	4	21	187	229
BN	Black-necked Grebe	11	24	19	21	17
UV	Unidentified grebe	0	0	0	1	0
CA	Cormorant	7,823	11,137	16,445	17,591	17,333
SA	Shag	315	1,008	2,001	2,233	2,777
XU	Unidentified Cormorant/Shag	0	0	0	1	0
BI	Bittern	4	3	6	6	24
NT	Night Heron	0	0	0	0	0
QH	Squacco Heron	0	0	0	1	1
EC	Cattle Egret	0	2	0	1	3
ET	Little Egret	2,049	3,286	4,368	4,423	2,865
HW	Great White Egret	2	1	4	9	7
H.	Grey Heron	2,436	2,758	3,938	4,178	3,716
UR	Purple Heron	1	1	0	0	0
OR	White Stork	0	0	1	0	0
IB	Glossy Ibis	0	0	3	1	3
NB	Spoonbill	28	47	43	21	34
FL	Greater Flamingo	0	0	0	0	0
WA	Water Rail	46	69	124	284	575

Table 3. continued

	Dec	Jan	Feb	Mar	Apr	May	Jun
sites	1,525	1,965	1,959	1,804	1,151	986	973
TB	0	0	2	0	1	0	1
SV	7,798	9,032	9,753	8,124	1,437	566	477
IE	0	0	0	0	0	0	0
RQ	461	346	371	316	38	72	49
PO	15,715	20,577	19,306	9,702	1,355	1,261	1,547
NG	1	1	3	2	1	0	0
FD	2	0	2	1	0	0	0
TU	47,364	61,795	56,636	47,787	24,141	10,173	10,193
SP	1,831	1,377	1,304	433	251	10	1
AY	0	3	2	2	1	0	0
ZD	4	11	5	4	4	0	1
EE	14,482	14,386	15,060	17,258	14,115	12,994	14,404
EF	0	1	0	2	21	26	12
KE	0	1	0	0	0	1	1
LN	1,002	1,011	1,006	765	86	15	5
CX	4,050	9,608	11,562	19,588	8,954	925	810
FS	0	1	0	1	0	2	0
VS	53	783	417	361	196	358	166
UX	0	304	8	0	0	0	0
DX	0	0	0	0	1	0	0
GN	7,035	10,184	12,564	11,078	1,290	25	56
HO	1	1	1	2	0	1	0
SY	145	232	196	105	1	0	0
RM	2,107	2,521	2,764	3,252	1,236	501	642
GD	2,361	4,643	4,040	2,862	732	350	603
RY	108	99	49	30	27	20	28
UM	56	87	215	15	3	6	10
RH	434	443	416	638	163	47	38
BV	52	72	45	78	36	3	6
ND	100	93	124	88	76	27	2
UL	4	0	2	4	0	0	0
PJ	0	0	0	0	0	0	0
LG	3,439	2,866	2,673	2,316	1,163	921	883
GG	6,494	4,692	6,976	6,887	4,634	3,539	3,721
RX	9	9	7	7	5	6	0
SZ	186	114	252	143	24	3	0
BN	71	51	62	59	41	23	24
UV	0	0	0	0	0	0	0
CA	10,408	12,680	13,699	10,872	5,574	5,677	6,553
SA	1,100	1,408	1,416	930	382	424	370
XU	0	1	2	1	0	1	0
BI	92	56	46	31	13	6	3
NT	0	0	0	0	1	1	1
QH	0	0	0	0	0	0	0
EC	0	0	1	0	0	0	0
ET	628	869	938	1,198	798	714	830
HW	5	10	8	6	0	0	3
H.	1,789	2,833	3,216	2,788	1,993	1,873	2,075
UR	0	0	0	0	2	0	1
OR	0	0	0	0	0	0	0
IB	0	1	0	0	0	0	0
NB	18	26	17	19	8	10	30
FL	0	1	0	0	1	1	1
WA	317	195	171	164	45	33	29

Table 3. continued

	Species	Jul	Aug	Sep	Oct	Nov
	Number of sites visited	*944*	*1,011*	*1,554*	*1,794*	*1,822*
AK	Spotted Crake	0	2	0	0	0
CE	Corncrake	0	0	0	0	0
MH	Moorhen	5,165	7,202	10,970	11,530	12,503
CO	Coot	48,326	69,428	102,730	106,819	114,436
AN	Crane	0	2	0	5	3
KF	Kingfisher	160	223	426	389	444
	TOTAL WILDFOWL	**274,974**	**385,311**	**649,975**	**1,298,145**	**1,496,155**

	Species	Jul	Aug	Sep	Oct	Nov
	Number of sites visited	*944*	*1,011*	*1,554*	*1,794*	*1,822*
OC	Oystercatcher	41,056	159,698	233,028	246,014	238,924
AV	Avocet	2,499	2,136	1,596	7,183	7,076
TN	Stone Curlew	3	7	0	0	0
KP	Kentish Plover	0	0	0	0	0
LP	Little Ringed Plover	310	107	14	2	1
RP	Ringed Plover	1,431	11,220	11,537	8,950	6,520
ID	American Golden Plover	0	0	0	1	0
GP	Golden Plover	3,847	19,401	25,492	64,763	144,916
GV	Grey Plover	792	13,174	23,798	32,620	27,577
L.	Lapwing	21,220	51,237	60,997	91,347	185,251
KN	Knot	25,158	149,919	225,769	261,164	199,291
SS	Sanderling	2,035	8,686	11,827	7,531	9,012
LX	Little Stint	1	19	76	50	6
TK	Temminck's Stint	0	1	0	0	0
BQ	Buff-breasted Sandpiper	0	0	0	3	0
BP	Baird's Sandpiper	0	0	0	1	0
PP	Pectoral Sandpiper	1	0	13	2	0
CV	Curlew Sandpiper	4	19	272	73	2
PS	Purple Sandpiper	52	101	152	444	882
DN	Dunlin	40,280	49,791	57,183	184,640	275,621
RU	Ruff	113	277	312	337	522
JS	Jack Snipe	0	1	3	51	87
SN	Snipe	164	856	1,964	4,917	6,029
LD	Long-billed Dowitcher	0	0	0	0	0
WK	Woodcock	2	2	0	6	29
BW	Black-tailed Godwit	8,302	19,929	27,477	32,799	29,351
BA	Bar-tailed Godwit	5,831	27,453	35,005	40,001	29,332
WM	Whimbrel	662	1,048	282	40	14
CU	Curlew	35,759	58,898	67,810	83,396	63,134
CS	Common Sandpiper	1,190	1,032	360	102	66
PQ	Spotted Sandpiper	0	0	1	0	0
GE	Green Sandpiper	436	768	328	258	176
DR	Spotted Redshank	94	243	147	157	59
GK	Greenshank	543	1,443	1,470	1,082	467
LY	Lesser Yellowlegs	0	0	0	1	0
OD	Wood Sandpiper	8	34	7	1	0
RK	Redshank	19,141	49,797	74,616	88,627	80,147
TT	Turnstone	673	5,436	7,961	11,157	10,714
WF	Wilson's Phalarope	0	0	1	1	0
NK	Red-necked Phalarope	0	0	1	0	0
PL	Grey Phalarope	0	0	6	1	8
	TOTAL WADERS	**211,607**	**632,733**	**869,505**	**1,167,722**	**1,315,214**

Table 3. continued

	Dec	Jan	Feb	Mar	Apr	May	Jun
sites	*1,525*	*1,965*	*1,959*	*1,804*	*1,151*	*986*	*973*
AK	0	0	0	0	0	0	0
CE	0	0	0	0	1	1	1
MH	9,226	9,112	8,578	8,624	4,446	3,206	3,358
CO	94,714	98,248	75,578	51,782	20,785	18,313	26,636
AN	2	2	2	3	1	0	0
KF	176	130	123	125	64	61	88
	1,325,880	1,450,623	1,071,049	800,093	281,283	155,155	208,842

	Dec	Jan	Feb	Mar	Apr	May	Jun
sites	*1,525*	*1,965*	*1,959*	*1,804*	*1,151*	*986*	*973*
OC	161,517	213,280	194,863	124,715	54,564	34,803	31,749
AV	4,567	6,849	6,382	4,091	2,723	2,043	1688
TN	0	0	0	0	1	2	0
KP	0	0	0	0	2	1	0
LP	0	0	0	13	414	346	349
RP	3,890	4,341	4,474	2,563	5,472	15,997	1,979
ID	0	0	0	0	0	0	0
GP	8,675	52,113	43,575	25,544	1,996	35	24
GV	21,572	34,741	26,327	29,594	18,633	11,248	1,747
L.	59,713	268,020	222,106	27,750	6,337	4,292	6,662
KN	105,882	239,445	228,069	154,579	80,938	12,098	4,898
SS	6,162	7,361	6,885	8,332	7,201	6,163	1,878
LX	1	2	0	2	1	3	4
TK	0	0	0	0	0	8	0
BQ	0	0	0	0	0	0	0
BP	0	0	0	0	0	0	0
PP	0	0	0	0	0	0	2
CV	0	0	1	0	0	7	0
PS	736	1,353	1,505	1,516	240	56	2
DN	215,053	309,306	248,297	110,426	41,306	78,879	2,646
RU	134	248	340	350	144	23	7
JS	28	39	34	33	0	0	0
SN	3,173	2,426	2,737	3,106	341	75	59
LD	0	1	0	0	0	0	0
WK	207	72	43	18	0	1	1
BW	20,366	24,079	21,369	17,130	16,518	2,455	1,999
BA	19,305	57,657	61,563	21,344	5,089	4,153	1,963
WM	16	53	17	8	553	985	100
CU	36,923	73,852	74,608	58,561	18,740	4,517	6,122
CS	28	23	25	32	250	280	267
PQ	0	0	0	0	0	0	0
GE	58	93	81	84	101	8	41
DR	33	55	36	38	61	3	12
GK	249	288	262	258	159	71	50
LY	0	0	0	1	1	0	0
OD	0	0	0	0	3	14	1
RK	40,888	58,819	62,737	50,661	19,913	2,732	2,312
TT	6,849	10,945	9,301	8,982	4,448	1,100	512
WF	0	0	0	0	0	0	0
NK	0	0	0	0	0	0	0
PL	0	0	0	0	0	0	0
	716,025	1,365,461	1,215,637	649,731	286,149	182,398	67,074

Table 3. continued

	Species	Jul	Aug	Sep	Oct	Nov
	Number of sites visited	*824*	*869*	*1,329*	*1,515*	*1,533*
KI	Kittiwake	367	368	682	191	92
ON	Bonaparte's Gull	0	0	0	0	0
BH	Black-headed Gull	87,857	119,690	168,223	174,517	173,601
LU	Little Gull	3	27	5	14	3
FG	Franklin's Gull	1	0	0	0	0
MU	Mediterranean Gull	386	844	1,565	827	353
CM	Common Gull	4,712	13,388	20,493	37,653	36,526
IN	Ring-billed Gull	0	0	1	0	2
LB	Lesser Black-backed Gull	34,907	15,298	17,901	20,890	17,736
HG	Herring Gull	30,548	44,671	58,117	69,592	79,872
YG	Yellow-legged Gull	27	36	40	43	52
YC	Caspian Gull	0	1	0	1	2
IG	Iceland Gull	0	1	0	1	1
GZ	Glaucous Gull	0	0	1	0	3
GB	Great Black-backed Gull	2,617	3,838	7,389	8,318	9,463
UU	Unidentified gull	43	124	714	584	738
OU	Unidentified small gull	0	0	4	0	0
VU	Unidentified large gull	0	2	1	0	0
	TOTAL GULLS	**161,468**	**198,288**	**275,136**	**312,631**	**318,444**

	Species	Jul	Aug	Sep	Oct	Nov
	Number of sites visited	*809*	*847*	*1,235*	*1,383*	*1,345*
AF	Little Tern	1,145	330	23	3	0
WD	Whiskered Tern	0	1	0	0	0
BJ	Black Tern	1	24	63	11	0
WJ	White-winged Black Tern	0	1	0	0	0
TE	Sandwich Tern	3,762	6,158	2,590	183	7
CN	Common Tern	5,712	4,441	776	73	0
RS	Roseate Tern	4	4	2	0	0
AE	Arctic Tern	632	202	9	9	0
UI	Common/Arctic Tern	196	4	2	1	0
UT	Unidentified tern	1	0	0	0	0
	TOTAL TERNS	**11,453**	**11,165**	**3,465**	**280**	**7**

Table 3. continued

	Dec	Jan	Feb	Mar	Apr	May	Jun
sites	1,267	1,652	1,635	1,500	991	854	848
KI	49	102	33	561	565	439	538
ON	0	0	0	0	0	1	1
BH	143,771	224,169	192,414	149,174	61,399	38,744	39,653
LU	0	7	6	2	88	8	10
FG	0	0	0	0	0	0	0
MU	220	340	659	697	334	159	163
CM	52,115	51,709	43,647	31,650	4,818	3,184	3,018
IN	2	4	1	2	0	0	0
LB	10,944	12,156	7,964	17,746	21,451	22,097	19,210
HG	49,872	106,832	61,065	51,234	38,466	33,155	32,235
YG	43	32	10	7	6	10	9
YC	9	1	4	4	0	0	0
IG	0	8	3	6	0	0	0
GZ	3	5	2	2	1	1	1
GB	8,336	9,127	5,084	4,934	1,921	1,716	1,877
UU	3,427	187	2,651	219	283	14	33
OU	0	0	25	0	8	0	0
VU	0	0	0	0	26	2,027	0
	268,791	404,679	313,568	256,238	129,366	101,555	96,748

	Dec	Jan	Feb	Mar	Apr	May	Jun
sites	1,123	1,433	1,406	1,330	923	809	821
AF	0	0	0	0	25	881	967
WD	0	0	0	0	0	0	0
BJ	0	0	0	0	1	3	0
WJ	0	0	0	0	0	0	0
TE	1	1	2	61	1,429	3,614	6,322
CN	0	0	0	3	641	3,887	4,538
RS	0	0	0	0	0	0	4
AE	0	0	0	0	14	355	384
UI	0	0	0	0	0	2	23
UT	0	0	0	0	0	9	2
	1	1	2	64	2,110	8,751	12,240

Table 4. Total numbers of waterbirds recorded by WeBS Core Counts in Northern Ireland in 2010/11. Census totals are indicated by '*'. (I-WeBS totals in the Republic of Ireland available via www.bto.org/webs).

	Species	Jul	Aug	Sep	Oct	Nov
	Number of sites visited	*3*	*2*	*11*	*14*	*18*
MS	Mute Swan	10	4	1,167	1,140	958
WS	Whooper Swan	2	1	22	270	1,475
PG	Pink-footed Goose	0	0	15	21	2
NW	Greenland White-fronted Goose	0	0	0	0	0
JE	British/Irish Greylag Goose	0	0	127	294	803
SJ	Snow Goose	0	0	1	1	1
CG	Canada Goose	0	0	85	147	211
YE	Naturalised Barnacle Goose	0	0	0	375	375
DB	Dark-bellied Brent Goose	0	0	0	0	0
QN	Canadian Light-bellied Brent Goose	1	0	22,087	36,519	10,169
SU	Shelduck	20	7	450	1,919	2,018
WN	Wigeon	0	4	414	3,885	2,124
GA	Gadwall	0	0	157	169	183
T.	Teal	0	0	1,359	4,612	3,282
MA	Mallard	111	160	6,642	7,972	4,437
PT	Pintail	0	0	12	328	87
SV	Shoveler	0	0	47	70	114
PO	Pochard	0	0	414	1,202	4,746
TU	Tufted Duck	0	0	1,768	2,027	5,077
SP	Scaup	0	0	4	629	2,763
E.	Eider	0	0	732	1,324	2,073
LN	Long-tailed Duck	0	0	0	0	3
CX	Common Scoter	0	0	0	2	13
VS	Velvet Scoter	0	0	0	1	0
GN	Goldeneye	0	0	10	67	2,581
SY	Smew	0	0	0	0	1
RM	Red-breasted Merganser	0	0	308	340	417
GD	Goosander	0	0	0	0	0
RY	Ruddy Duck	0	0	4	11	9
RH	Red-throated Diver	0	0	4	13	46
ND	Great Northern Diver	0	0	0	1	4
LG	Little Grebe	0	0	380	544	532
GG	Great Crested Grebe	0	0	1,061	1,324	821
SZ	Slavonian Grebe	0	0	0	0	0
CA	Cormorant	53	102	1,680	1,855	1,862
SA	Shag	0	0	277	312	479
IB	Glossy Ibis	0	0	0	1	0
ET	Little Egret	13	21	58	63	55
H.	Grey Heron	47	25	322	372	398
WA	Water Rail	0	0	1	4	3
MH	Moorhen	0	0	196	274	162
CO	Coot	0	0	2,351	2,219	1,949
KF	Kingfisher	0	0	2	0	3
	TOTAL WILDFOWL	**257**	**324**	**42,889**	**71,631**	**52,309**

Table 4. continued

sites	Dec	Jan	Feb	Mar	Apr	May	Jun
	16	22	20	19	4	3	2
MS	799	1,572	1,101	699	4	29	24
WS	560	2,614	2,602	1,842	0	1	0
PG	51	0	25	22	0	0	0
NW	0	68	0	35	0	0	0
JE	337	1,210	1,614	2,010	0	0	0
SJ	0	0	2	1	0	0	0
CG	132	903	524	208	0	0	0
YE	370	364	8	369	0	0	0
DB	0	0	1	0	0	0	0
QN	1,687	3,558	3,136	3,713	160	0	0
SU	2,181	3,526	2,950	2,239	83	59	45
WN	999	3,527	3,190	1,920	0	0	2
GA	98	105	141	173	0	0	0
T.	1,745	4,707	2,475	1,925	14	0	0
MA	1,889	4,978	3,133	2,718	140	168	207
PT	190	270	449	84	0	0	0
SV	82	10	75	43	0	0	0
PO	19	5,075	4,857	1,439	0	0	0
TU	862	7,664	11,379	4,276	26	19	22
SP	1,155	1,904	1,112	2,266	0	0	0
E.	1,180	1,636	1,213	3,088	19	0	2
LN	5	2	12	15	0	0	0
CX	0	4	8	6	0	0	0
VS	0	0	0	0	0	0	0
GN	195	3,405	3,829	3,184	0	0	0
SY	0	2	3	3	0	0	0
RM	128	160	303	342	2	0	0
GD	0	0	4	0	0	0	0
RY	0	3	6	3	0	0	0
RH	8	48	5	47	0	0	0
ND	0	3	1	9	0	0	0
LG	158	413	158	139	12	10	18
GG	460	462	444	874	4	0	0
SZ	1	1	0	11	0	0	0
CA	178	1,172	1,189	1,034	40	41	6
SA	29	448	69	142	0	0	0
IB	0	0	0	0	0	0	0
ET	0	16	12	20	1	0	0
H.	47	281	152	111	5	7	6
WA	2	0	3	0	0	0	0
MH	163	167	97	161	2	5	4
CO	2,184	3,182	2,410	997	5	10	14
KF	0	3	0	1	0	0	0
	19,074	**55,100**	**49,905**	**39,259**	**536**	**349**	**352**

Table 4. continued

	Species	Jul	Aug	Sep	Oct	Nov
	Number of sites visited	*3*	*2*	*11*	*14*	*18*
OC	Oystercatcher	535	1,593	10,984	12,809	12,362
RP	Ringed Plover	10	8	149	252	369
GP	Golden Plover	0	0	166	3,829	4,600
GV	Grey Plover	0	0	7	34	54
L.	Lapwing	51	101	940	3,253	6,858
KN	Knot	5	7	16	983	713
SS	Sanderling	0	0	207	538	198
LX	Little Stint	0	0	6	1	0
PS	Purple Sandpiper	0	0	0	7	41
DN	Dunlin	85	39	1,100	1,691	4,001
BQ	Buff-breasted Sandpiper	0	0	2	0	0
RU	Ruff	0	2	0	0	0
JS	Jack Snipe	0	0	0	0	0
SN	Snipe	0	0	11	62	152
GE	Green Sandpiper	0	1	0	0	0
WK	Woodcock	0	0	0	0	0
BW	Black-tailed Godwit	57	50	479	1,032	570
BA	Bar-tailed Godwit	0	0	1,017	1,647	638
WM	Whimbrel	7	1	0	0	1
CU	Curlew	342	387	4,017	3,667	3,195
CS	Common Sandpiper	8	2	0	0	0
GK	Greenshank	32	30	87	119	99
RK	Redshank	814	691	3,455	5,720	6,191
TT	Turnstone	14	1	370	995	1,628
	TOTAL WADERS	**1,960**	**2,913**	**23,013**	**36,639**	**41,670**

	Species	Jul	Aug	Sep	Oct	Nov
	Number of sites visited	*3*	*2*	*11*	*11*	*15*
KI	Kittiwake	0	0	0	16	1
BH	Black-headed Gull	380	566	6,027	7,040	5,753
MU	Mediterranean Gull	0	0	1	0	0
CM	Common Gull	597	245	2,633	1,730	1,278
LB	Lesser Black-backed Gull	15	14	1,143	800	304
HG	Herring Gull	73	155	1,453	1,141	1,667
IG	Iceland Gull	0	0	0	0	0
GB	Great Black-backed Gull	112	166	258	260	245
	TOTAL GULLS	**1,177**	**1,146**	**11,515**	**10,987**	**9,248**

	Species	Jul	Aug	Sep	Oct	Nov
	Number of sites visited	3	2	9	10	8
BJ	Black Tern	0	0	4	0	0
TE	Sandwich Tern	78	66	26	36	3
CN	Common Tern	4	5	0	0	0
AE	Arctic Tern	2	0	0	0	0
	TOTAL TERNS	**84**	**71**	**30**	**36**	**3**

Table 4. continued

	Dec	Jan	Feb	Mar	Apr	May	Jun
sites	*16*	*22*	*20*	*19*	*4*	*3*	*2*
OC	6,877	14,130	9,236	7,235	151	295	46
RP	33	418	164	193	50	39	6
GP	10	3,797	2,569	4,490	644	0	0
GV	9	83	63	22	2	0	0
L.	3,448	11,902	7,235	532	0	0	0
KN	17	879	1,898	598	0	0	0
SS	60	213	322	1	15	42	0
LX	0	0	0	0	0	0	0
PS	3	93	13	51	0	0	0
DN	2,766	5,848	4,315	2,557	70	100	10
BQ	0	0	0	0	0	0	0
RU	0	0	0	0	0	0	0
JS	0	1	0	0	0	0	0
SN	173	83	15	3	0	0	0
GE	0	0	0	0	0	0	0
WK	0	1	0	0	0	0	0
BW	162	811	916	1,771	180	10	0
BA	304	2,124	1,206	1,684	158	0	0
WM	0	0	1	1	0	0	2
CU	1,500	5,272	4,398	3,392	64	7	20
CS	0	0	0	0	2	0	0
GK	17	60	60	89	0	0	0
RK	2,205	4,643	3,793	3,823	132	0	0
TT	264	1,337	632	1,385	24	0	0
	17,848	**51,695**	**36,836**	**27,827**	**1,492**	**493**	**84**

	Dec	Jan	Feb	Mar	Apr	May	Jun
sites	*13*	*21*	*18*	*18*	*4*	*3*	*2*
KI	0	0	0	4	0	0	0
BH	1,579	8,117	8,873	9,292	250	46	46
MU	0	0	3	1	0	0	0
CM	413	2,694	2,842	2,500	102	142	12
LB	22	189	150	488	9	11	11
HG	147	1,982	1,353	2,378	98	92	23
IG	0	0	0	1	0	0	0
GB	34	300	259	369	41	51	18
	2,195	**13,282**	**13,480**	**15,033**	**500**	**342**	**110**

	Dec	Jan	Feb	Mar	Apr	May	Jun
sites	*10*	*17*	*15*	*14*	*4*	*3*	*2*
BJ	0	0	0	0	0	0	0
TE	0	5	0	0	67	27	20
CN	0	0	0	0	0	1	0
AE	0	0	0	0	0	0	0
	0	**5**	**0**	**0**	**67**	**28**	**20**

SPECIES ACCOUNTS

Key to symbols commonly used in the species accounts.

In headers and footnotes:

Subspecies/Population in brackets with international 1% threshold (Appendix 1).

?   population size not accurately known

+   population too small for meaningful threshold

*   where 1% of the national population is < 50 birds, 50 is normally used as a minimum threshold for national importance

**   a site regularly holding > 20,000 waterbirds (excluding non-native species) qualifies as internationally important by virtue of absolute numbers

†   denotes that a qualifying level different to the national threshold has been used for the purposes of presenting sites in this report

In tables of important sites:

-      no data available

( )   incomplete count

†   same meaning as used for thresholds

▲   site was of a lower importance status in the previous five-year period

▼   site was of a higher importance status in the previous five-year period

[1,2]   count obtained using different survey methodology from WeBS Core Counts (see table below)

Sources of additional information used in compiling tables of important sites are listed below. Non-WeBS counts are shown in the tables by the number below given in superscript following the count.

1 WWT data
2 Uist Greylag Goose Management Committee
3 SNH data
4 Bean Goose Working Group
5 WWT studies
6 Supplementary daytime counts
7 Greenland White-fronted Goose Study Group
8 WWT publications
9 SOTEAG reports
10 WeBS Low Tide Counts
11 Roost counts
12 Supplementary daytime counts
13 Icelandic Goose Census
14 Firth of Clyde Eider counts (Chris Waltho)
15 R Godfrey (in litt)
16 International Swan Census (WWT)
17 All-Ireland Light-bellied Brent Goose Census
18 WWT unpublished data
19 Judith Smith, Gr. Manchester County recorder
20 SNH data
21 Paul Daw, County recorder for Argyll
23 Roost counts
24 Supplementary counts
26 B McMillan (in litt.)
28 BTO/CCW Carmarthen Bay surveys
29 WWTC/CCW Carmarthen Bay surveys
30 Supplementary data
31 Supplementary counts
32 RSPB data
33 A Stevenson (in litt.)
34 WWT UK-breeding Greylag Goose Survey
37 W Aspin (in litt.)
39 D Tate (in litt.)
43 Norman Elkins (Fife Bird Club)
46 S.J.Turner, West Midland Bird Club
47 Birdguides (www.birdguides.com)
49 Norfolk bird report; White-fronted Goose counts
50 RSPB Bean Goose counts

Lesser Whistling Duck

Dendrocygna javanica

Escape

Native Range: S & E Asia

One was at Poole Harbour in October; the third year out of the last four that this species (and presumably that individual) has been seen there.

Mute Swan

Cygnus olor

International threshold (British population):	320
International threshold (Irish population):	100
Great Britain threshold:	740
All-Ireland threshold:	110

GB max: 23,440   Nov
NI max: 1,572   Jan

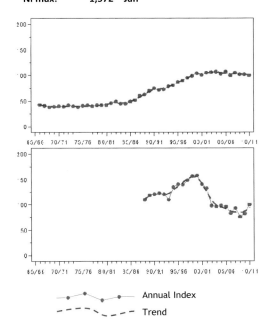

Figure 3.a, Annual indices & trend for Mute Swan in GB (above) & NI (below).

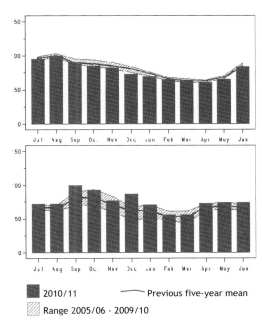

Figure 3.b, Monthly indices for Mute Swan in GB (above) & NI (below).

Mute Swans in Britain and Ireland are largely sedentary, and hence the populations are considered separate from both one another and from birds on the Continent (Scott & Rose 1996). Consequently, all sites of national importance in Britain and All-Ireland importance in Northern Ireland are also classed as being of importance internationally.

During the last decade, the annual indices for Mute Swan in Britain have shown little in the way of variation. In 2010/11, the peak WeBS site count of Mute Swans was 951, recorded at both Loughs Neagh & Beg and Somerset Levels. At the latter site, this was the lowest count since 2003/04 and a notable contrast to the maximum recorded there just two years previously.

Elsewhere in south-west England, the peak at Fleet & Wey failed to reach the 1,000 mark for the fourth year in succession. Among the other principal sites for this species, the maximum recorded at Rutland Water was the highest ever and that at Abberton Reservoir was the most for 11 years.

In Northern Ireland, the December peak at Upper Lough Erne proved to be a site record, contributing to a small rise in the national index. The peak at Strangford Lough, the most important site in Northern Ireland for the species in terms of absolute numbers, was the highest there for three years.

	06/07	07/08	08/09	09/10	10/11	Mon	Mean
Sites of international importance in the UK							
Somerset Levels	1,164	1,098	1,252	1,174	951	Nov	1,128
Fleet and Wey	1,013	867	990	897	922	Oct	938
Loughs Neagh and Beg	770	1,012	702	898	951	Sep	867
Ouse Washes	508 [6]	1,151	(1,010)	625 [6]	437	Mar	746
Rutland Water	588	499	562	555	637	Aug	568
Stour Estuary	347	544	512	632	575	Sep	522
Loch Leven	542	520	544	434	(428)	Oct	510
Tweed Estuary	583	364	410	632	456	Aug	502
Loch Bee (South Uist)	401	399	605		481	Oct	472
Upper Lough Erne	457	354	351	396	650	Dec	442
Dungeness and Rye Bay	410	476	489	417	358	Jul	430
Severn Estuary	421	477	383	381	334	Dec	399
Abberton Reservoir	(399)	311	348	326	428	Aug	362
Lower Lough Erne	266	311	(149)	(133)	(245)	Jan	289
Strangford Lough	(59)	252	111	221	186	Nov	193
Upper Quoile River	121	144					133
Sites no longer meeting table qualifying levels in WeBS-Year 2010/11							
Humber Estuary	350	266	377	453	115	Nov	312 ▼
Hornsea Mere	375	290	155	318 [6]	196	Jun	267 ▼

Black Swan

Cygnus atratus

Escape
Native Range: Australia

Black Swans were noted at 66 WeBS sites in Britain in 2010/11, including two in Wales and three in Scotland. A monthly maximum of 46 was noted in September. This represents a drop in distribution for the third year in a row, contrasting with the pattern shown by Bird Atlas 2007-11 (D. Balmer, pers. comm.). The majority of WeBS records were of singles or pairs but maxima of six were at Abberton Reservoir (Jul) and seven at Stour Estuary (Sep). Given the proximity of these sites, it is possible that the same birds were involved.

Sites with 4 or more birds during 2010/11

Stour Estuary	7, Sep	Ramsbury Lake	5, Nov
Abberton Reservoir	6, Jul	Rochester Pools	5, Nov
Fleet and Wey	5, Jul		

Bewick's Swan

Cygnus columbianus

International threshold	
(W Siberia, N Europe):	220
Great Britain threshold:	70
All-Ireland threshold:	20*

GB max:	6,490	Feb
NI max:	0	
% young:	10.8	**Brood size:** 1.7

50 is normally used as a minimum threshold

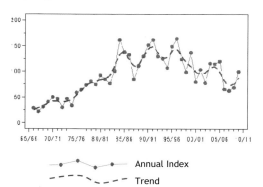

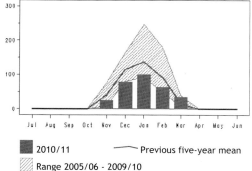

Figure 4.a, Annual indices & trend for Bewick's Swan in GB.

Figure 4.b, Monthly indices for Bewick's Swan in GB.

Bewick's Swans breed in the northern Russian tundra and winter primarily in Britain and The Netherlands. The most recent census of the British wintering population, coordinated by WWT as part of the International Swan Census, was undertaken during winter 2009/10, when the number present was estimated to be 7,000 birds (C. Hall, pers. comm.).

Neil Calbrade

In 2010/11, the WeBS index rose compared to the last three years, indicative of a response to the cold winter. In the last two decades the British trend has fluctuated downwards, and over the same period declining numbers have also been noted in Ireland (Boland & Crowe 2012) and at key wintering sites in the north of the Netherlands (Hornman *et al.* 2011). These international declines have led to this amber-listed species (Eaton *et al.* 2009) being the focus of dedicated conservation initiatives (Rees & Beekman 2010).

An increasing proportion of Bewick's Swans that winter in the UK are now concentrated in the fenlands in eastern England. Whereas peak counts at most sites across the UK have declined in recent years, those at the two principal sites of Ouse Washes and Nene Washes have remained stable or increased. At both of these locations, the birds use wetlands for roosting and agricultural fields for diurnal foraging. In 2010/11, the peaks logged during fenland roost counts were 6,176 (Feb) at Ouse Washes and 418 (Dec) at Nene Washes. The high number present at Ouse Washes was possibly due to a shift of birds from The Netherlands in response to the coldest winter in north-west Europe for 35 years (M. Hornman, pers. comm.).

Elsewhere, the peaks reported from Severn Estuary (311, Jan), Dee Estuary (92, Jan) and Somerset Levels (63, Feb) all represented the most at those sites for several years, and were also indicative of a cold weather response. The latter site, with a historic peak of 452 swans in January 1982, was traditionally one of the most favoured sites in Britain for this species before experiencing sharp declines during the 1980s and 1990s.

Breeding success was assessed at three wintering sites in the UK during 2010/11; WWT Slimbridge, WWT Martin Mere/Ribble Estuary, and Ouse Washes. Across these three sites the proportion of young birds was 10.8%, slightly lower than the previous ten-year average and therefore an indication of relatively poor breeding success in 2010. Mean brood size was typical of recent years, at 1.7 young per pair (Newth 2011a).

	06/07	07/08	08/09	09/10	10/11	Mon	Mean
Sites of international importance in the UK							
Ouse Washes	3,407 [11]	5,341 [11]	3,468 [11]	5,109 [11]	6,176 [11]	Feb	4,700
Nene Washes	703 [11]	642 [11]	305 [11]	962 [11]	418 [11]	Dec	606
Severn Estuary	196	180	238	303	311	Jan	246
Sites of national importance in Great Britain							
Ranworth and Cockshoot Broads					(116)	Dec	(116) ▲
Dungeness and Rye Bay	130	127	83	99	(100)	Dec	110
Breydon Water and Berney Marshes	147 [11]	87 [12]	5	131 [12]	38 [12]	Mar	82
Sites below table qualifying levels but exceeding threshold in WeBS-Year 2010/11 in Great Britain							
Dee Estuary (England and Wales)	48	82	56	55	92	Jan	67

Whooper Swan
Cygnus cygnus

International threshold (Iceland population): 270
Great Britain threshold: 110
All-Ireland threshold: 130

GB max:	9,700	Feb
NI max:	2,614	Jan
% young:	14.4	Brood size 2.1

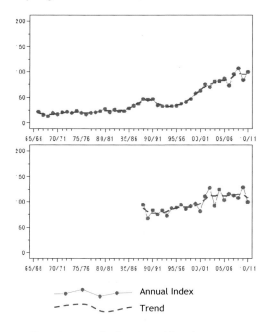

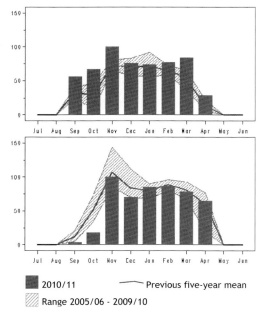

Annual Index
Trend

2010/11 — Previous five-year mean
Range 2005/06 - 2009/10

Figure 5.a, Annual indices & trend for Whooper Swan in GB (above) & NI (below).

Figure 5.b, Monthly indices for Whooper Swan in GB (above) & NI (below).

The number of Whooper Swans wintering in Britain and Ireland has increased steadily over the course of the last 25 years. Almost all originate from the increasing population breeding in Iceland, and a small number of Scandinavian birds also winter in eastern England. A census, coordinated by WWT as part of the International Swan Census, was carried out during 2009/10, when the number present in the UK was estimated to be 16,502 birds (Hall *et al.* in press). This represented an increase of 9.6% compared to the previous estimate from a census in 2004/05.

In 2010/11, the WeBS index for sites in Britain remained at the high level of recent years. The relatively high monthly index values from September to November imply a large and early arrival took place, with numbers counted then slightly reduced during December and January through displacement of birds by the prevailing freezing conditions to uncounted sites. The maximum at the Ouse Washes roost, 7,271 in

February, represents the largest ever total there. Maxima at the other sites of international importance were largely similar to recent years, except for Loch of Strathbeg, where the count of 1,188 in November was a site record; the Core count presumably coinciding with a peak of southbound passage that occurs in northern Scotland in autumn.

Jill Pakenham

Following an increase in the international population estimate (Wetlands International 2012), Solway Estuary and East Fenton Farm Reservoir no longer surpass the threshold for international importance.

In Northern Ireland, the peak at Loughs Neagh & Beg was typical, but at Lough Foyle, where numbers usually peak in October or November, the peak was the lowest ever recorded.

Breeding success was assessed at a number of sites in Britain and Ireland in 2010/11. At the three British sites monitored on an annual basis (Ouse Washes, WWT Caerlaverock, and WWT Martin Mere/Ribble Estuary) the proportion of young birds was 14.4%. This is slightly lower than the previous five-year average and therefore an indication of relatively poor breeding success in 2010. Mean brood size was also slightly less than expected, at 2.1 young per pair (Newth 2011b).

	06/07	07/08	08/09	09/10	10/11	Mon	Mean
Sites of international importance in the UK							
Ouse Washes	3,756[11]	3,960[11]	5,979[11]	5,615[16]	7,271[11]	Feb	5,316
Martin Mere and Ribble Estuary	1,451	1,819	1,703	2,296	2,052	Jan	1,864
Loughs Neagh and Beg	1,731	1,734	(1,592)	1,192	1,669	Mar	1,584
Lough Foyle	1,042	1,167	1,240	2,033	506	Feb	1,198
Upper Lough Erne	956	680	636	643	793	Jan	742
Loch of Strathbeg	285	92	252	182	1,188	Nov	400
Loch Eye	55	399[13]	797[13]	4	448	Oct	341
Nene Washes	216[11]	110[11]	462[11]		450[11]	Nov	310
Loch Leven	220	242	350[12]	357	224	Nov	279
Strangford Lough	199	432	251[10]	183	319	Jan	277
Sites of national importance in Great Britain							
Solway Estuary	(194)	(97)	(231)	298	215	Mar	257 ▼
East Fenton Farm Reservoir	143	340[12]	182	240	150	Dec	211 ▼
Solway Firth - Newton and Border Marsh			200[13]				200
River Earn, Forteviot - Kinkell			(5)		198	Nov	198 ▲
Norham West Mains	196						196
Loch Heilen	(197)	84	(59)	300	(25)	Jan	194 ▼
Lower Teviot Valley	36	98	(129)	433[12]			189
Wigtown Bay	(164)	267	(195)	177	101	Mar	185 ▼
R Clyde: Carstairs to Thankerton	188	173	109	(86)	268	Nov	185
Cromarty Firth	6	19[13]	(67)	(331)	335[13]	Nov	173 ▲
Dornoch Firth	241	(86)	190	37	222	Oct	173
Wedholme Flow	0	0	19	557[11]	250	Nov	165
River Tweed - Kelso to Coldstream	162	230	252	134	32	Nov	162
Montrose Basin	147	(182)	103	151	224	Mar	161
Black Cart Water (Gryfe-White Cart)	106[12]	98[12]	207[12]	221[12]	132	Nov	153
Dalreoch			216[13]	67[13]			142
Loch a` Phuill (Tiree)	152[12]	103	94	115	184	Dec	130
Lower Derwent Ings	104	88	93	174	151	Mar	122 ▲
Morecambe Bay	(84)	158	82	(118)	(73)	Feb	120
River Eden - Grinsdale to Sandsfield	59	186	108	108	94	Mar	111
Sites no longer meeting table qualifying levels in WeBS-Year 2010/2011							
Rossie Bog		99	(78)	(162)[12]	67[12]	Mar	109
Sites below table qualifying levels but exceeding threshold in WeBS-Year 2010/11 in Great Britain							
Vasa Loch, Shapinsay	147	85	40	62	130	Dec	93
Mersey Estuary	78	75	52	54	118	Jan	75
Loch Eaval and Loch Hosta (North Uist)	27	16	79	47	117	Nov	57
Loch Insh and Spey Marshes	96	148	97	42	112	Feb	99

Chinese Goose

Anser cygnoides

Escape
Native Range: E Asia

Chinese Geese (the domestic strain of Swan Goose) were recorded at 11 WeBS sites, with a monthly maximum of ten birds in January. All records involved one or two birds.

Taiga Bean Goose

Anser fabalis fabalis

International threshold	
(NE Europe population):	420
Great Britain threshold:	4
All-Ireland threshold:	+

GB max: **376**   Jan
NI max: **0**
% young: 31.0   Brood size: 2.1

There are two regular sites for wintering Taiga Bean Geese (*Anser f. fabalis*) in the UK; Slamannan Plateau in central Scotland and Yare Valley in Norfolk. Birds are highly faithful to both of these areas, where their numbers are monitored by the Bean Goose Working Group and RSPB, respectively. Unless specifically reported as being of the *fabalis* race, all other 'bean geese' are assumed to be of the race *rossicus* (Tundra Bean Goose); similarly, all 'bean geese' reported from the Slamannan and Yare Valley areas are assumed to relate to Taiga Bean Geese.

In 2010/11, a site maximum of 267 Taiga Bean Geese was recorded at Slamannan Plateau in October. This is comparable to recent years and slightly higher than the mean for the previous decade. At Yare Valley however, the peak of 137 in January represented a significant increase compared to the previous year, and may have been associated with a cold weather movement. Further evidence for this is provided by the fact that having arrived relatively late in the winter (in November), the majority had migrated back to the continent by mid February. Monitoring of the Slamannan Plateau population by the Bean Goose Working Group indicated that approximately 31% of the population were first-year birds in 2010/11, an improvement on the previous year (Reed 2011a).

Away from these two key areas, single Taiga Bean Geese were identified at two other sites during Core counts; Humber Estuary (Jan) and Waughton (Feb).

Sites of national importance in Great Britain	06/07	07/08	08/09	09/10	10/11	Mon	Mean
Slamannan Area	255 [4]	300 [4]	265 [4]	260 [4]	267 [4]	Oct	269
Middle Yare Marshes	111 [50]	136 [50]	133 [50]	81 [50]	137 [50]	Jan	120

Tundra Bean Goose

Anser fabalis rossicus

International threshold	
(W & C Siberia population):	5,500
Great Britain threshold:	3
All-Ireland threshold:	+

GB max: **45**   Jan
NI max: **0**

Unless submitted otherwise, records of 'bean geese' away from the two key wintering areas of Taiga Bean Goose (*Anser f. fabalis*) are assumed to relate to Tundra Bean Goose (*Anser f. rossicus*). Since 2008/09, the two sub-species have been listed separately in the annual WeBS report. Small, but regular, numbers of Tundra Bean Geese are noted during the course of most winters in the UK, primarily at sites in the east. Most records tend to relate to birds in flocks of other geese. However, during periods of cold weather on the continent influxes of discrete, larger, groups can occur.

Considering that weather-related influxes were noted in The Netherlands (Hornman *et al.* 2012) and Switzerland (Keller & Müller 2012), a larger arrival of Tundra Bean Geese into the UK might have been expected during the midwinter period of 2010/11. The majority seen during WeBS Core counts were singles, but several small flocks were noted including 12 at North Warren & Thorpeness Mere (Jan-Feb).

Sites with 3 or more birds in 2009/10

Breydon Water & Berney Marshes	17, Jan	Lower Derwent Ings	4, Dec
North Warren & Thorpeness Mere	12, Jan	Alde Complex	4, Jan
Humber Estuary	8, Nov	Swale Estuary	3, Feb
Abberton Reservoir	6, Jan	Achlochan	3, Jan

Pink-footed Goose
Anser brachyrhynchus

International threshold (Greenland/Iceland population):			3,500
Great Britain threshold:			3,600
All-Ireland threshold:			+

GB max:	288,798	Oct
NI max:	51	Dec
% young:	19.9	Brood size: 2.3

The annual census of Pink-footed Geese is carried out through the Goose & Swan Monitoring Programme, coordinated by WWT. Late 2010 saw counts undertaken in October, November and December, representing the 51st consecutive Icelandic-breeding Goose Census (Mitchell 2011a).

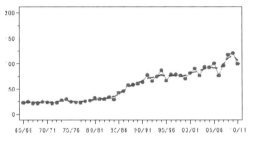

Figure 6.a, Annual indices & trend for Pink-footed Goose in GB.

Despite some recent fluctuations in numbers, partly due to variation in coverage, the long-term trend for the species has been one of steady increase. During 2010/11, the population using sites in Britain (including estimates for non-counted sites) was considered to be 297,798 birds, an marked decrease compared to the high of over 360,000 estimated the previous year. Birds were relatively early to arrive in autumn 2010. In September, 32,882 were recorded at Loch of Strathbeg, while by October, a site record peak ofover 65,000 had gathered at Montrose Basin.

Although it is possible that large numbers of Pink-footed Geese may have been in inaccessible and uncounted areas of Iceland during October, there was no marked increase in the overall census totals between October and November. This suggests that the decrease noted between years was real, at least to some extent, and not merely attributable to a late departure from Iceland (Mitchell 2011a).

Typically, Pink-footed Geese shift locations within the UK during the course of the winter. However, the severe weather in December 2010 clearly affected the expected distribution at the start of the midwinter period. For example, the Solway Firth experienced a huge influx of nearly 50,000 geese, as birds escaped the frozen waterbodies and extensive snow cover to the north. Further south, the peak counts in Norfolk where several sites have become increasingly important for this species in recent decades, included 30,000 at Holkham Marshes and 37,350 at Snettisham.

Tommy Holden

The combination of consistent annual breeding success, targeted nature reserve management, and changes in availability of agricultural foraging resources (Fox *et al.* 2005, Gill *et al.* 2006) have contributed to the rise of the wintering Pink-footed Goose population in Britain since the mid 1980s. However, with the midwinter periods of 2009/10 and 2010/11 having been particularly harsh (notably so in Scotland), with prolonged snow cover and freezing temperatures, over-winter mortality is likely to have risen in the last two years. We will have to wait to determine the extent to which the overall population size may have been affected by these recent winters.

It is interesting to recall that a recent population model developed using counts and demographic data for Pink-footed Goose (Trinder *et al.* 2005), predicted that the population would reach equilibrium at approximately 220,000 birds. The same work indicated that there is only a very small chance that numbers would fall below 50,000 by the year 2030.

Breeding success was assessed at several locations throughout Scotland and England. The proportion of young within flocks was 19.9% and the mean brood size for pairs with young was 2.3, both figures higher than the previous year and the mean of the preceding decade (Mitchell 2011a).

	06/07	07/08	08/09	09/10	10/11	Mon	Mean
Sites of international importance in the UK							
Southwest Lancashire	39,030[13]	17,877	90,455[13]	69,790[13]	17,160[13]	Nov	46,862
Loch of Strathbeg	37,396	39,370[13]	53,454[13]	60,626[13]	35,000[13]	Mar	45,169
Snettisham	33,485[13]	47,530[13]	51,950[13]	28,700[13]	37,350[13]	Jan	39,803
Holkham Marshes	60,000[13]	46,400[13]	19,510[13]	19,630[13]	30,000[13]	Jan	35,108
West Water Reservoir	(56,900)	27,960[13]	47,361[13]	26,400[13]	16,650[13]	Oct	35,054
Montrose Basin	25,000[13]	23,945[13]	38,911[13]	6,500	65,060[13]	Oct	31,883
Aberlady Bay		23,415[13]	32,244[13]	15,721[13]	20,622[13]	Sep	23,001
Loch of Skene	(22,930)[13]	19,000[13]	18,560[13]	16,780[13]	27,500[13]	Nov	20,954
Solway Estuary	23,313[13]	5,004	5,751	6,633	50,000[13]	Dec	18,140
Breydon Water and Berney Marshes	17,800[11]	22,785[12]	21,400[11]	14,230[11]	12,250[11]	Jan	17,693
West Freugh				(16,000)[12]	(22)	Feb	(16,000)
Carsebreck and Rhynd Lochs	12,600[13]	11,200[13]	15,200[13]	18,250[13]	16,550[13]	Oct	14,760
Scolt Head	17,200[13]	7,870[13]	23,000[13]	10,750[13]			14,705
Findhorn Bay	(3,800)[13]	7,800[13]	9,850[13]	14,500[13]	6,300[13]	Oct	9,613
Brow Well			120[13]	124[13]	26,570[13]	Dec	8,938 ▲
Loch Leven	14,600[13]	1,000	17,618[13]	4,539	5,168[13]	Oct	8,585
Martham Broad			8,500[13]				8,500
Beauly Firth				12,800[13]	3,370[13]	Oct	8,085
Wigtown Bay	(6,695)	11,720[13]	(4,943)	5,941	6,120	Jan	7,927
Kilconquhar Loch	90	7,010[13]	14,000[13]	9,540[13]	6,730[13]	Dec	7,474
Morecambe Bay	(7,145)	3,376	(7,255)	(2,757)	10,689	Oct	7,116
Loch of Lintrathen	7,040[13]	8,410[13]	10,745[13]	3,550[13]	5,380[13]	Nov	7,025
Priestside					7,000[13]	Dec	7,000 ▲
Winter Loch, St Fergus Gas Terminal	6,620[13]						6,620
Hule Moss	2,250[13]	6,850[13]	6,250[13]	9,350[13]	7,550[13]	Nov	6,450
Ythan Estuary and Slains Lochs	1,600	2,000		10,000	10,970	Oct	6,143
Dupplin Lochs	1,450[13]	2,100[13]		18,500[13]	870[13]	Nov	5,730
Middlemuir (New Pitsligo Moss)		4,500[13]	3,500[13]		9,000[13]	Oct	5,667
Holme and Thornham	4,000[13]		4,170[13]	8,000[13]			5,390
Simonswood Peat Moss	3,000[13]	4,500[13]			8,500[13]	Nov	5,333
Horsey Mere	5,430[13]				5,125[13]	Dec	5,278
Fala Flow	2,170[13]	3,650[13]	1,510[13]	13,084[13]	5,604[13]	Oct	5,204
Holme		3,865[13]			6,500[13]	Dec	5,183
Eden Estuary	9	430[13]	20,520[11]	650[13]	3,400[13]	Nov	5,002
Lochhill	760	5,000[12]	7,100[12]	7,000[12]			4,965
Wedholme Flow	0	1,300	6,000[12]	10,000	7,000	Mar	4,860
Humber Estuary	4,151	3,703	7,108	3,944	4,180	Nov	4,617
Lindisfarne	(6,132)	6,900[13]	3,500[13]	3,500[13]	2,630[13]	Oct	4,532
Biggar Moss	0	6,500	7,000				4,500
Norton Marsh	6,650[13]	4,850[13]	2,720[13]	2,831[13]			4,263
Sites no longer meeting table qualifying levels in WeBS-Year 2010/2011							
River Tay - Haughs of Kercock	3,702[13]	3,165[13]	2,704[13]	2,500[13]	1,308[13]	Nov	2,676
Loch Spynie	9,000[13]	150[13]	1,000[13]	3[13]			2,538
Forth (Skinflats)	2,950[13]	2,176[13]	4,463[13]	775[13]	365[13]	Nov	2,146
Sites below table qualifying levels but exceeding threshold in WeBS-Year 2010/11 in Great Britain							
Munlochy Bay	2,600[13]	2,500[13]	750[13]	3,500[13]	5,000[13]	Oct	2,870
Ythan Estuary	5,700	2,300	750	(2,110)	4,200	Jan	3,238
Loch Connell		4,500[12]	3	(3,000)	4,000	Mar	2,876
Loch Tullybelton	2,700[13]	2,800[13]	4,000[13]	150[13]	3,800[13]	Nov	2,690

European White-fronted Goose

Anser albifrons albifrons

GB max:	3,087	Jan
NI max:	0	
% young:	25.9	Brood size: 2.3

International threshold	
(NW Siberia/ NE Europe population):	12,000
Great Britain threshold:	24
All-Ireland threshold:	+

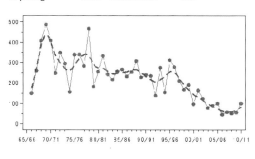

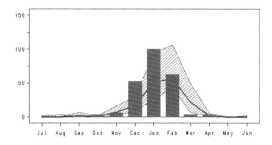

Annual Index

Trend

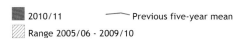

2010/11   Previous five-year mean

Range 2005/06 - 2009/10

Figure 7.a, Annual indices & trend for European White-fronted Goose in GB.

Figure 7.b, Monthly indices for European White-fronted Goose in GB.

Much has been written in past WeBS reports about how the steady decline in numbers of wintering European White-fronted Geese in Britain is at least partly attributable to short stopping, in response to milder winter conditions further east in northwestern Europe. This distributional shift in core wintering range has resulted in an associated increase in wintering numbers in The Netherlands (Hornman *et al.* 2011). In view of this trend, cold weather events might be anticipated to result in an opposing response, and 2010/11 was no exception. A marked influx was noted across eastern England during the frozen conditions that affected much of north-west Europe, yielding a British monthly maximum of 3,087 birds in January 2011.

Although the maximum reported from Severn Estuary (650, Jan) was higher than the recent five-year average, this total was surpassed at two sites in eastern England. The peak aggregations at Alde Compex (779, Jan) and North Warren & Thorpeness Mere (483, Jan) both represent record WeBS counts for those sites, and the count of 758 at Swale Estuary in February is the most there since 1998/99. Historically, the Swale Estuary was used by larger numbers of European White-fronted Geese, exemplified by the regular presence of

1,000+ wintering birds during the 1980s and early 1990s that included a site maximum of 2,550 geese in February 1987. However, as with other formerly important sites, numbers there decreased as short-stopping became more prevalent.

Records were widely distributed across a variety of sites in England during winter 2010/11 (54 in total, compared to an average of 24 sites in the previous five years). As can be seen from the table below, a number of noteworthy flocks were recorded away from traditionally favoured sites during the very cold December to January period. These included groups of 30+ on the south coast of England where the species rarely occurs nowadays.

European White-fronted Geese were aged at two sites (WWT Slimbridge and North Warren, Suffolk) during the winter. Overall, 25.9% were first-winter birds, a similar figure to the previous year and indicative of a reasonably productive breeding season compared to the longer-term average. Brood size data were also collected at Slimbridge, and ranged from one to five goslings with an average of 2.3 young per successful pair (Reed 2011b). Notably, in Denmark, brood size in October 2010 was estimated to be somewhat greater, at 3.64 young per successful pair (P. Clausen, pers. comm.).

	06/07	07/08	08/09	09/10	10/11	Mon	Mean
Sites of national importance in Great Britain							
Severn Estuary	542 [5]	527 [5]	503 [5]	676 [5]	650 [5]	Jan	580
Swale Estuary	355	315	160	523	758	Feb	422
Heigham Holmes	570 [49]	800 [49]	200 [49]	150 [49]	230 [49]	Dec	390
North Warren and Thorpeness Mere	180	452 [6]	245	293	483	Jan	331
Alde Complex	0	(58)	206	(7)	779	Jan	328
Dungeness and Rye Bay	151	194	239	388	(0)		243
North Norfolk Coast	200	275	226	96	257	Dec	211
Middle Yare Marshes	66	193	72	90	202	Jan	125
Pegwell Bay	0	118	0	120 [6]	81 [6]	Dec	64
Lower Derwent Ings	0	1	0	136	120	Dec	51
Breydon Water and Berney Marshes	0	61 [6]	0	28 [6]	155 [6]	Dec	49
Arun Valley	4	1	(0)	(0)	(102)	Jan	36 ▲
Buckden and Stirtloe Pits				35 [6]			35
Thames Estuary	0	24	17	28	90	Jan	32
Minsmere	0	0	0	0	139	Jan	28 ▲
Hamford Water	1	0	1	0	135	Dec	27 ▲
Sites no longer meeting table qualifying levels in WeBS-Year 2010/2011							
Stodmarsh	0	32	0	0	68	Dec	20
Ouse Washes	7	0	41 [6]	0	23 [6]	Jan	14
Sites below table qualifying levels but exceeding threshold in WeBS-Year 2010/11 in Great Britain							
Stodmarsh	0	32	0	0	68	Dec	20
Crouch-Roach Estuary	0	1	0	0	58	Dec	12
Humber Estuary	0	0	0	3	56	Feb	12
Cuckmere Estuary	0	0	0	0	35	Jan	7
Dingle Marshes and Walberswick NNR	0	0	0	0	35	Jan	7
North West Solent	1	0	0	0	34	Jan	7
Otmoor	(0)	(5)	0	14 [6]	29	Jan	14
Cotswold Water Park (East)	0	0	0	0	28	Feb	6
The Wash	2	0	0	0	25	Dec	5

Greenland White-fronted Goose

Anser albifrons flavirostris

International threshold (Greenland population):	240
Great Britain threshold:	130
All-Ireland threshold:	110

GB max:	13,269	Dec
NI max:	68	Jan
% young:	22.9	Brood size: 3.1

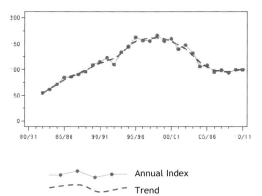

Figure 8.a, Annual indices & trend for Greenland White-fronted Goose in GB.

Greenland White-fronted Geese breed in the low arctic coastal fringe of west Greenland, and migrate southwards through south and west Iceland during September and October. The species then winters exclusively in Britain and Ireland, favoured locations being Islay on the west coast of Scotland and Wexford Slobs in Ireland.

2010/11 represented a year of stability for the UK's internationally important population of wintering Greenland White-fronted Geese, which as well as being Red-listed in the UK (Eaton *et al.* 2009) also qualifies as 'Endangered' under IUCN criteria (Birdlife International 2012). The two years since the low point in 2008/09 have seen a slight improvement in the national index and it would appear that the steep decline which characterised the period of 1998/99 to 2006/07 has come to an end. A ban on hunting in Iceland has probably helped to enable numbers to stabilise in recent years. Previously, hunting pressure had represented an unsustainable source of mortality in combination with a long period of low productivity – considered responsible for the decline noted since mid 1990s (Fox *et al.* 2012).

The annual census organised by the Greenland White-fronted Goose Study Group, was carried out in December 2010 and March 2011. The peak of 13,269 geese in December represents an increase of 6.1% compared to the maximum recorded in 2009/10. Typically, over half of the Scottish population was on Islay, while the peak count from the most southerly wintering site in Britain, the Dyfi Estuary, was slightly lower than recent years.

The percentage of young on Islay (22.9%) was the highest for 25 years and the fourth highest since records began in 1962. Mean brood size of 3.05 also implies a successful breeding season. The spring of 2010 was exceptionally mild and snow-free in west Greenland, so geese arrived to good feeding conditions. Warm temperatures persisted through the summer and probably also contributed to high productivity (Fox *et al.* 2012).

	06/07	07/08	08/09	09/10	10/11	Mon	Mean
Sites of international importance in the UK							
Island of Islay	7,902 [5]	7,980 [5]	8,590 [5]	7,262 [5]	8,027 [5]	Jan	7,952
Machrihanish	1,716 [5]	1,285 [11]	1,477 [5]	2,180 [5]	1,866 [5]	Mar	1,705
Rhunahaorine	940 [5]	1,451 [5]	879 [5]	1,017 [5]	961 [5]	Dec	1,050
Tiree	974 [5]	803 [5]	979 [5]	787 [5]	898 [5]	Nov	888
Isle of Coll	687 [5]	445 [5]	336 [5]	284 [5]	301 [5]	Nov	411
West Freugh/Stranraer Lochs	360 [5]	247 [5]	273 [5]	350 [10]	470 [5]	Jan	340
Sound of Gigha	105 [5]	194 [5]	330	337 [5]	679	Mar	329 ▲
Isle of Lismore	273 [5]	240 [5]	280 [5]	300 [5]	245 [5]	Mar	268
Keills Peninsula and Isle of Danna	300 [5]	202 [5]	239 [5]	214 [5]	259 [5]	Nov	243 ▲
Sites of national importance in Great Britain							
Bute	209 [5]	240 [5]	210 [5]	215 [5]	230 [5]	Nov	221
Loch Lomond	210 [5]	223 [11]	220 [5]	200 [5]	210 [11]	Nov	213
Clachan and Whitehouse	186 [5]	120 [5]	170 [5]	182 [5]	359 [5]	Jan	203
Loch Ken	206 [5]	177 [5]	194 [5]	186 [5]	203 [5]	Feb	193
Westfield Marshes	155 [5]	173 [5]	176 [5]		180 [5]	Nov	171
Loch of Mey	176 [5]	146 [5]	240 [5]	170 [5]	118 [5]	Mar	170
South Uist: Loch Bee/Kilaulay	160 [5]	184 [5]	150 [5]	123 [5]	100 [5]	Nov	143
Sites no longer meeting table qualifying levels in WeBS-Year 2010/2011							
Loch Gorm				14	145	Nov	80
Sites below table qualifying levels but exceeding threshold in WeBS-Year 2010/11 in Great Britain							
Loch Gorm				14	145	Nov	80

Lesser White-fronted Goose
Anser erythropus

Vagrant and escape
Native Range: SE Europe, Asia

Presumed escapes were seen at four sites in 2010/11, including a long-stayer throughout much of the year at Llyn Traffwll and two at Saltfleet (Oct-Nov).

Greylag Goose (Icelandic)
Anser anser

International threshold (Iceland population):   980
Great Britain threshold: 850
All-Ireland threshold: 50

GB max: 104,450   Nov
NI max: 0**
% young: 22.4   Brood size: 2.1

**small numbers remain difficult to distinguish from resident birds*

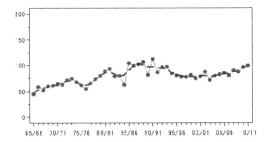

Figure 9.a, Annual indices & trend for Icelandic Greylag Goose in GB.

Counts of Icelandic Greylag Goose were undertaken in late 2010 as part of the 51st consecutive Icelandic-breeding Goose Census (IGC), coordinated by WWT. This census incorporates monitoring of sites in Britain, Ireland, the Faeroes, Norway and Iceland.

Howard Lacey

Following adjustments for the presence of birds from other populations and the addition of estimated counts, a total population estimate of 110,662 geese was derived from the higher November total (Mitchell *et al.* 2011). This includes 16,000 in Iceland and small numbers elsewhere, but represents an overall increase of 1.1% compared to the previous year. Trinder *et al.* (2010) analysed IGC data from the last 15

years, the time in which the majority of Iceland Greylag Geese began wintering on Orkney. This shift in winter distribution has probably meant that fewer Greylag Geese are being shot in Britain, as there are fewer wildfowlers on Orkney than other parts of Scotland. Despite a large annual harvest in Iceland, a presumed reduction in the number shot in other parts of the winter range combined with relatively high breeding success in recent years has probably been sufficient to reverse the decline noted in this population during the 1990s.

During early November, birds were aged at several localities across northern Scotland. Breeding success was similar to the recent average, with flocks containing 22.4% young and a mean brood size of 2.1 young per successful pair (Mitchell 2011a).

It should be stated that there is an increasing number of British Greylag Geese present in Scotland, with Mitchell *et al.* (2011) estimating there to be c. 47,400 British Greylag Geese in Scotland in the summers of 2008 and 2009. With large concentrations in Orkney (c. 10,000) and Shetland (c. 5,000), where Iceland Greylag Geese are known to winter, separating the two populations for monitoring continues to be a challenge.

	06/07	07/08	08/09	09/10	10/11	Mon	Mean
Sites of international importance in the UK							
Orkney	55,521 [13]	67,540 [13]	68,349 [13]	69,519 [13]	80,744 [13]	Dec	68,334
Loch Leven	620	700	1,195 [13]	18,573 [13]	(1,364)	Jul	5,272
Bute	1,670 [13]	1,960 [13]	3,800 [13]	2,550 [13]	8,010 [13]	Dec	3,598
Dornoch Firth	2,858	3,310 [13]	6,379	1,825	3,596 [13]	Nov	3,594
Strathearn (West)	3,170 [13]	1,400 [13]					2,285
Cromarty Firth	832 [13]	5,268 [13]	992	2,501 [13]	914 [13]	Nov	2,101
Loch Fleet Complex	1,762	2,100 [13]	1,110 [13]	2,143	2,255 [13]	Nov	1,874
Inner Firth of Tay	157 [13]	636 [13]	2,640 [13]	1,943 [13]			1,344
West Freugh				1,000 [6]			1,000
Sites of national importance in the UK							
Gadloch	1,100 [13]	600	1,990	785	401	Oct	975
Forth Estuary	(471)	875	936 [13]	(783)	1,101	Sep	971
Island of Westray	1,030 [13]	735 [13]					883
Sites no longer meeting table qualifying levels in WeBS-Year 2010/2011							
Mill Dam & Balfour Mains Pools	676	1,095	850	374	580	Feb	715
Loch of Skene	(500) [13]	520 [13]	790 [13]	760 [13]	530 [13]	Nov	650
Sites below table qualifying levels but exceeding threshold in WeBS-Year 2010/11 in Great Britain							
Montrose Basin	250 [13]	226	161 [13]	275	2,519	Jan	686
Loch Ryan	1	92	0	301 [6]	1,484	Dec	376
Loch of Spiggie	344 [13]	625	443	630	940	Oct	596

Greylag Goose (British/Irish)

Anser anser

Pooled 're-established' and 'NW Scotland' populations
Great Britain threshold: **1,400**[†]
All-Ireland threshold: **?**[†]

GB max:	39,448	Oct
NI max:	2,010	Mar
% young:	27.5*	
Brood size:	3.2*	

*NW Scotland only

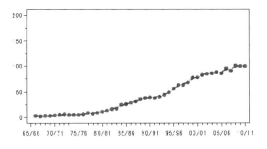

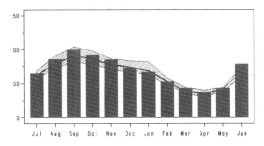

Annual Index
Trend

2010/11 — Previous five-year mean
Range 2005/06 - 2009/10

Figure 10.a, Annual indices & trend for British/Irish Greylag Goose

Figure 10.b, Monthly indices for British/Irish Greylag Goose

British/Irish Greylag Goose, listed as such in the annual WeBS report since 2009/10, refers to a combination of the populations previously referred to as 're-established' and 'North West Scotland' Greylag Geese. As these populations have spread towards each other in Scotland, it is no longer possible to make a clear distinction between them (Mitchell *et al.* 2010, 2012). Until such time that the British population of Greylag Goose is recognised internationally, sites will be here as surpassing the threshold for national importance only.

The annual index for resident Greylag Goose at WeBS sites is now showing signs of having reached stability, whereas the breeding population in the wider countryside continues to increase (Baillie *et al.* 2012). During WeBS Core counts, the largest aggregations were noted during the post-breeding period when birds form moulting flocks. Following the change in the classification of resident Greylag Geese in Britain, six sites continue to surpass the revised threshold for national importance (Musgrove *et al.* 2011). These include Nosterfield Gravel Pits, Lower Derwent Ings and North Norfolk Coast in England, and Tiree and the Uists in Scotland. Numbers have declined on Tiree and the Uists due to an increase in the number of birds shot under licence (Mitchell 2011b).

	06/07	07/08	08/09	09/10	10/11	Mon	Mean
Sites of national importance in Great Britain[†]							
Tiree	4,005[32]	3,694[32]	3,370[32]	2,848[32]	2,639[32]	Aug	3,311
Nosterfield Gravel Pits	1,898	2,819	1,953	3,885	2,024	Aug	2,516
North Uist	2,318[34]	2,294[34]	2,783[34]	2,488[34]	2,150[34]	Aug	2,406
South Uist	1,719[34]	1,141[34]	1,971[34]	2,482[34]	1,661[34]	Aug	1,795
Lower Derwent Ings	1,780	1,056	1,472	2,468	1,980	Dec	1,751
North Norfolk Coast	1,725	1,270	2,203	1,159	1,859	Aug	1,643
Other sites with mean peak counts of 800+ birds in Great Britain[†]							
King`s Dyke Pits, Whittlesey	1,338	(0)	(90)	(46)	(12)	Mar	1,338
The Wash	1,337	1,159	1,200	1,291	1,362	Jun	1,270
Humber Estuary	(785)	(906)	945	1,401	(1,111)	Nov	1,173
Point of Ayre Gravel Pit	900	1,165	1,630	1,250	56	Jul	1,000
Tophill Low Reservoirs	1,190	1,230	1,000[6]	(890)	474	Oct	974
Ouse Washes	810	687[6]	1,496	1,061	750	Oct	961
Dungeness and Rye Bay	773	1,409	964	740	787	Aug	935
Hay-a-Park Gravel Pits	825	1,503	606	1,007	720	Sep	932

	06/07	07/08	08/09	09/10	10/11	Mon	Mean
Livermere and Ampton Water		1,285	784	642			904
Windermere	985	767	843	1,184	586	Jun	873
Bolton-on-Swale Gravel Pits	615	1,585	716	732	630	Dec	856
Morecambe Bay	(617)	(585)	1,139	538	861	Nov	846
Sutton and Lound Gravel Pits	494	563	1,095	868	1,131	Aug	830
Alton Water	1,056	1,068	613	807	555	Oct	820
Sites with mean peak counts of 50+ birds in Northern Ireland[†]							
Loughs Neagh and Beg	662	1,284	(917)	1,294	726	Mar	992
Lough Foyle	974	716	750	194	1,184	Mar	764
Strangford Lough	277 [5]	431	513	462	520	Nov	441
Belfast Lough	196 [5]	134	86	87	90	Dec	119
Tullyratty Lake	213	5					109
Lower Lough Erne	140	38	(14)	(30)	(12)	Jan	89
Clea Lakes					78	Nov	78
Upper Lough Erne	73	64	21	26	102	Jan	57
Sites below table qualifying levels but exceeding threshold in WeBS-Year 2010/11 in Great Britain[†]							
River Avon - Fordingbridge to Ringwood	113	150	193	167	920	Nov	309
Abberton Reservoir	103	239	212	870	801	Aug	445
Other sites surpassing table qualifying levels in Winter 2010/2011 in Northern Ireland[†]							
Larne Lough	(15)	21	11	37	(106)	Dec	44

[†] *as the British threshold (1,400) is relatively high and no All-Ireland threshold has been set, qualifying levels of 800 & 50 have been chosen to select sites in Great Britain and Northern Ireland respectively, for presentation in this report.*

Bar-headed Goose

Anser indicus

Escape
Native Range: S Asia

Bar-headed Geese were recorded at 35 WeBS sites in Britain, with a monthly peak of 30 birds in October. Maxima of six were present at Loch of Lowes and Par Sands Pools & St Andrews Road, both in September.

Snow Goose

Anser caerulescens

Escape and possible vagrant
Native Range: N America

Reported from 19 WeBS sites, most records of Snow Goose involved one or two birds, the notable exception being 22 at Fairburn Ings in January. None of the records received in 2010/11 are considered to relate to birds of genuine provenance.

Ross's Goose

Anser rossii

Escape and possible vagrant
Native Range: N America

Single Ross's Geese were reported from ten sites, with a monthly peak of five birds in October. The only possibly wild bird was one at North Norfolk Coast in midwinter.

Emperor Goose

Anser canagicus

Escape
Native Range: Alaska, NE Siberia

The resident flock was present at South Walney Island (Morecambe Bay) throughout 2010/11, peaking at 14 in August. Elsewhere, one was at Walthamstow Reservoirs in October.

Canada Goose
Branta canadensis

Naturalised introduction[†]
Native Range: N America

GB max:	65,548	**Oct**
NI max:	903	**Jan**

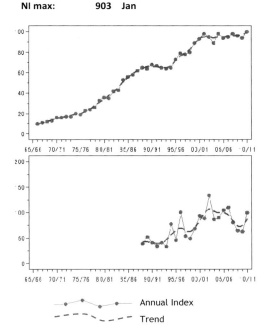

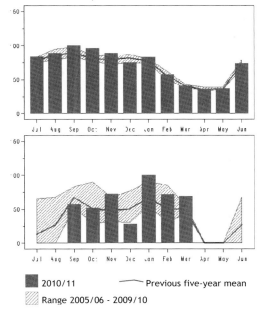

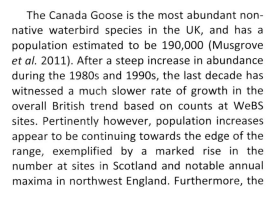

- Annual Index
- - - Trend

■ 2010/11　　　　⌒ Previous five-year mean
▨ Range 2005/06 - 2009/10

Figure 11.a, Annual indices & trend for Canada Goose in GB (above) & NI (below).

Figure 11.b, Monthly indices for Canada Goose in GB (above) & NI (below).

The Canada Goose is the most abundant non-native waterbird species in the UK, and has a population estimated to be 190,000 (Musgrove *et al.* 2011). After a steep increase in abundance during the 1980s and 1990s, the last decade has witnessed a much slower rate of growth in the overall British trend based on counts at WeBS sites. Pertinently however, population increases appear to be continuing towards the edge of the range, exemplified by a marked rise in the number at sites in Scotland and notable annual maxima in northwest England. Furthermore, the adjacent population in The Netherlands is also increasing at a fast rate (Hornman *et al.* 2012).

In 2010/11, maxima at most of the prinicipal sites listed below were close to or slightly above average. The highest count was 4,078 at Mersey Estuary in July; following the all-time WeBS high recorded there in the previous month (Holt *et al.* 2011). Peaks of 1,000+ were received from a further 13 sites, including for the first time during WeBS counts at Lee Valley Gravel Pits (Jul) and Atcham Bridge to Wroxeter (Jan).

	06/07	07/08	08/09	09/10	10/11	Mon	Mean
Sites with mean peak counts of 700+ birds in Great Britain							
Mersey Estuary	2,160	2,706	3,500	4,519	4,078	Jul	3,393
Dyfi Estuary	2,420	2,799	3,319	2,478	2,966	Nov	2,796
Dee Estuary (England and Wales)	1,810	2,536	3,204 [10]	(2,303)	2,688	Oct	2,560
Ribble Estuary	(1,245)	(1,494)	1,625	1,828	2,207	Jan	1,887
Colliford Reservoir	2,439	1,637	632	1,409	897	Jun	1,403
Lee Valley Gravel Pits	(488)	(516)	1,200	(549)	(1,108)	Jul	1,200
Arun Valley	1,076	570	(939)	(1,535)	1,390	Oct	1,143
Medway Estuary	824	1,413	(1,123)	1,103	(398)	Feb	1,116
Rutland Water	1,118	1,009	1,063	1,084	1,083	Sep	1,071
Lower Derwent Ings	688	573	703	1,697	1,005	Oct	933
Bewl Water	548	1,039	(669)	1,072 [12]	(1,011)	Dec	918

	06/07	07/08	08/09	09/10	10/11	Mon	Mean
Ouse Washes	575	558	1,463 [12]	823 [12]	1,158	Nov	915
Alde Complex	684	1,131	1,248	851	566	Dec	896
Harewood Lake		1,080	630	999	851	Oct	890
R. Severn: Atcham Bridge to Wroxeter	600	650	1,200	800	1,100	Jan	870
Abberton Reservoir	(213)	1,036	480	355	1,502	Aug	843
Doxey Marshes SSSI	802	726	987	884	650	Sep	810
Taw-Torridge Estuary	986	(565)	647	944	540	Jan	779
Windermere	747 [12]	796	967	878 [12]	495	Aug	777
Osberton	1,212	790	850	542	481	Sep	775
Pitsford Reservoir	832	587	877	807	743	Sep	769
Fal Complex	655	1,035	442	490	1,015	Sep	727
The Wash	677	559	644	792	938	Nov	722
Sites with mean peak counts of 50+ birds in Northern Ireland							
Upper Lough Erne	665	390	301	202	486	Jan	409
Lower Lough Erne	365	286	(71)	(78)	41	Oct	231
Strangford Lough	247	161	166	230 [10]	(242)	Jan	209
Lough McNean Lower	44	148	27	60	140	Jan	84
Sites below table qualifying levels but exceeding threshold in WeBS-Year 2010/11 in Great Britain							
Teifi Estuary	454	195	500	600	1,000	Sep	550
Tamar Complex	309	276	257	432	955	Sep	446
Loch of Lowes	14	85	42	47	951	Sep	228
Drakelow Gravel Pit	78 [12]	232	199	310	906	Sep	345
Camel Estuary	129	197	817	641	888	Aug	534
Sandbach Flashes	191	235	364	450	850	Oct	418
Nosterfield Gravel Pits	726	340	378	686	810	Dec	588
Batemill Sand Quarry	265	160	147	308	754	Aug	327
Roadford Reservoir	552	593	594	432	750	Jan	584
Somerset Levels	367	700	547	508	746	Jan	574
R. Severn and R. Vyrnwy Confluence	72	(168)	255	(130)	745	Oct	357
Netherfield Gravel Pits	17	56	57	88	743	Oct	192
Brading Harbour	408	310	219	426	735	Jan	420
Tees Estuary	504	447	443	761	730	Nov	577
Thames Estuary	494	353	405	582	708	Sep	508

[†] as no British or All-Ireland thresholds have been set qualifying levels of 700 and 50 have been chosen to select sites, in Great Britain and Northern Ireland respectively, for presentation in this report

---

Lesser Canada Goose
Branta hutchinsii

Vagrant and escape
Native Range: N America

Records were received from four WeBS sites, none likely to have related to birds of wild origin.

Hawaiian Goose
Branta sandvicensis

Escape
Native Range: Hawaii

One was at Rochester Pools (Mar to May).

Greenland Barnacle Goose
Branta leucopsis

International threshold (Greenland population): 710
Great Britain threshold: 580
All-Ireland threshold: 90

GB max: 44,844 Dec
NI max: 0
% young: 11.2 Brood size: 2.3

Wintering exclusively at sites in northwest Scotland and Ireland, ringing studies have shown Greenland Barnacle Geese to be faithful to specific wintering sites, with 70% of birds returning to the same site between winters.

In 2010/11, counts were carried out at most of the important areas in Scotland, which in spring 2008 (the last complete census) had held 92.5% of the total number of Greenland Barnacle Geese in Scotland. Two comprehensive counts of Islay are organised by Scottish Natural Heritage (SNH) each winter; those in 2010/11 were 44,844 birds in December 2010 and 35,661 in March 2011. The adopted island estimate is taken to be the mean of these two counts, hence 40,252 birds. This is 7% greater than the adopted estimate of the previous winter, but 20% lower than the all-time maximum of 50,232 geese in 2006/07.

Results from productivity assessments carried out on Islay in 2010/11 indicate a reasonably good breeding season in 2010; 11.2% young being higher than the previous 10-year mean of 8.5%. Notably, since 2001, annual breeding success based on assessments on Islay has been <10% in seven out of the last ten years. With the addition of data from Tiree and Inishkea (Ireland), the mean overall estimate for 2010 is reduced slightly to 10.4%. Mean brood size on Islay was also relatively high at 2.26 young per successful pair, whereas on Tiree it was considerably lower (1.39 young per successful pair) (Mitchell 2011c).

	06/07	07/08	08/09	09/10	10/11	Mon	Mean
Sites of international importance in the UK							
Island of Islay	52,709[32]	44,961[32]	44,896[32]	40,727[32]	44,844[32]	Dec	45,627
Tiree	4,323[32]	3,393[32]	3,725[32]	3,729[32]	4,190[32]	Dec	3,872
North Uist	2,119[32]	3,630[32]	3,393[32]	2,392[32]	2,546[32]	Feb	2,816
South Walls (Hoy)	1,710[32]	1,874[32]	1,800[32]	1,600[32]	1,861[32]	Feb	1,769
Colonsay/Oronsay	1,332[32]	1,200[32]	1,874[32]	2,100[32]	2,056[32]	Dec	1,712
Isle of Coll	2,456[32]	800[32]	968[32]	880[32]	775[32]	Dec	1,176
Sites of national importance in the UK							
Keills Peninsula and Isle of Danna	627[3]	711[3]	550[3]	600[3]	715[3]	Dec	641 ▼
Sites no longer meeting table qualifying levels in WeBS-Year 2010/2011							
Balnakiel Farm	130	809	(0)	(0)	500	Feb	480

Svalbard Barnacle Goose
Branta leucopsis

International threshold (Svalbard population):	300
Great Britain threshold:	330

GB max:	35,640	Oct
NI max:	0	
% young:	10.8	Brood size: 2.5

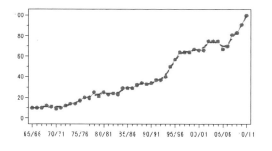

Figure 12.a, Annual indices & trend for Svalbard Barnacle Goose in GB.

The population of Svalbard-breeding Barnacle Geese increased for the fifth consecutive year. Consequently, in 2010/11, the annual index reached its highest ever value. Twenty-five co-ordinated counts were undertaken between September 2010 and May 2011 across the Inner Solway Estuary, and used to derive an adopted population total of 35,900 birds (Griffin 2011). This represents the largest ever estimate, and is an increase of 9% on the comparable estimate for the previous winter.

Although the population is increasing, the core feeding areas for Svalbard Barnacle Geese on the Solway have remained broadly the same. Rockcliffe Marsh at the eastern end of the Solway is especially heavily used by geese throughout the winter, and in late April/early May during a period of rapid turnover when at least 99% of the population visit the site for up to a week before departing for Svalbard (WWT data). As Rockcliffe Marsh is expanding due to saltmarsh accretion, it is becoming increasingly difficult to monitor the area. Therefore, it would be timely to consider the use of aerial counts coupled with high definition photography of the flocks, in order to assess the true population size and provide a comparison with ground counts.

In 2010/11, breeding success was assessed throughout the winter at WWT Caerlaverock and other sites around the Solway; 10.8% young and a mean brood size of 2.5 young per successful pair, represents the best breeding season since 2007.

	06/07	07/08	08/09	09/10	10/11	Mon	Mean
Sites of international importance in the UK							
Solway Firth	29,370 [1]	29,815 [1]	31,111 [1]	29,170 [1]	35,640 [1]	Oct	31,021
Lindisfarne	1,202	(190)	70	(300)	42	Jan	438
Sites no longer meeting table qualifying levels in WeBS-Year 2010/2011							
Loch of Strathbeg	181	121 [8]	62	67	31	Oct	92

Naturalised Barnacle Goose

Naturalised establishment[†]

Branta leucopsis

GB max: 1,802 Jan
NI max: 375 Oct

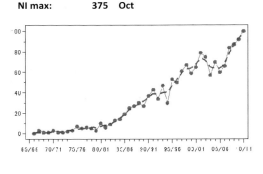

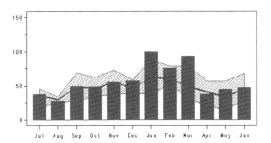

Annual Index

Trend

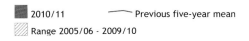

2010/11

Range 2005/06 - 2009/10

Previous five-year mean

Figure 13.a, Annual indices & trend for Naturalised Barnacle Goose in GB.

Figure 13.b, Monthly indices for Naturalised Barnacle Goose in GB.

Barnacle Geese are treated as naturalised on the basis of geographical location, with those outside the normal ranges of the Svalbard and Greenland populations assigned as such. As a result, it should be borne in mind that is possible that some extra-limital birds from the Svalbard and Greenland populations, are incorrectly assigned, though this is considered unlikely.

The national index for naturalised Barnacle Geese rose again in 2010/11, to its highest ever level. A similarly steep rise has been witnessed across the North Sea in The Netherlands (Hornman *et al.* 2012). Counts of 300+ were noted at three sites during WeBS Core counts in 2010/11; Willington, Minsmere, and North Warren & Thorpeness Mere. Maxima in excess of 100 birds were noted at a further eight sites. In Northern Ireland, a highest ever peak was recorded at Strangford Lough.

	06/07	07/08	08/09	09/10	10/11	Mon	Mean
Sites with mean peak counts of 50 or more birds in Great Britain[†]							
Humber Estuary	318	631	200	(349)	(172)	Nov	383
Minsmere	17	240	650	260	300	Jan	293
Willington		5	287	(227)	382	Jan	225
North Warren and Thorpeness Mere	90	147	230	195	(312)	Oct	195
Roxton Lake	128	170	246	172	159	Jun	175
Severn Estuary	126	126	150	192	152	Mar	149
Derwent Water	137	184	160	137	97	May	143
Ullswater	186	230	82	170	3	Jan	134
Hamford Water	19	0	146	221	273	Mar	132
Frampton Pools	114	118	108	146	122	Mar	122
Benacre Broad	359	52	0	70	120	Sep	120

	06/07	07/08	08/09	09/10	10/11	Mon	Mean
Bassenthwaite Lake	1	12	140	52	163	Mar	74
Dungeness and Rye Bay	44	92	79	83	63	Dec	72
Hornsea Mere	72	73	67	67	76	Nov	71
Pegwell Bay	0	46	0	3 [12]	300 [12]	Dec	70
Morecambe Bay	18 [7]	23	196	53	57	Jan	69
Duddon Estuary	(10)	65	(0)	(38)	(0)		65
Osberton	68	71	51	74	31	Nov	59
Alde Complex	19	(0)	(1)	108	40	Oct	56
Lound Waterworks	104	50	37	45	41	Jan	55
Barcombe Mills Reservoir	53	56	53	56	54	Jan	54
Sites with mean peak counts of 50 or more birds in Northern Ireland[†]							
Strangford Lough	279	275	325	365	375	Oct	324
Sites below table qualifying levels but exceeding threshold in WeBS-Year 2010/11 in Great Britain[†]							
Priory Country Park (Barkers Lane Gravel Pit)		0	0	0	140	Sep	35
Colne Estuary	0	2	0	0	89 [12]	Dec	18
Crouch-Roach Estuary	2	14	·36	50	60	Oct	32
Lower Derwent Ings	6	1	0	56	59	Feb	24

[†] as no British or All-Ireland thresholds have been set a qualifying level of 50 has been chosen to select sites for presentation in this report

---

Dark-bellied Brent Goose
Branta bernicla bernicla

International threshold (W Siberia & W Europe):	2,400
Great Britain threshold:	910
All-Ireland threshold:	+

GB max:	71,550	Feb	
NI max:	1	Feb	
% young:	12.7	Brood size:	2.7

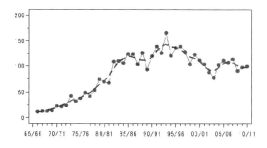

Figure 14.a, Annual indices & trend for Dark-bellied Brent Goose in GB.

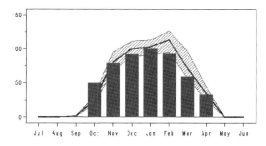

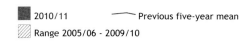

Figure 14.b, Monthly indices for Dark-bellied Brent Goose in GB.

Dark-bellied Brent Geese winter along the coasts of western Europe, the majority at sites on the Atlantic west coast of France, the south and east coasts of England, southwest Netherlands and the Wadden Sea. The species is now at the same status as the early 1980s, when it was in the ascendancy before reaching a notable peak in 1993/94. Since then numbers have fallen somewhat, but the last decade has seen relative stability. A very similar overall pattern has been recorded on the Wadden Sea in The Netherlands over the same period (Hornman *et al.* 2012).

Twelve sites in Britain qualified as being of international importance in 2010/11. Typically, these were all located between the Humber Estuary on the east coast and Portsmouth Harbour on the south coast. The maximum from The Wash was close to the recent average; annual peaks of 20,000+ were regular up until 2007/08 inclusive. Elsewhere, perhaps the most notable count was the record 23,057 at Thames Estuary, which recalls a similarly high peak there in 2007/08. A further thirteen sites surpassed the qualifying threshold for national importance, following the demotion of Colne Estuary, Swale

Estuary and Northwest Solent after the lowest annual peaks for several years at those three sites.

Results from age assessments undertaken at wintering sites in the UK indicate that flocks of Dark-bellied Brent Geese in 2010 comprised 12.7% young birds, above the recent average and 7.4% higher than the previous year. Mean brood size was 2.7 young per successful pair, also higher than in 2009/10 and slightly above the previous ten-year mean of 2.06 (Reed 2011c). Although monitoring indicated that rodent and predators numbers were generally low in arctic Russia during 2010, high densities were recorded at a scattering of sites (Soloviev & Tomkovich 2011). Because breeding success of Dark-Bellied Brent Geese is greatly influenced by interactions between rodent abundance and predator pressure, it is probable that low levels of predation at these particular sites enabled geese to breed successfully.

	06/07	07/08	08/09	09/10	10/11	Mon	Mean
Sites of international importance in the UK							
The Wash	20,870	21,101	13,993	15,438	16,104	Oct	17,501
Thames Estuary	8,100	22,047	11,684	12,541	23,057	Oct	15,486
Chichester Harbour	9,605	12,171	8,757	8,569	11,434	Jan	10,107
Blackwater Estuary	7,293	8,278	6,692	7,564	(5,410)	Jan	7,457
North Norfolk Coast	7,091	7,614	6,614	5,830	(5,669)	Dec	6,787
Hamford Water	4,089	4,157	5,698 [10]	(5,572)	(5,935)	Dec	5,090
Humber Estuary	(4,586)	(2,430)	(2,801)	(3,245)	(2,370)	Jan	(4,586)
Langstone Harbour	4,906	5,263	4,165	3,846	3,947	Nov	4,425
Crouch-Roach Estuary	(4,471)	4,534	4,241	3,149	4,368 [10]	Jan	4,073
Dengie Flats	2,901	(3,560)	2,364	3,871	2,499	Feb	3,039
Pagham Harbour	2,744	2,341	2,522	3,015	2,453	Mar	2,615
Portsmouth Harbour	3,162	(2,500)	2,538 [10]	(2,030)	2,054	Feb	2,585
Sites of national importance in Great Britain							
Fleet and Wey	1,554	1,810	2,200	2,190 [10]	2,416	Dec	2,034
Colne Estuary	1,296	2,536	2,076	2,839	1,135	Feb	1,976 ▼
Swale Estuary	2,310	1,857	2,115	(1,782)	1,448	Oct	1,933 ▼
North West Solent	1,808	2,101	1,885	2,050	1,800	Jan	1,929 ▼
Stour Estuary	2,063	2,038	1,726	1,891	1,875	Mar	1,919
Medway Estuary	(1,076)	(1,367)	(959)	(1,509)	(1,684)	Mar	(1,684)
Newtown Estuary	1,662	2,115	1,469	1,382	1,707	Feb	1,667
Orwell Estuary	1,500 [10]	(1,405)	1,266	1,503 [10]	(1,610)	Jan	1,470
Exe Estuary	1,374	1,820	1,614	1,317	1,219	Dec	1,469
Deben Estuary	1,759	(1,409)	1,038	1,173	1,883	Jan	1,463
Beaulieu Estuary	3,439	774	689	798	746	Feb	1,289
Southampton Water	1,151	1,674	869	1,055 [12]	1,649	Jan	1,280
Jersey Shore	733	1,317		1,481 [11]	1,467 [11]	Nov	1,250
Poole Harbour	1,146	(721)	(812)	(938)	(882)	Dec	1,146
Sites no longer meeting table qualifying levels in WeBS-Year 2010/2011							
Burry Inlet	937	764	860	927	555	Jan	809
Sites below table qualifying levels but exceeding threshold in WeBS-Year 2010/11 in Great Britain							
Holland Marshes	4	1,250	20	200 [11]	1,250 [11]	Jan	545
Bracklesham Bay		5	1	135	925	Dec	267

C.J.F. Coombs

Canadian Light-bellied Brent Goose

Branta bernicla hrota

International threshold	
(Canada & Greenland):	400
Great Britain threshold:	7
All-Ireland threshold:	220

GB max:	1,018	Jan	
NI max:	36,519	Oct	
% young:	3.2	Brood size:	2.1

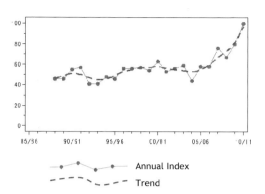

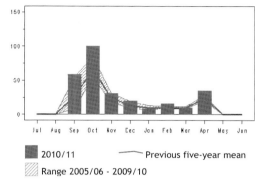

Figure 15.a, Annual indices & trend for Nearctic Light-bellied Brent Goose in Northern Ireland.

Figure 15.b, Monthly indices for Nearctic Light-bellied Brent Goose in Northern Ireland.

The population of Light-bellied Brent Geese which breeds on the Arctic islands of north-east Canada migrate across Greenland and Iceland, and winters mostly in Ireland. As the winter progresses, increasing numbers move southwards and use sites in western Britain, Channel Islands, and on the Atlantic coasts of France and Spain.

The International Census of East Canadian High Arctic Light-bellied Brent Geese took place in October 2010 for a ninth consecutive year, and involved coverage of sites in Iceland, Ireland and UK. A total population of 38,216 geese was counted, slightly higher than that in 2009/10.

Typically, the majority were in Northern Ireland, principally at Strangford Lough (28,600) and Lough Foyle (2,650). On the other side of the Irish Sea, site maxima were noted at Dee Estuary and Inland Sea & Alaw Estuary, while 200+ were at Morecambe Bay for the third year in succession. The international population estimate has been increased from 26,000 to 40,000 (Wetlands International 2012).

Annual breeding success tends to be either good or very poor. In 2010/11, just 3.2% birds were considered to be young, indicative of another poor year following the worst since the mid-1970s recorded in 2009/10.

	06/07	07/08	08/09	09/10	10/11	Mon	Mean	
Sites of international importance in the UK								
Strangford Lough	24,658	30,457	20,702	21,375	33,750	Oct	26,188	
Lough Foyle	2,177	3,251	2,550	3,862	2,652	Oct	2,898	
Dundrum Inner Bay	575	1,108	1,232	982	948	Feb	969	
Outer Ards Shoreline	577	946	781	580	621	Mar	701	
Carlingford Lough	542	483	626	330 [6]	(160)	Apr	495	
Sites of national importance in Great Britain								
Larne Lough	256	369	655	219	376	Nov	375	▼
Killough Harbour	282						282	▼
Traeth Melynog			351	187	238	Jan	259	▼
Morecambe Bay	(65)	(129)	(236)	276	205	Dec	241	▼
Foryd Bay	47	181	295 [6]	170	270	Nov	193	
Inland Sea and Alaw Estuary	79 [6]		174	209	227	Mar	172	
Dee Estuary (England and Wales)	104	199	174	130	214	Mar	164	
Cymyran Strait (Four Mile Bridge to Sea)		0	0	204	182	Jan	97	
Loch Ryan	(37)	52	0	110	102	Nov	66	
Jersey Shore	23	36		85 [6]	57 [6]	Nov	50	
Cleddau Estuary	(7)	12	51	36	41	Dec	35	

	06/07	07/08	08/09	09/10	10/11	Mon	Mean	
Broadford Bay	0	(0)	122	0	0		31	
Scarlett Pt to Strandhall			40	18			29	
Lavan Sands	15	24	28	54	21	Feb	28	
Fleet and Wey			35[6]	7[6]			21	
Dinas Dinlle to Afon Llifon				18[6]	15[6]	Mar	17	
Inner Loch Indaal					17[6]	Nov	17	▲
Tamar Complex					16[6]	Feb	16	
Derbyhaven Bay			0	23			12	
Severn Estuary	2	11	0	10	11	Mar	7	▲
Garlieston Bay				7[6]			7	
South Ford	0	0	1		27	Oct	7	▲
Sites no longer meeting table qualifying levels in WeBS-Year 2010/2011								
Swansea Bay	0	0	11	(3)	7	Apr	5	
Ribble Estuary	(0)	(1)	8	(2)	0		4	
No data since 2006/07: Ayr to North Troon, Loch Gruinart, Loch Riaghain (Tiree)								
Sites below table qualifying levels but exceeding threshold in WeBS-Year 2010/11 in Great Britain								
Wigtown Bay	(0)	0	0	8	10	Nov	5	
Fishguard Harbour		0	5	2	8	Oct	4	
Swansea Bay	0	0	11	(3)	7	Apr	5	

Svalbard Light-bellied Brent Goose

Branta bernicla hrota

International threshold (Svalbard):	75
Great Britain threshold:	34

GB max:	5,637	Oct
NI max:	0	
% young:	11.6	Brood size: -

*50 is normally used as a minimum threshold

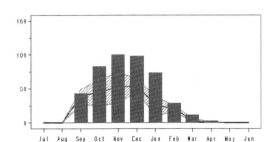

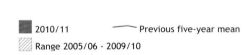

Figure 16.a, Annual indices & trend for Svalbard Light-bellied Brent Goose in GB.

Figure 16.b, Monthly indices for Svalbard Light-bellied Brent Goose in GB.

The population of Light-bellied Brent Geese which breeds in Svalbard, north-east Greenland and Franz Josef Land, has shown a trend of fluctuating increase over the last 30 years. The main wintering sites were traditionally in Denmark, but Lindisfarne has gradually increased in importance with numbers there rising from 200 birds in the 1950s to typically 3,000+ during the 2000s.

In 2010/11, the annual index value rose to its highest ever value and the peak count at Lindisfarne of 5,612 in October was the most ever recorded. The latter total represents an increase of 13% compared to the previous peak of the year before. Typically, both Eden Estuary and Inner Moray & Inverness Firth supported small flocks during the winter, consolidating their status as sites of national importance. However, as shown below, a major feature of the midwinter period was the presence of several flocks of 80+ at less expected sites on the east coast of Britain, particularly Northumberland. These counts (as well as the record aggregation at Lindisfarne) provide an indication of an exodus of geese from Denmark and elsewhere across the North Sea during the frozen conditions. A similar response has been observed in previous cold winters (P. Clausen, pers. comm.); prior to 2010/11, the last marked influx into the UK was in January 1987.

Breeding success was assessed by monitoring of birds at Lindisfarne and two other sites on the east coast of Britain, and at 11.6% was a marked improvement on the previous year. The percentage of young in wintering flocks has generally been low over the past ten years, only exceeding 10% on four occasions since 1992/93. No brood size data were collected.

	06/07	07/08	08/09	09/10	10/11	Mon	Mean
Sites of international importance in the UK							
Lindisfarne	(3,350)	(3,798)	3,879	(4,935)	5,612	Oct	4,809
Sites of national importance in Great Britain							
Inner Moray and Inverness Firth	43	14	99	52	64	Jan	54
Humber Estuary	(8)	2	3	30	154	Jan	47 ▲
Howick to Beadnell	0	0	6	5	201	Dec	42 ▲
Eden Estuary	18	69	29 [6]	41	42	Dec	40
Sites below table qualifying levels but exceeding threshold in WeBS-Year 2010/11 in Great Britain							
Breydon Water and Berney Marshes	0	0	0	0	155 [12]	Jan	31
Beadnell to Seahouses	0	1	12	0	140	Feb	31
Boulmer to Howick	0	0	0	0	(119)	Jan	24
Seahouses to Budle Point	18	0	0	22	110	Feb	30
Alnmouth to Boulmer	3	0	0	1	(80)	Feb	17
Newton Pool	0	0	0	0	63 [12]	Dec	63

Black Brant
Branta bernicla nigricans

Vagrant
Native Range: N America and E Asia

Black Brants were recorded in flocks of Dark-bellied Brent Geese at ten sites along the English coast between The Wash and Dorset. Records spanned November to March, and all related to singles apart from two at Fleet & Wey in February.

Red-breasted Goose
Branta ruficollis

Vagrant and escape
Native Range: SE Europe, Asia

Red-breasted Geese were seen at 12 WeBS sites in England. Typically the provenance of most is doubtful, most obviously a group of five recorded in Suffolk and Essex throughout the year. However, a potential genuine vagrant may have been responsible for sightings at Southampton Water (Jan), Yar Estuary (Feb) and Northwest Solent (Feb).

Egyptian Goose
Alopochen aegyptiaca

Naturalised introduction
Native Range: Africa

GB max:	724	Sep
NI max:	0	

In 2010/11, the national index for Egyptian Goose rose to its highest ever point, and there is every indication that this species will continue to expand across Britain in the years ahead. A record 200 WeBS sites held the species, representing an increase of >50% in the number of sites over the course of the last two years. As was the case in 2009/10, this distribution included single locations in both Wales and Scotland.

Typically, many of the largest counts emanated from Norfolk, although the listing of Eversley & Yateley Gravel Pits, Rutland Water and Summerleaze Gravel Pits near to the top of the table below is strong evidence of the steady expansion taking place away from the East Anglian core. The above average monthly index value for September infers high breeding success of this increasing population, presumably aiding the range expansion.

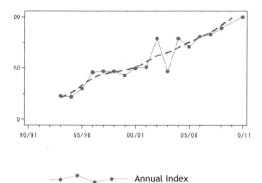

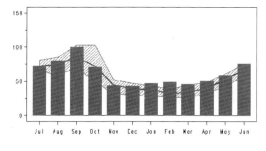

	Annual Index
- - - -	Trend

▓	2010/11	⌐ Previous five-year mean
▨	Range 2005/06 - 2009/10	

Figure 17.a, Annual indices & trend for Egyptian Goose in GB.

Figure 17.b, Monthly indices for Egyptian Goose in GB.

	06/07	07/08	08/09	09/10	10/11	Mon	Mean
Sites with mean peak counts of 10 or more birds in Great Britain							
North Norfolk Coast	211	125	(162)	133	153	Aug	157
Breydon Water and Berney Marshes	55	134 [12]	83 [12]	256 [11]	192 [11]	Sep	144
Eversley Cross and Yateley Gravel Pits	69	96	156	117	162 [11]	Sep	120
Rutland Water	64	56	96	63	77	Sep	71
Cranwich Gravel Pits			59	93	53	Aug	68
Yare Valley - Marlingford to Bawburgh	52 [12]	(61)	68 [12]	52	97	Jul	67
Middle Yare Marshes	65	81	(30)	(50)	51	Oct	66
The Wash	39	(32)	32	78	42	Sep	48
Nar Valley Fisheries Lakes				30	41	Aug	36
Summerleaze Gravel Pits	2	60	62	35	11	Feb	34
Nunnery Lakes	36	36	26	37	28	Jul	33
Trinity Broads	(8)	26	33	19	48	Jun	32
Bawsey Country Park					29	Jun	29
Whitlingham Country Park	24	24	21	35	14	Apr	24
Busbridge Lakes	17	17	25	22	(27)	Dec	22
Lound Waterworks	14	5	25	19	32	Aug	19
Wimbledon Park Lake		21	10	15	25	Jun	18
Rocester Pools	0			21	32	Jul	18
Clapham Common			12	19	18	Dec	16
Spade Oak Gravel Pit (Little Marlow)	11	19	22	19	8	Nov	16
Redgrave Lake	7	17	11	12	33	Sep	16
Queen Mary Reservoir	0	47	2	20	5	May	15
Earith Gravel Pits		21 [12]	8 [12]	16	15	Aug	15
Sites below table qualifying levels but exceeding threshold in WeBS-Year 2010/11 in Great Britain							
Lee Valley Gravel Pits	4	6	14	8	38	Dec	14
Lackford Lakes Nature Reserve	17	6	9	11	27	Sep	14
Wellington Country Park	9	9	12	8	17	Jul	11
Sevenoaks Wildfowl Reserve	5	7	5	12	17	Jul	9
Dart Estuary	6	(10)	8	6	15	Aug	9
Castle Marshes Reserve	3	2	2	8	23	Feb	8
River Avon - Fordingbridge to Ringwood	0	0	3	9	19	Oct	6

[†] *as no British or All-Ireland thresholds have been set a qualifying level of 15 has been chosen to select sites for presentation in this report*

Paradise Shelduck
Tadorna variegata

Escape
Native Range: New Zealand

One was at Petworth Park (Mar).

Australian Shelduck
Tadorna tadornoides

Escape
Native Range: Australia

One was at Petworth Park (Jan, Mar).

Ruddy Shelduck
Tadorna ferruginea

Escape and possible vagrant
Native Range: Asia, N Africa, S Europe

Ruddy Shelducks were noted at 19 WeBS sites during the year, all in England apart from one at Carmarthen Bay in November. A typical late-summer peak included four birds at Rostherne Mere in August.

Common Shelduck
Tadorna tadorna

International threshold (NW Europe population):		3,000
Great Britain threshold:		610
All-Ireland threshold:		150

GB max:	52,041	Jan
NI max:	3,526	Jan

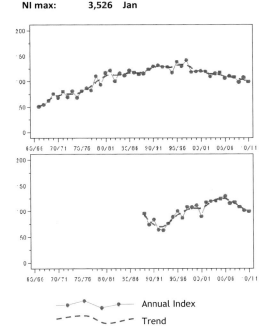

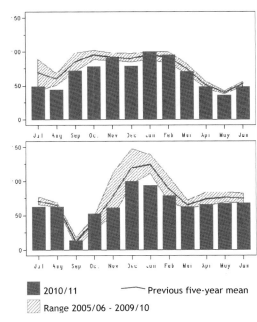

Annual Index

Trend

2010/11 · Previous five-year mean

Range 2005/06 - 2009/10

Figure 18.a, Annual indices & trend for Shelduck in GB (above) & NI (below).

Figure 18.b, Monthly indices for Shelduck in GB (above) & NI (below).

The majority of British and Irish breeding Shelduck are known to migrate to the Helgoland Bight of the Wadden Sea to moult, where they are joined by birds from Scandinavia and the Baltic. Although several sites on this side of the North Sea, such as the Mersey, Humber and Severn estuaries, are also of importance for moulting birds, the monthly indices indicate that below average numbers were present in Britain during late-summer in 2010/11.

Perhaps in response to the general trend for milder winters in north-west Europe (up until 2009/10), the number of Shelduck wintering in The Netherlands has increased since the mid 1990s (Hornman *et al.* 2012), implying a shift in distribution across the North Sea in that time. However, in January 2011 there was an apparent influx of Shelducks into Britain, presumably from the Wadden Sea due to the cold weather conditions prevalent at the time.

Eight sites in Britain continue to surpass the threshold for international importance. Although the October total recorded at Dee Estuary represents the fourth highest ever annual peak from that site, reported maxima from the other sites of international importance were less favourable. The apparent marked drop at Mersey Estuary is especially noticeable. If it is a genuine decline, it cannot be explained by the recent increase noted on the Dee. Elsewhere in north-west England, numbers have also decreased markedly on the Ribble Estuary since the 1990s.

Shelducks can show marked responses to subtle changes in habitat quality. A decline in numbers using The Wash has been linked to over-exploitation of the cockle and mussel fishery there (Atkinson et al. 2010). During the 1980s, mid winter maxima of 15,000+ Shelducks were a feature of the site, peaking at an exceptional 21,304 birds in December 1985; the most ever noted through WeBS.

In Northern Ireland, numbers have steadily declined over the course of the last five years, returning the species to an equivalent status to the mid 1980s when monitoring began there.

	06/07	07/08	08/09	09/10	10/11	Mon	Mean
Sites of international importance in the UK							
Dee Estuary (England and Wales)	10,869	9,425	9,457	11,688	12,234	Oct	10,735
Mersey Estuary	(16,721)	(10,644)	(4,237)	(3,613)	2,395	Aug	7,522
Morecambe Bay	(8,880)	5,804	(8,409)	(8,367)	6,081	Nov	7,508
The Wash	6,855	6,656	6,046	6,155	(5,228)	Jan	6,428
Humber Estuary	4,823	5,804	(2,892)	(6,137)	(4,095)	Aug	5,588
Strangford Lough	3,413 [10]	6,084 [10]	5,583 [10]	3,069 [10]	3,101 [10]	Dec	4,250
Severn Estuary	3,711	(5,414)	3,943	5,148	2,945	Mar	4,232
Forth Estuary	(3,546)	3,283	2,774	4,047	3,322	Sep	3,394
Sites of national importance in Great Britain							
Ribble Estuary	2,577	2,216	2,878	(2,327)	3,094	Jul	2,691
Blackwater Estuary	2,623	(2,369)	2,642	(2,342)	(1,936)	Jan	2,633
Stour Estuary	1,641	2,402	3,499 [10]	2,396 [10]	(1,652)	Jan	2,485
Lindisfarne	1,868	(1,406)	(2,302)	(1,451)	2,086	Nov	2,085
Thames Estuary	1,870	2,498	(1,941)	1,362	(1,792)	Feb	1,918
Medway Estuary	(1,290)	(1,631)	(1,604)	(1,673)	(1,884)	Jan	(1,884)
Hamford Water	(1,496)	2,450	1,838	1,401	1,264	Jan	1,738
Swale Estuary	1,406	2,003	1,926	1,636	1,667	Feb	1,728
Solway Estuary	2,888	1,902	(708)	763	558	Feb	1,528
North Norfolk Coast	1,361	1,222 [10]	981	1,027	1,106	Mar	1,139
Montrose Basin	(1,106)	(1,098)	806	1,191	1,365	Feb	1,121
Crouch-Roach Estuary	577	823	1,029	935	2,115 [10]	Dec	1,096
Alde Complex	1,181	1,120	(1,041)	1,020	982	Mar	1,076
Poole Harbour	(1,043)	(788)	(899)	(715)	(790)	Jan	(1,043)
WWT Martin Mere	1,075	780	1,290	1,050	1,012	Jan	1,041
Wigtown Bay	751	880	1,017	1,338	462	Oct	890
Orwell Estuary	727 [10]	(419)	807 [10]	849 [10]	922	Jan	826
Colne Estuary	326	1,600 [10]	(406)	813	547	Feb	822
Burry Inlet	690	780	962	759 [10]	646	Feb	767
Duddon Estuary	363	498	790	911	866	Feb	686
Deben Estuary	837	754	554	467	635	Feb	649
Chichester Harbour	643	449	560	926	638	Dec	643
Cleddau Estuary	497	607	763	580	765	Jan	642
Blyth Estuary	677	794	(493)	413	(346)	Dec	628 ▲
Sites of all-Ireland importance in Northern Ireland							
Larne Lough	832	486	931	819	728	Feb	759
Belfast Lough	(378)	265	691	916 [10]	375	Jan	562
Carlingford Lough	(349)	477	434	278	237	Feb	357
Lough Foyle	264	322	364	122	139	Feb	242
Sites no longer meeting table qualifying levels in WeBS-Year 2010/2011							
Tees Estuary	816	588	599	517	485	Mar	601
Sites below table qualifying levels but exceeding threshold in WeBS-Year 2010/11 in Great Britain							
Dengie Flats	238	192	248	238	876	Jan	358
Lavan Sands	395	424	379	445	653	Feb	459
Other sites surpassing table qualifying levels in Winter 2010/2011 in Northern Ireland							
Dundrum Inner Bay	70	188	109	116	150	Feb	127

John Harding

Muscovy Duck
Cairina moschata

Escape
Native Range: S America

Recorded at 47 WeBS sites in 2010/11, a monthly peak of 65 Muscovy Ducks was noted in January. Peaks were ten at Hesketh Park Lake, and eight at Brayford Pool and Bucklands Pond.

	06/07	07/08	08/09	09/10	10/11	Mon	Mean
Sites with mean peak counts of 5 or more birds in Great Britain							
Brayford Pool, Lincoln	26	17	14	11	8	Jul	15
Hesketh Park Lake		11	14	15	10	Jul	13
Fort Henry Ponds and Exton Park Lakes	43	5	1	0	0		10
Sites below table qualifying levels but exceeding threshold in WeBS-Year 2010/11 in Great Britain							
Bucklands Pond, Nailsea	3	3	3	3	8	Jan	4
Tarns Dub	0	0	0	0	6	Nov	1

Wood Duck
Aix sponsa

Escape
Native Range: N America

Wood Ducks were seen at 12 WeBS sites in 2010/11, including locations in both Wales and Scotland . All were single birds apart from two at Connaught Water in July.

Mandarin Duck
Aix galericulata

Naturalised introduction
Native Range: E Asia

GB max:	703	Nov
NI max:	0	

Records of Mandarin Ducks were received from 189 sites in 2010/11, representing an increase of 22% compared to the previous year. This total is indicative of a range expansion, but could also partly reflect both increased WeBS coverage of small wooded lakes and ponds and potential displacement during the frozen 2010/11 midwinter period. Most sites were in England, with just two sites in Scotland and four in Wales. A monthly maximum of 703 birds was logged in November, and the national index was at a similarly high level to the past two years.

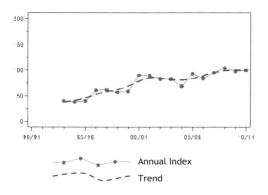

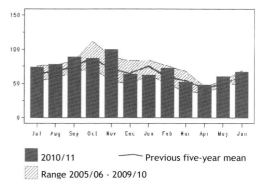

Figure 19.a, Annual indices & trend for Mandarin in GB.

Figure 19.b, Monthly indices for Mandarin in GB.

In 2010/11, counts of 50+ were received from nine sites. These included marked increases in the peaks, both in November, reported from Stockgrove Country Park (121) and Linacre Reservoirs (135). These counts were surpassed only by that from the traditional haunt of Forest of Dean Ponds where a supplementary count of

245 (Oct) represents the most ever reported. Notably, following the speculation in last year's report, a count of 100+ from the River Severn at Trimpley provides some evidence of the concentrations of this species probably present elsewhere in the English/Welsh border region.

	06/07	07/08	08/09	09/10	10/11	Mon	Mean
Sites with mean peak counts of 20 or more birds in Great Britain[†]							
Forest of Dean Ponds	236[12]		232[12]	74[12]	245[12]	Oct	197
Bradley Pools		251[12]	75[12]	120[12]	98[12]	Dec	136
R.Severn, Trimpley					101[12]	Dec	101
Brookleys Lake	11[46]	98[46]	51[46]	160[46]	86	Nov	81
Trimpley Reservoir				64	(38)	Dec	64
Stockgrove Country Park		3	67	39	121	Nov	58
Linacre Reservoirs	25	35	23	45	135	Nov	53
Dee Flood Meadows	83	48	35	47	30	Sep	49
Busbridge Lakes	41	31	52	36	61	Feb	44
Bough Beech Reservoir	60[12]	42	48	50[12]	6	May	41
Kedleston Park Lake		80[12]	54[12]	23[12]	8[12]	Mar	41
Harewood Lake		25	44	62	32	Oct	41
Arun Valley	25	53	71	28	22	Apr	40
Darwell Reservoir	74	33	41		0		37
Blackbrook Reservoir	16	13	8	64[12]	79[12]	Jul	36
Connaught Water (Epping Forest)	44	40	38	27	17	Dec	33
Wimpole Park					33	Jan	33
Headley Mill Pond	15	64	28	22[12]	18	Feb	29
Strawberry Hill Ponds	44	33	17	41	12	Feb	29
Blatherwyke Lake	3	21	48	32	32	Feb	27
Osterley Park Lakes	14	21	37	32	19	Aug	25
Sites below table qualifying levels but exceeding threshold in WeBS-Year 2010/11 in Great Britain							
Radnor Mere	6	15	12	26	33	Jan	18
Mere Farm Quarry - Chelford	0	0	0	0	25	Dec	5

[†] *as no British or All-Ireland thresholds have been set a qualifying level of 25 has been chosen to select sites for presentation in this report*

Maned Duck

Escape

Chenonetta jubata

Native Range: Australia

One was at Testwood Lakes (Sep-Oct).

Eurasian Wigeon
Anas penelope

International threshold (W Siberia and NE Europe population): 15,000
Great Britain threshold: 4,400
All-Ireland threshold: 820

GB max: 391,660   Jan
NI max: 3,885   Oct

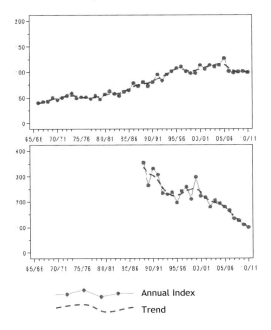

Figure 20.a, Annual indices & trend for Wigeon in GB (above) & NI (below).

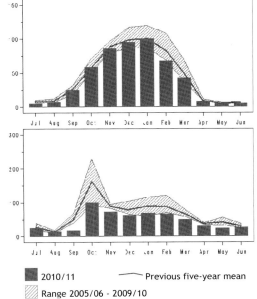

■ 2010/11   — Previous five-year mean
▨ Range 2005/06 - 2009/10

Figure 20.b, Monthly indices for Wigeon in GB (above) & NI (below).

Following the record high index value reached in 2005/06, numbers of Wigeon in Britain have been stable, at approximately 10% lower in the five years since. In 2010/11, four sites continued to meet the citerion for international importance. At the principal site, Ribble Estuary, the peak recorded in November was close to the recent site average, although some way short of the total logged there two years previously.

The two top inland sites, Ouse Washes and Somerset Levels, both held maxima in January that were well in excess of typical numbers for those sites, presumably associated with the frozen conditions prevalent across north-west Europe at the time. The count at Somerset Levels is exceptional, if one considers that the previous maximum there was 39,546 in January 2003 (itself 10,000+ more birds than the next highest count, noted the following year). At Ouse Washes, although the peak in 2010/11 was the highest since the site maximum of over 55,000 five years before, historically the site has regularly been used by peaks in excess of 30,000

Wigeon. Among the 17 additional sites that surpass the threshold for national importance, further evidence of responses to the cold weather was provided by the midwinter peaks at Nene Washes (following a similarly high maximum during a cold spell in 2009/10), Severn Estuary and Dungeness & Rye Bay.

It is possible that the December peak at the latter site and some others indicates a fresh influx of birds from frozen continental Europe at that time. Interestingly, further support for Britain being used as a refuge is provided by the fact that the monthly indices show a larger than expected exodus of Wigeon in February, after the cold period. Wigeon wintering in Britain largely comprise breeding birds from Scandinavia, northeast Europe and western Russia – it might therefore be expected that this species would show a climatic-induced shift in winter distribution towards the breeding range core, as identified in some waders by Maclean *et al.* (2008).

However, recent work by the research group *Nordic Waterbirds and Climate Network*

(NOWAC) indicates that, of the six common dabbling duck species, Wigeon has shown the least change in core distribution within Europe in response to climate (Dalby *et al.* 2012). However, record numbers in Switzerland in recent years (e.g. Keller & Burkhardt 2010) tends to suggest some degree of change either in distribution or overall abundance, and the wintering population in Northern Ireland is in steep decline. Given that Wigeon have been shown to respond to temperature in the breeding season, when breeding success is correlated with temperature in breeding areas (Mitchell *et al.* 2008), further research is required to examine the population dynamics and responses to environmental change (whether associated with climate change or more localised factors) of the species in winter.

	06/07	07/08	08/09	09/10	10/11	Mon	Mean
Sites of international importance in the UK							
Ribble Estuary	(57,385)	85,964	97,512	64,633	80,148	Nov	82,269
Somerset Levels	27,391	28,882	21,186	26,073	51,189	Jan	30,944
Ouse Washes	26,984	19,800	(29,658)	24,175[12]	43,010[12]	Jan	28,725
Breydon Water and Berney Marshes	18,184[12]	21,400[12]	21,074[12]	22,770[12]	24,231[12]	Jan	21,532
Sites of national importance in Great Britain							
Swale Estuary	7,041	11,560	12,134	25,848	14,800	Dec	14,277
Nene Washes	8,180	10,497	9,096	22,571	20,460	Jan	14,161
Lower Derwent Ings	14,200	11,600	9,614	14,803	17,803	Mar	13,604
North Norfolk Coast	16,750	11,998	10,304	7,557	11,148	Dec	11,551
Dornoch Firth	9,763	11,115	(12,303)	8,221	15,440	Oct	11,368
Lindisfarne	10,840	(12,000)	10,194	(7,990)	(8,922)	Nov	11,011
The Wash	6,612	8,961	(5,124)	13,224	8,062	Oct	9,215
Severn Estuary	9,343	10,008	8,672[10]	7,676	(10,284)	Jan	9,197
Cromarty Firth	8,510	10,510	(9,109)	4,626	7,915	Oct	8,134
Alde Complex	8,280	6,337	5,345	9,128	(9,672)	Dec	7,752
Morecambe Bay	(6,201)	(6,260)	9,110	(7,179)	6,137	Jan	7,624
Cleddau Estuary	7,643	7,130	7,429	8,227	7,580	Nov	7,602
Dungeness and Rye Bay	5,193	4,010	2,711	(5,574)	(13,852)	Dec	6,268
Thames Estuary	3,566	9,293	4,428	6,641	5,653	Jan	5,916
Inner Moray and Inverness Firth	5,863	7,666	6,555	3,546	5,884	Oct	5,903
Middle Yare Marshes	3,890	6,507	5,511	7,904	5,545	Feb	5,871
Blackwater Estuary	6,580	5,667	5,836	4,722	3,713	Jan	5,304
Sites of all-Ireland importance in Northern Ireland							
Lough Foyle	5,406	2,835	3,118	1,273	1,409	Oct	2,808
Strangford Lough	3,476	1,582	1,540	1,559	2,178	Oct	2,067
Loughs Neagh and Beg	1,878	1,614	1,427	1,528	1,156	Jan	1,521
Sites no longer meeting table qualifying levels in WeBS-Year 2010/2011							
Abberton Reservoir	654	6,572	5,815	4,906	2,143	Oct	4,018
Dee Estuary (England and Wales)	5,797	(2,461)	1,776	3,512	2,568	Oct	3,413
Sites below table qualifying levels but exceeding threshold in WeBS-Year 2010/11 in Great Britain							
Fleet and Wey	3,087	2,285	3,089	5,131	8,244	Dec	4,367
Hamford Water	(2,102)	2,718	2,491[10]	1,894	(5,599)	Dec	3,176
Rutland Water	2,278	2,773	3,414	4,883	5,480	Dec	3,766

American Wigeon
Anas americana

Vagrant
Native Range: N & C America

Singles were noted at three sites: Rutland Water (Jan-Feb), North Norfolk Coast (Jan) and Loch Bee, South Uist (Apr).

Chiloe Wigeon
Anas sibilatrix

Escape
Native Range: S America

Records from three sites included a peak of six birds at Hereford Quarry (Sep).

Gadwall

Anas strepera

GB max: 20,526 Jan
NI max: 183 Nov

International threshold
(NW Europe population): 600
Great Britain threshold: 250
All-Ireland threshold: 20*

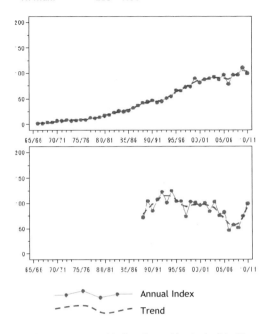

Figure 21.a, Annual indices & trend for Gadwall in GB (above) & NI (below).

— Annual Index
--- Trend

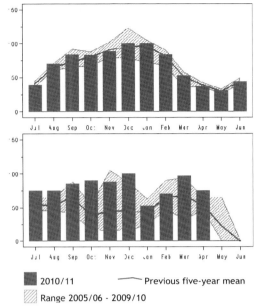

■ 2010/11   — Previous five-year mean
▨ Range 2005/06 - 2009/10

Figure 21.b, Monthly indices for Gadwall in GB (above) & NI (below).

Following a sustained rise over the past thirty years, the rate of increase in Gadwall numbers in Britain appears to be slowing. Monitoring schemes elsewhere in Europe, e.g. The Netherlands (Hornman *et al.* 2012) and Switzerland (Keller & Müller 2012), have also shown marked increases in the population of this species which continue to be maintained.

In general, the monthly indices suggest no marked net influx or exodus of Gadwall into or from Britain during the cold winter of 2010/11. Based on five-year means, seven sites in the UK are of international importance for Gadwall. These sites included Pitsford Reservoir for the first time, following an all-time high of 1,044 birds there in October 2010. Rutland Water again hosted the largest aggregation of the year (1,289, Dec), albeit considerably fewer than the exceptionally high number present during winter 2009/10. The historic maximum from Rutland Water relates to an unprecedented count of 2,181 birds in November 1997. River Avon (Fordingbridge to Ringwood) and Abberton

Reservoir both held maxima of 1,000+ (for the first and second times, respectively). The notable January peak from the River Avon is indicative of a shift in distribution from other frozen wetlands. Maxima were typical of recent years at the other sites of international importance. Based on the numbers present at Dungeness & Rye Bay in both 2009/10 and 2010/11, it would seem likely that site will also surpass the threshold for international importance in the near future.

Seven further sites are of national importance. In addition, unusually high counts emanated from a number of other less typical locations during the winter, perhaps linked to displacement of birds (either from within Britain or perhaps elsewhere in Europe) due to the adverse weather conditions. These included all-time maxima at Whitlingham Country Park (720, Dec) and Sonning Eye & Henley Road Gravel Pits (551, Jan).

The relatively small population of Gadwall in Northern Ireland, most of which use Loughs

Neagh & Beg and Strangford Lough, has shown a notable increase in the past two years. Will the species continue to increase there, and thereby mirror the upward trend that has characterised other northwest European countries?

Outwith winter, a site-record total of 375 at North Norfolk Coast in May is a useful indication of the increasing national breeding population of Gadwall, which is no longer assessed and reported on by the *Rare Breeding Birds Panel* (Holling *et al.* 2012).

	06/07	07/08	08/09	09/10	10/11	Mon	Mean
Sites of international importance in the UK							
Rutland Water	904	992	1,520	2,119	1,289	Dec	1,365
Ouse Washes	220	970	1,508	998	729	Feb	885
River Avon - Fordingbridge to Ringwood	755	725	653	854	1,149	Jan	827
Abberton Reservoir	(535)	483	493	797	1,128	Sep	725
Lee Valley Gravel Pits	518	703	700	669	896	Dec	697
Thames Estuary	451	(431)	687	909	(357)	Feb	682
Pitsford Reservoir	444	264	352	916	1,044	Oct	604 ▲
Sites of national importance in Great Britain							
Dungeness and Rye Bay	362	485	417	1,014	715	Dec	599
Somerset Levels	424	706	614	485	317	Feb	509
Tees Estuary	433	464	342	480	433	Sep	430
Sutton and Lound Gravel Pits	425	437	282	539	399	Feb	416
Fen Drayton Gravel Pits	553	387	442	361	303	Dec	409
Cotswold Water Park (West)	330	(217)	(395)	420	(427)	Feb	393
Orwell Estuary	340 [10]	268	722 [10]	414	194	Oct	388
Minsmere	410	468	388	434	216	Jul	383
Loch Leven	309	284	345 [12]	417	422	Sep	355
Whitlingham Country Park	111	114	230 [12]	547	720	Dec	344 ▲
North Norfolk Coast	186	314	388	418	375	May	336
Blackwater Estuary	231	395	154	488	(372) [12]	Dec	328
Woolston Eyes	(84)	397	192	439	103	Nov	283
Middle Tame Valley Gravel Pits	(131)	(108)	275	(94)	(117)	Sep	275
Nene Washes	151	277	170	494	234	Mar	265 ▲
Little Paxton Gravel Pits	215	324	280	307	173	Jan	260
Ouse Fen and Pits (Hanson/RSPB)	(49)	203	317	293	219	Feb	258 ▲
Chew Valley Lake	150	245	210	295	375	Oct	255 ▲
Sonning Eye and Henley Road GPs	100		108	241	551	Jan	250 ▲
Sites of all-Ireland importance in Northern Ireland							
Loughs Neagh and Beg	143	132	164	144	158	Mar	148
Strangford Lough	68 [10]	86 [10]	60 [10]	69	87	Nov	74
Sites no longer meeting table qualifying levels in WeBS-Year 2010/2011							
Alton Water	166	109	226	330	123	Nov	191
Sites below table qualifying levels but exceeding threshold in WeBS-Year 2010/11 in Great Britain							
Fleet and Wey	78	42	49	133	591	Dec	179
Bewl Water	89	158	183	345 [12]	347 [12]	Dec	224
Brent Reservoir	107	114	109	329	315	Oct	195
Crouch-Roach Estuary	17	111	138	132	290	Jan	138
Buckden and Stirtloe Pits			187	214	286 [12]	Oct	229
Watermead Country Park North	142	120	95	186	275	Dec	164
Dogmersfield Lake	115	35	70	195	255	Nov	134
Other sites surpassing table qualifying levels in Winter 2010/2011 in Northern Ireland							
Hillsborough Main Lake	2	0	13	18	22	Jan	11

Baikal Teal

Anas formosa

Vagrant and escape
Native Range: Asia

A Baikal Teal, of unknown origin, was reported from Rochester Pools (Kent) in January and March. There have been three previous WeBS records of this species, including one at Minsmere in 2001 which was considered to be a genuine vagrant.

Eurasian Teal

Anas crecca

International threshold
(NW Europe population): 5,000
Great Britain threshold: 2,100
All-Ireland threshold: 450

GB max: 162,401 Jan
NI max: 4,707 Jan

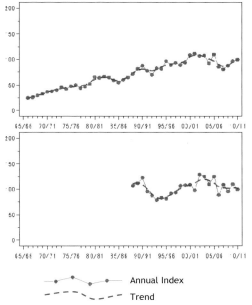

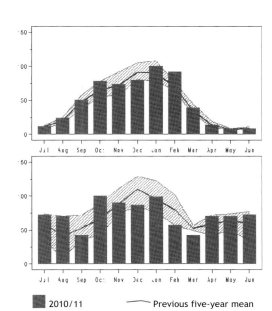

Annual Index

Trend

2010/11   Previous five-year mean

Range 2005/06 - 2009/10

Figure 22.a, Annual indices & trend for Teal in GB (above) & NI (below).

Figure 22.b, Monthly indices for Teal in GB (above) & NI (below).

Most Teal that spend the winter in Great Britain originate from breeding areas either in Iceland, Scandinavia (especially Finland) or northwest Russia. However, Guillemain *et al.* (2005) showed that any splitting into distinct 'north-western European' and 'Mediterranean' sub-populations (e.g. Scott & Rose 1996) was inappropriate, and that all birds wintering in west Europe are best considered as belonging to a single larger population. Hence, in extremely cold winters, such as 2010/11, some Teal are likely to be forced to make use of the whole flyway to flee cold conditions.

The count of 45,884 at Somerset Levels in February 2011 is the largest site total ever. Duck numbers have probably responded to habitat management in that area, but this high total may also represent a response to the cold weather in December and January which could have resulted in waterfowl concentrating in south-west England. Alternatively, it may represent increased flocking (and hence associated detectability) during the frozen conditions when Teals may be forced onto open water. At other times, vegetated ditches are favoured by Teal, but such habitats can be difficult to count effectively in unfrozen conditions.

John Harding

After a period of steady increase, the national index for Teal in Britain has been stable in recent years. Reasons for this apparent change in trajectory are unclear, but may be linked at least in part to three relatively cold winters, particularly those of 2009/10 and 2010/11. Only continued monitoring will determine if the species reverts to showing a decline during winters characterised by weather conditions more typical of the recent era.

Based on current five-year mean peak counts, five other sites in the UK hold internationally important numbers of Teal, and a further 20 sites surpass the threshold for national importance.

	06/07	07/08	08/09	09/10	10/11	Mon	Mean	
Sites of international importance in the UK								
Somerset Levels	21,581	17,663	24,029	13,680	45,884	Feb	24,567	
Ribble Estuary	(6,959)	8,045	6,072	8,064	5,256	Nov	6,879	
Hamford Water	(1,969)	3,255	10,684 [10]	3,952	(7,289)	Dec	6,295	
Swale Estuary	(3,728)	4,470	5,485	7,030	5,831	Oct	5,704	
Loch Leven	2,527	4,920	7,580 [12]	5,591	6,151	Sep	5,354	
Morecambe Bay	(2,338)	2,934	7,327	(4,009)	(3,169)	Oct	5,131	▲
Sites of national importance in Great Britain								
Lower Derwent Ings	4,221	3,714	3,393	6,411	6,361	Mar	4,820	
Thames Estuary	3,940	(3,373)	4,393	5,917	(4,111)	Dec	4,750	
Severn Estuary	4,233	5,428	4,710	3,882	(4,568)	Jan	4,564	
Ouse Washes	4,333 [12]	3,135	5,351	2,492 [12]	5,245 [12]	Mar	4,111	▼
North Norfolk Coast	3,638	3,278 [10]	3,524	5,708	4,307	Nov	4,091	
Blackwater Estuary	(2,786)	(2,207)	(4,002)	(2,730)	(4,052)	Jan	(4,052)	
Alde Complex	3,560	3,334	3,961	4,986	4,071	Nov	3,982	
Nene Washes	1,677	2,078	1,851	9,012	3,916	Jan	3,707	
Mersey Estuary	(3,593)	(2,072)	(2,000)	(3,230)	(2,988)	Jan	(3,593)	▼
Humber Estuary	(2,009)	2,365	(3,385)	(3,538)	(4,782)	Oct	3,518	
The Wash	2,138	2,537	(2,308)	5,811	3,176	Jan	3,416	
Dee Estuary (England and Wales)	3,719	2,144	3,129 [10]	4,413	3,348	Oct	3,351	
Abberton Reservoir	2,662	3,410	872	4,975	3,924	Oct	3,169	
Breydon Water and Berney Marshes	3,620 [12]	5,612 [12]	3,216 [12]	1,337 [12]	1,017 [12]	Mar	2,960	
Mersehead RSPB Reserve	3,900	1,045		3,560	2,080	Nov	2,646	
Hickling Broad	2,000		3,150	2,401			2,517	
Solway Estuary	(2,265)	(839)	(1,648)	1,342	3,306	Nov	2,324	
Forth Estuary	2,531	1,877	2,370	2,293	2,551	Jan	2,324	
Poole Harbour	(874)	(1,923)	(1,715)	(1,415)	(2,297)	Dec	(2,297)	▲
Arun Valley	2,129	(2,343)	1,985	(2,026)	(1,831)	Jan	2,152	
Sites of all-Ireland importance in Northern Ireland								
Strangford Lough	1,724	1,752	1,347	1,790	2,104 [10]	Jan	1,743	
Lough Foyle	915	1,562	2,000	2,020	1,325	Oct	1,564	
Loughs Neagh and Beg	1,049	1,297	889	1,345	1,030	Oct	1,122	
Belfast Lough	488	640	479	618	723	Oct	590	
Carlingford Lough	440	565	571	309	487	Feb	474	
Sites no longer meeting table qualifying levels in WeBS-Year 2010/2011								
Inner Moray and Inverness Firth	(1,890)	(2,208)	1,944	1,338	2,859	Dec	2,087	
WWT Martin Mere	1,430	1,200	2,005	2,640	2,500	Nov	1,955	
Sites below table qualifying levels but exceeding threshold in WeBS-Year 2010/11 in Great Britain								
Chew Valley Lake	515	360	435 [12]	1,425	3,500	Oct	1,247	
North West Solent	1,100	1,461	1,116	1,520	3,400	Dec	1,719	
Inner Moray and Inverness Firth	(1,890)	(2,208)	1,944	1,338	2,859	Dec	2,087	
WWT Martin Mere	1,430	1,200	2,005	2,640	2,500	Nov	1,955	
Cleddau Estuary	1,389	1,991	1,171	(1,347)	(2,246)	Dec	1,699	
Other sites surpassing table qualifying levels in Winter 2010/2011 in Northern Ireland								
Larne Lough	189	168	543	217	578	Jan	339	

Green-winged Teal

Anas carolinensis

Vagrant
Native Range: N America

Singles were recorded at 11 sites in Britain between November and April. These included long-stayers at WWT Caerlaverock (Nov-Dec), Forth Estuary (Dec-Jan), Mill Dam & Balfour Mains Pools (Jan-Feb), and Solway Estuary (Feb-Mar).

Mallard
Anas platyrhynchos

International threshold (NW Europe):   45,000
Great Britain threshold: 6,800[†]
All-Ireland threshold: 380

GB max: 133,775   Jan
NI max: 7,972   Oct

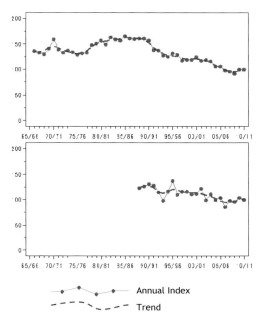

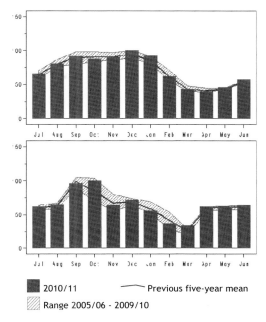

Annual Index

Trend

2010/11   Previous five-year mean

Range 2005/06 - 2009/10

Figure 23.a, Annual indices & trend for Mallard in GB (above) & NI (below).

Figure 23.b, Monthly indices for Mallard in GB (above) & NI (below).

The WeBS trend indicates that the number of Mallards wintering in Britain has steadily declined since the early 1990s. However, the index appears to have stabilised in recent years, presumably at least partly in response to two cold winters; marked increases in the monthly indices for Britain in midwinter (December 2010 and January 2011) are certainly suggestive of an arrival of birds from the continent in response to the cold weather during that period. This concurs with the assumption that the recent downward trend for Mallard is primarily related to a drop in continental immigration (Sauter *et al.* 2010). Alternatively, such conditions may also concentrate Mallard on larger wetlands that generally receive better coverage through WeBS, birds having been forced off smaller sites that are more likely to be frozen. However, ring-recovery data up to the late-1990s suggested that 75% of the birds in Britain and Ireland during the winter months were continental immigrants (Wernham *et al.* 2002) so the potential effects of a very harsh winter, such as

2010/11, are obvious. As documented in previous WeBS reports, the apparent fall in the UK's wintering population contrasts with the breeding numbers which increased by 33% between 1984 and 2009 (Baillie *et al.* 2012).

The largest WeBS count in the UK during 2010/11 was from Lower Derwent Ings where 4,350 were present in December, considerably more than has been recorded at the site in recent years. Counts of 3,000+ were regular there during the 1980s and 1990s, and the historic maximum dates back to a high of 8,142 in March 1982 (when the species' national abundance was at its peak). Maxima at the majority of the other most important sites, including Loughs Neagh & Beg (the only other site to have ever held 8,000+ Mallard), were more typical of recent years. Also notable was the highest peak ever from Cotswold Water Park (West) and the largest for several years from Loch Leven (most since 1989/90), Ellesmere Lakes (1979/80), and Inner Moray & Inverness Firth (2002/03).

	06/07	07/08	08/09	09/10	10/11	Mon	Mean
Sites of all-Ireland importance in Northern Ireland							
Loughs Neagh and Beg	4,351	3,767	1,911	4,287	4,242	Oct	3,712
Strangford Lough	(1,010)	1,950	2,177	2,125	1,630	Nov	1,971
Lough Foyle	1,036	830	965	995	1,079	Sep	981
Lower Lough Erne	551	702	(295)	(226)	346	Oct	533
Belfast Lough	(344)	457	447	419	299	Jan	406
Sites with mean peak counts of 2,000+ birds in Great Britain[†]							
Severn Estuary	3,661	2,954	3,091	3,086	3,334	Oct	3,225
Ouse Washes	2,606 [12]	2,918 [12]	(3,024)	3,336 [12]	3,182 [12]	Jan	3,013
The Wash	2,417	2,316	(2,586)	3,030	(1,886)	Jan	2,588
Lower Derwent Ings	2,890	1,272	2,001	1,865	4,350	Dec	2,476
Morecambe Bay	(1,837)	(1,240)	(1,926)	2,145	2,380	Jan	2,263
WWT Martin Mere	2,211	2,000	1,665	2,250	2,640	Jan	2,153
Clifford Hill Gravel Pits Consolidated	2,027	1,733	2,048	2,199	2,205	Sep	2,042
Humber Estuary	(1,911)	2,166	1,644	2,417	1,799	Jan	2,007
Sites below table qualifying levels but exceeding threshold in WeBS-Year 2010/11 in Great Britain[†]							
Loch Leven	1,620	1,261	1,178	675	2,169	Sep	1,381
Other sites surpassing table qualifying levels in Winter 2010/2011 in Northern Ireland							
Upper Lough Erne	304	370	302	221	417	Jan	323

[†] *as no sites exceed the British threshold, a qualifying level of 2,000 has been chosen to select sites for presentation in this report*

Chestnut Teal
Anas castanea

Escape
Native Range: S Australia

Singles were at Westport Lake (Aug) and Fen Drayton Gravel Pits (Nov).

Northern Pintail
Anas acuta

International threshold (NW Europe population):	600
Great Britain threshold:	290
All-Ireland threshold:	20

GB max: 19,655 Jan
NI max: 449 Feb

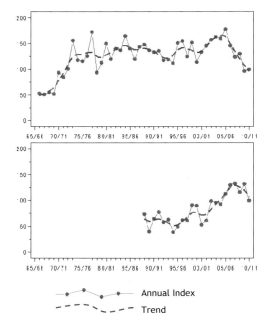

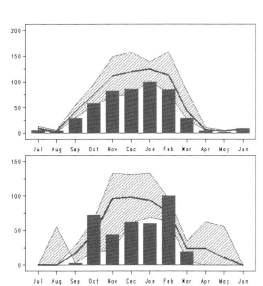

Figure 24.a, Annual indices & trend for Pintail in GB (above) & NI (below).

Figure 24.b, Monthly indices for Pintail in GB (above) & NI (below).

In 2010/11, numbers of Pintail in Britain were at a similarly low level as the previous year when the annual index dropped to its lowest value for over thirty years. As recently as 2005/06, the species reached a historic peak; the reasons for a rapid change of fortunes are unclear. The monthly indices show that numbers were below average throughout the autumn and winter, not only during the freezing midwinter period that resulted in clearer effects on other species.

The relative lack of Pintail at WeBS sites in Britain in October and November would tend to suggest either a decrease in overall population size or a shift in core wintering range; also implied by an increase in The Netherlands in recent years (Hornman et al. 2011). If the latter was the case, the UK would perhaps have been expected to receive an influx of Pintails during the onset of frozen conditions across northwest Europe in December. Alternatively, some of the UK's normal wintering population may have moved southwards to Iberia or northern Africa.

Fifteen sites in Britain are of international importance. At the two most important sites, the reported maxima in 2010/11 were again lower than those which have typified recent years. The year's peak count was from Solway Estuary where the December total of 4,262 was the highest for six years; the historic peak at that site relates to a count of 6,570 in December 2001. Fifteen further sites are of national importance; annual maxima at these were generally close to or slightly below average.

The index for Northern Ireland dropped in comparison to 2009/10, with Strangford Lough in particular supporting below average numbers.

	06/07	07/08	08/09	09/10	10/11	Mon	Mean	
Sites of international importance in the UK								
Burry Inlet	4,692	6,244	4,058	2,750	(2,680)	Jan	4,436	
Dee Estuary (England and Wales)	6,172	(4,334)	3,932	2,960	3,669	Nov	4,213	
Morecambe Bay	2,609	(2,543)	2,593	3,186	2,830	Oct	2,805	
Ribble Estuary	(1,094)	3,639	2,178	(2,124)	2,074	Jan	2,630	
Solway Estuary	2,429	1,047	(888)	(977)	4,262	Dec	2,579	
Duddon Estuary	(2,317)	(1,153)	2,481	(629)	(1,209)	Nov	2,481	
Nene Washes	1,931	1,267	1,951	2,400	1,237	Jan	1,757	
Ouse Washes	1,823 [12]	1,713 [12]	(1,697)	743 [12]	1,187	Feb	1,433	
Mersehead RSPB Reserve	1,010	1,445		1,690	479	Feb	1,156	
Loch Leven	217	213	1,554 [12]	1,396	676	Sep	811	
Severn Estuary	(1,161)	668	655 [10]	(494)	456	Nov	735	
The Wash	1,215	652	(560)	294	(104)	Jan	720	
Medway Estuary	(582)	663	(351)	(353)	(400) [12]	Dec	663	
Dee Flood Meadows	916	750	196	227	1,060	Feb	630	▲
Somerset Levels	530	985	682	534	332	Jan	613	
Sites of national importance in Great Britain								
Swale Estuary	731	597	630	381	521	Dec	572	
North Norfolk Coast	753	697 [10]	421	437	503	Jan	562	
Wigtown Bay	166	834	642	689	240	Nov	514	
Blackwater Estuary	(401)	(201)	(488)	(203)	(353)	Feb	(488)	
Pagham Harbour	566	(464)	(447)	337	552	Feb	485	
Lower Derwent Ings	656	674	298	278	405	Mar	462	
WWT Martin Mere	580	380	380	550	294	Dec	437	
Stour Estuary	467	303	486 [10]	345 [10]	449	Jan	410	
Arun Valley	574	(322)	227	(142)	(302)	Jan	401	
North West Solent	484	407	320	279	500	Jan	398	
Traeth Bach	325	341	403	233	(151)	Jan	326	▲
Alde Complex	441	447	276	281	154	Nov	320	
Lindisfarne	445	327	(272)	(200)	154	Oct	309	
River Avon: Ringwood to Christchurch	(456)	507	245	(274)	58	Jan	308	
Cromarty Firth	205	(171)	287	(246)	(420)	Nov	290	▲
Sites of all-Ireland importance in Northern Ireland								
Strangford Lough	496	395	449	487	301	Feb	426	
Lough Foyle	123	157	185	112	156	Jan	147	
Sites no longer meeting table qualifying levels in WeBS-Year 2010/2011								
Orwell Estuary	753 [8]	158	125 [10]	170 [10]	85	Nov	258	
Foryd Bay	330	152	360 [12]	160	190	Dec	238	
Sites below table qualifying levels but exceeding threshold in WeBS-Year 2010/11 in Great Britain								
Inner Moray and Inverness Firth	314	232	236	211	305	Feb	260	

Yellow-billed Pintail

Anas georgica

Escape
Native Range: S America

One was as at Cherwell Valley in August.

White-cheeked Pintail

Anas bahamensis

Escape
Native Range: S America

Singles were seen at four sites.

Garganey

Anas querquedula

	International threshold (W Siberia and Europe population):	20,000
	Great Britain threshold:	+[t]
	All-Ireland threshold:	+[t]

GB max:	45 May
NI max:	0

Being summer migrants to the UK, Garganey are reported for the calendar year, here 2010. Records were received from 58 WeBS sites, a similar number to the previous three years. All were in England, with the exception of four singles in Scotland (all in spring) and one on the Isle of Man (in August). For the third year in a row, the species was seen in February, the herald of a spring passage involving records from 25 sites. Typically, highest counts were noted post breeding season; peaks of eight at Grafham Water (Aug), and three at both Maxey Pits (Aug) and Lee Valley Gravel Pits (Sep). The species was noted at four sites in October.

Thelma Sykes

	2006	2007	2008	2009	2010	Mon	Mean
Sites with mean peak counts of 4 or more birds in Great Britain							
Dungeness and Rye Bay	9	9	8	7	(2)	Apr	8
Other sites surpassing table qualifying levels in Summer 2010 in Great Britain							
Nene Washes	(2)	(5)	0	0	(8)	Apr	3
Grafham Water	0	0	0	0	8	Aug	2
Chew Valley Lake	6	1	1	4	4	Sep	3
Stodmarsh	1	2	0	5	4	Aug	2

[t] *as no British or All-Ireland thresholds have been set a qualifying level of four has been chosen to select sites for presentation in this report*

Blue-winged Teal

Anas discors

Vagrant
Native Range: N America

Singles were recorded at Gilmourton Ponds (Feb), North Norfolk Coast (Apr) and Chew Valley Lake (Jun). Three in a WeBS-year has been surpassed just twice before.

Northern Shoveler
Anas clypeata

International threshold (NW & C Europe population): 400
Great Britain threshold: 180
All-Ireland threshold: 20*

GB max: 11,104 Oct
NI max: 114 Nov

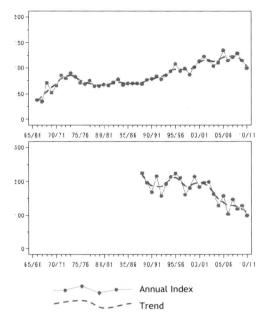

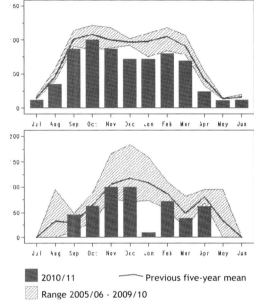

●—● Annual Index
--- Trend

■ 2010/11   ⎯ Previous five-year mean
▨ Range 2005/06 - 2009/10

Figure 25.a, Annual indices & trend for Shoveler in GB (above) & NI (below).

Figure 25.b, Monthly indices for Shoveler in GB (above) & NI (below).

Contrary to the longer term trend, the national index for Shoveler in Britain fell for the second year in succession. It remains to be seen if this represents merely a temporary response to two cold winters, as might be expected. The monthly indices show the sensitivity of this species to frozen conditions; the marked drop-off in the number recorded at British WeBS sites in December being especially pertinent. It is likely that an influx of Shoveler into more southern areas of Europe, such as France and Iberia, took place at this time, but data from those countries are currently unavailable to be able to validate this assertion. Prior to these two relatively cold winters, it was considered that a greater proportion of Shoveler were wintering at sites in more northern latitudes in response to milder conditions. For example, the species has also steadily increased in The Netherlands over the longer term (Hornman *et al.* 2011).

Nine sites surpassed the threshold for international importance. Maxima at most of these were slightly below average, most notably at Somerset Levels where the peak of just 396 in

February was the lowest since 1996/97 and considerably less than the historic peak there of 2,190 in January 2003. The January 2011 total of just 242 Shoveler contrasts with an exceptional peak of Wigeon at the site during the same WeBS Core count; a good example of the different response of these two dabbling species to a period of severe weather. Among the regular dabbling ducks wintering in north-west Europe, Shoveler (along with Teal) has shown the most marked redistribution in response to recent climate change (Dalby *et al.* 2012).

Among the growing list of sites that surpass the threshold for national importance, the peaks at Chew Valley Lake (620, Oct), Minsmere (340, Nov), and Grafham Water (268, Dec) were especially notable. Elsewhere, evidence of a response to the onset of freezing conditions in December was also provided by the maxima noted during that month at several other sites in southern England, including inland at Chichester Gravel Pits and King George VI Reservoir, and on/near the coast at North-west Solent, Fleet & Wey and Eastbourne Park Lakes.

In Northern Ireland, the trend showed a further decline in wintering numbers, typifying the recent situation there for Shoveler and several other dabbling duck species. The cold weather conditions appear to have had a particularly profound effect in Northern Ireland during January.

	06/07	07/08	08/09	09/10	10/11	Mon	Mean
Sites of international importance in the UK							
Ouse Washes	696 [12]	1,071	2,039	503	1,186 [12]	Mar	1,099
Somerset Levels	1,520	1,806	971	713	396	Feb	1,081
Abberton Reservoir	(152)	604	606	566	918	Sep	674
Breydon Water & Berney Marshes	540 [12]	754	570 [12]	546 [12]	568 [12]	Nov	641
Dungeness and Rye Bay	553	581	588	735	506	Mar	593
Severn Estuary	600	796	526	497	426	Dec	572
Rutland Water	495	620	525	773	323	Sep	547
Thames Estuary	524	(227)	486	355	(352)	Mar	455
Medway Estuary	(509)	(156)	298	(51)	(105)	Sep	404 ▲
Sites of national importance in Great Britain							
Chew Valley Lake	300	180	270 [12]	435	620	Oct	361
Ribble Estuary	532	188	478	271	346	Oct	363
Lower Derwent Ings	301	341	333	612	364	Mar	390
Swale Estuary	(144)	331	(216)	459	291	Jan	375
Nene Washes	448	384	272	330	79	Nov	303
North Norfolk Coast	380	258	297	309	282	Nov	305
Stodmarsh	400	147	284	220	254	Oct	261
Alde Complex	441	295	260	156	161	Jan	263
Crouch-Roach Estuary	(78)	(259)	330	227	200	Nov	254
Fairburn Ings	226	54	304	453	123	Dec	232
Pitsford Reservoir	329	148	148	349	362	Oct	267
Burry Inlet	101	309	(283)	300 [12]	(61)	Feb	248
Middle Yare Marshes	(84)	(174)	(352)	174	(261)	Oct	240
R. Avon: Fordingbridge-Ringwood	153	312	245	245	122	Oct	216
Tees Estuary	309	170	225	300	151	Sep	231
Tring Reservoirs	130	256	250	219	182	Sep	207
Trinity Broads	(27)	338	162	(63)	220	Dec	240 ▲
Llynnau Y Fali	135	59	419	213	208	Mar	207
Minsmere	218	138	157	171	340	Nov	205 ▲
Arun Valley	278	217	215	197	208	Feb	223
Grafham Water	170	157	121	200	268	Dec	183
Cotswold Water Park (West)	222	176 [12]	251	184	87	Oct	184
Lee Valley Gravel Pits	164	184	145	222	229	Dec	189
London Wetland Centre	185	327	158	139	162	Feb	194
Loch Leven	279	205	192	80	273	Sep	206
Middle Tame Valley Gravel Pits	(68)	111	270	(10)	(10)	Feb	191
Theale Gravel Pits	157 [12]	73	140	351	180	Feb	180
Sites of all-Ireland importance in Northern Ireland							
Strangford Lough	139 [10]	73	69 [10]	123	76	Dec	96
Loughs Neagh and Beg	34	90	57	32	47	Sep	52
Belfast Lough	15	28	49	31	14	Mar	28
Sites no longer meeting table qualifying levels in WeBS-Year 2010/2011							
Blagdon Lake	542	137	76	41	45	Nov	168
Staines Reservoirs	149	65	232	147	153	Dec	149
Morecambe Bay	174	22	326	38	38	Dec	160
Sites below table qualifying levels but exceeding threshold in WeBS-Year 2010/11 in Great Britain							
Chichester Gravel Pits	(67)	78	(185)	128	291	Dec	171
King George VI Reservoir	40	26	42	61	290	Dec	92
Norh West Solent	152	108	125	131	255	Dec	154
Fleet and Wey	137	193	152	105	247	Dec	167
Colne Fen Gravel Pits	29	6	22	68	197 [12]	Sep	64
North Warren & Thorpeness Mere	151	171	92	175	194	Jan	157
Aqualate Mere	49	164	58	135	188	Oct	119
Eastbourne Park Lakes	38	48	(69)	(65)	186	Feb	91

Ringed Teal
Callonetta leucophrys

Escape
Native Range: S America

Two were at Rumworth Lodge Reservoir in July and one was on River Lune in September.

Red-crested Pochard
Netta rufina

Naturalised introduction and vagrant
Native range: S & E Europe

GB max: 470   Nov
NI max: 0

Red-crested Pochard is a patchily distributed species throughout central and southern Europe. The majority of UK records, including those pertaining to the ancestors of the core of the population at Cotswold Water Park, are generally considered to relate to escapes. However, the species has shown a change in winter distribution in recent decades, involving a shift in range core from the western Mediterranean to the region north of the Alps and the use of a greater number of sites (Keller 2000), increasing the likelihood of wild birds reaching Britain.

In total, the species was recorded at 89 WeBS sites in 2010/11, exactly the same total as the previous year. These included two sites in Scotland (Castle Park and Loch Connell) and one on the Channel Islands (Les Mondrins GP).

In 2010/11, numbers reported from Cotswold Water Park were greater than the previous year and approached the all-time high noted in 2008/09. Although less rapid than the increase that has taken place in Switzerland (Keller & Müller 2012), Red-crested Pochard continues to steadily expand in terms of both population and range in England.

The species is now firmly established in the east Midlands and southeast England; the expansion away from the traditional stronghold exemplified by the WeBS maxima noted in 2010/11 at Sutton & Lound Gravel Pits (Nottinghamshire), Hanningfield Reservoir (Essex), Knight & Bessborough Reservoirs (London), and Thrapston Gravel Pits (Northamptonshire).

	06/07	07/08	08/09	09/10	10/11	Mon	Mean
Sites with mean peak counts of 10 or more birds in Great Britain							
Cotswold Water Park (West)	207	170[12]	327	252	205	Nov	232
Cotswold Water Park (East)	106	72	104	91	194	Dec	113
Lower Windrush Valley Gravel Pits	26	(26)	(36)	(90)	(32)	Jan	42
Rutland Water	10	8	13	84	58	Dec	35
Sutton and Lound Gravel Pits	22	13	10	42	88	Sep	35
St James`s Park			22	32	25	Sep	26
Hanningfield Reservoir	17	10	11	21	33	Aug	18
Chimney Corner GP				17			17
Arnot Park Lake	16	14	9	9	6	Oct	11
Sites below table qualifying levels but exceeding threshold in WeBS-Year 2010/11 in Great Britain							
Cheddar Reservoir	0	1	0	21	16[12]	Dec	8
Knight and Bessborough Reservoirs	0	0	0	0	16	Nov	3
Thrapston Gravel Pits			0	0	14	Dec	5
Hornsea Mere	0	0	0	1	14	Aug	3
Trinity Broads	0	0	0	0	10	Jan	2

[†] *as no British or All-Ireland thresholds have been set a qualifying level of 10 has been chosen to select sites for presentation in this report*

Common Pochard

Aythya ferina

GB max: 20,577 Jan
NI max: 5,075 Jan

International threshold
(N Europe population): 3,000
Great Britain threshold: 380
All-Ireland threshold: 380

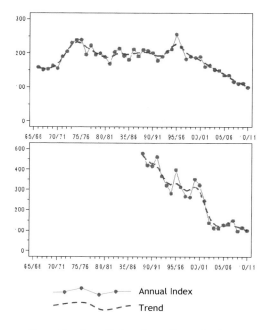

Figure 26.a, Annual indices & trend for Pochard in GB (above) & NI (below).

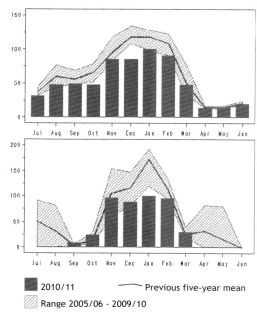

Figure 26.b, Monthly indices for Pochard in GB (above) & NI (below).

The trends for Pochard in both Britain and Northern Ireland indicate alarming declines have occurred since the 1990s. In 2010/11, the annual index for Britain reached an all-time low, with numbers approximately half of what they were twenty years ago. The precise mechanism driving both this decline and an apparent shift in distribution towards central Europe is uncertain, but it may be related at least in part to a changing climate. Pertinently, a similar decline has taken place in The Netherlands (Hornman *et al.* 2011), yet further east numbers have not fallen (e.g. Keller & Burkhardt 2011).

Pochard are very sensitive to frozen conditions (Keller *et al.* 2009). The monthly indices for Britain (and Northern Ireland) in 2010/11 show that numbers were particularly low in December during the onset of cold weather when the majority of freshwater wetlands were frozen. The species presumably responded similarly in other parts of Europe, and numbers are likely to have swelled further

south in the species' wintering range (but no data are yet available).

In Northern Ireland, after a slight recovery in peak numbers during the previous year, 2010/11 saw the lowest ever monthly maximum reported from Loughs Neagh & Beg. As recently as 1990/91 over 40,000 birds were counted at this site. The decline is considered primarily attributable to the effects of eutrophication which may have impacted on the invertebrates consumed by Pochard and other diving waterfowl (Maclean *et al.* 2006, Tomankova *et al.* in prep.).

Across Britain, virtually all the other major sites reported below average maxima, notable exceptions being Rutland Water, and both the Thames and Severn estuaries. The estimated international population size was recently revised downwards by 14% (Wetlands International 2012). Following the associated lowering of the threshold for international importance, Ouse Washes now qualifies as being internationally important for the first time.

	06/07	07/08	08/09	09/10	10/11	Mon	Mean
Sites of international importance in the UK							
Loughs Neagh and Beg	8,884	9,023	5,799	9,288	5,002	Jan	7,599
Ouse Washes	4,197	2,987	2,367 [12]	3,151 [12]	2,461 [12]	Feb	3,033 ▲
Sites of national importance in Great Britain							
Loch Leven	3,666	1,650	4,326	1,281	1,300	Sep	2,445
Abberton Reservoir	3,167	2,355	850	1,134	1,306	Sep	1,762
Dungeness and Rye Bay	1,049	728	1,019	1,356	979	Aug	1,026
Chew Valley Lake	1,220	600	530	1,065	1,305	Nov	944
Fleet and Wey	879	980	718	674	921	Dec	834
Thames Estuary	484	854	588	714	(907)	Dec	709
Middle Tame Valley Gravel Pits	296	783	1,042	(18)	(11)	Nov	707
Loch of Harray	532	468	454	1,184	754	Nov	678
Cotswold Water Park (East)	993	884	685	421	379	Dec	672
Severn Estuary	786	583	617	593	(734)	Jan	663
Cotswold Water Park (West)	(641)	553	568	639	489	Nov	578
Hornsea Mere	710	650	560	550	410	Mar	576
Cheddar Reservoir	443	80	230	435	1,215 [12]	Dec	481 ▲
Lower Windrush Valley Gravel Pits	467	(409)	(316)	(312)	(207)	Feb	467
Loch of Boardhouse	623	441	665	312	71	Oct	422
Brogborough Clay Pit				645	147	Nov	396
Pitsford Reservoir	365	505	328	407	335	Sep	388
Hanningfield Reservoir	463	226	538	323	375	Dec	385 ▲
Sites below table qualifying levels but exceeding threshold in WeBS-Year 2010/11 in Great Britain							
Rutland Water	233	291	352	274	504	Dec	331

Ring-necked Duck

Aythya collaris

Vagrant
Native Range: N America

Ring-necked Ducks were recorded at nine sites; Loch Gelly (Jul), Chew Valley Lake (Sep-Nov), Kirkby-on-Bain Gravel Pits (Oct), Bardney Pits (Nov), Nosterfield Gravel Pits (Dec-Jan), Dornoch Firth (Feb), Bosherston Lakes (Feb), Talley Lakes (Feb-Mar), and Stithians Reservoir (Mar-Apr).

Ferruginous Duck

Aythya nyroca

Vagrant and escape
Native Range: N America, Asia

Ferruginous Ducks were seen at eight sites in England. Records from Chew Valley Lake, where the species may have bred in recent years (Davis & Vinicombe 2011), included three present in October. Other records were from Minsmere (Jul-Aug), Woburn Park Lakes (Sep), Wintersett & Cold Hiendley Reservoirs (Oct), Trinity Broads (Nov), Leathes Ham (Dec), Queen Mary Reservoir (Dec) and Lakenheath Fen (Feb). Typically, some may have been escapees.

Tufted Duck

Aythya fuligula

International threshold (NW Europe population):	**12,000**
Great Britain threshold:	**1,100**
All-Ireland threshold:	**370**

GB max:	61,795	Jan
NI max:	11,379	Feb

Annual maxima and indices for Tufted Duck in Britain have exhibited a shallow increase over the course of the last forty years. In northern Europe, the species has responded strongly to climate change, with wintering numbers in Scandinavia having increased exponentially in the last three decades in response to ice-free conditions (Lehikoinen *et al.* in prep.). No strong response was detected in Britain in 2010/11 despite freezing midwinter conditions that prevailed across north-west Europe in November, December and January. However, a marked increase in numbers in Northern Ireland during February 2011 may be linked, to some degree, to a shift in distribution in response to weather conditions during winter 2010/11.

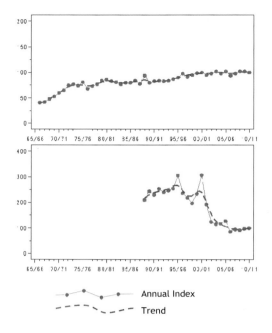

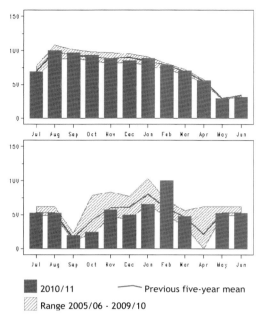

Figure 27.a, Annual indices & trend for Tufted Duck in GB (above) & NI (below).

Figure 27.b, Monthly indices for Tufted Duck in GB (above) & NI (below).

In 2010/11, the peak at Rutland Water was consistent with the recent average but that at Abberton Reservoir was the lowest for four years. The associated drop in five-year average at Abberton means the site is leap-frogged by Loch Leven in the table of sites below, where the peak of 6,455 in September was the most ever seen there. Among the ten further sites that surpass the threshold for national importance, Ouse Washes yielded its lowest maximum for seven years. In contrast, the October peak at Chew Valley Lake, where waterbirds have been monitored for over 50 years, was the most ever.

In Northern Ireland, the February peak of 8,078 at Loughs Neagh & Beg was consistent with the previous year. In common with other diving ducks, a sharp drop in numbers of Tufted Ducks took place at the site from 2001/02 onwards, but recent colder winters appear to have resulted in a degree of stability in the Northern Irish trend. The record WeBS count of 29,393 dates back to December 1989. In contrast, continuing the trend of recent years the maximum at Upper Lough Erne, 2,836 in February, represented a new high for that site.

	06/07	07/08	08/09	09/10	10/11	Mon	Mean
Sites of national importance in Great Britain							
Rutland Water	9,758	5,134	3,678	7,216	5,449	Jan	6,247
Loch Leven	3,553	4,140	3,610	3,601	6,455	Sep	4,272
Abberton Reservoir	1,187	3,796	3,928	5,078	2,790	Sep	3,356
Ouse Washes	2,057	3,328	(2,978)	1,647	1,548	Mar	2,312
Middle Tame Valley Gravel Pits	1,243	1,766	3,372	(162)	(68)	Mar	2,127
Hanningfield Reservoir	2,194	486	3,269	2,275	1,596	Aug	1,964
Chew Valley Lake	1,325	1,480	1,350	1,480	2,420	Oct	1,611
Walthamstow Reservoirs	1,516	900	2,103		1,873 [12]	Jul	1,598
Grafham Water	521	1,464	1,591	2,242	1,815	Dec	1,527
Lee Valley Gravel Pits	1,215	1,231	1,519	1,673	1,565	Nov	1,441
Cotswold Water Park (West)	1,372	1,343	1,354	1,541	1,445	Mar	1,411
Pitsford Reservoir	1,374	774	1,654	1,749	1,164	Aug	1,343
Staines Reservoirs	1,865	1,074	1,097	730	1,097	Aug	1,173

	06/07	07/08	08/09	09/10	10/11	Mon	Mean
Sites of all-Ireland importance in Northern Ireland							
Loughs Neagh and Beg	6,441	6,076	5,126	8,968	8,078	Feb	6,938
Upper Lough Erne	1,478	1,772	1,895	2,240	2,836	Feb	2,044
Lower Lough Erne	705	638	(183)	(201)	(455)	Jan	672
Sites below table qualifying levels but exceeding threshold in WeBS-Year 2010/11 in Great Britain							
Woolston Eyes	377	370	580	392	2,600 [12]	Jan	864
Sonning Eye and Henley Road GPs	886		649	879	1,533	Jan	987
Queen Mary Reservoir	6	372	65	186	(1,325)	Dec	391
Loch of Stenness	351	597	250	112	(1,165)	Dec	495

Scaup

Aythya marila

International threshold (N Europe population):	3,100
Great Britain threshold:	52
All-Ireland threshold:	45

GB max:	1,831	Dec
NI max:	2,763	Nov

*50 is normally used as a minimum threshold

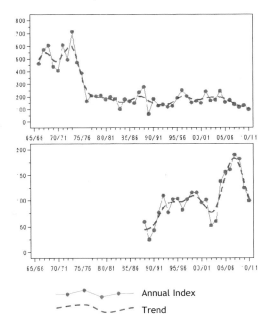

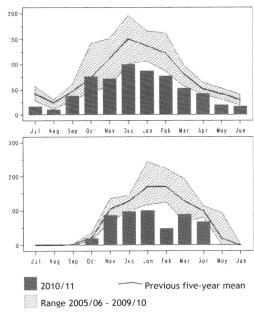

Figure 28.a, Annual indices & trend for Scaup in GB (above) & NI (below).

Figure 28.b, Monthly indices for Scaup in GB (above) & NI (below).

Following a relative period of stability, the WeBS trend for Britain indicates a shallow decline in the number of Scaup over the last seven years. However, as with all seaducks, there is an inherent susceptibility to the effects of bad weather and associated poor viewing conditions; interpretation of Scaup totals therefore needs to be undertaken with caution. This contemporary situation is in contrast to that prior to the mid 1970s when up to 25,000 birds were regular on the Forth Estuary. The disappearance of that aggregation was largely responsible for the rapid drop in the value of the national index at the time, occurring in isolation from the stable trend elsewhere in the country. Parts of the Scottish coastline suffer from sporadic, incomplete, or indeed no WeBS coverage. For example, a supplementary count of 4,000 birds at Solway Estuary in January 2010 provides an indication of the potential numbers not routinely monitored through the survey.

Typically, the maximum WeBS Core count of the year emanated from Loughs Neagh & Beg in Northern Ireland. Up until 2009/10, the wintering population at that site had been on an upward trend considered to be associated with the recovery of the Icelandic breeding population. However, for two successive years the peak total has now dropped below 3,000 birds. Only further years of monitoring will determine if Scaup at Loughs Neagh & Beg return to the level that saw the species become the most abundant *Aythya* duck wintering there in 2008/09.

Away from the key sites, notable maxima from northwest England included 70 at Dee Estuary (Jan) and 44 at Morecambe Bay (Dec). The peak count at an inland site (other than Loughs Neagh & Beg) was 15 at Rutland Water (Feb) where the species is regular in winter.

	06/07	07/08	08/09	09/10	10/11	Mon	Mean
Sites of international importance in the UK							
Loughs Neagh and Beg	4,349	5,587	6,335	2,997	2,254	Mar	4,304
Solway Estuary	(1,060)	(499)	(257)	(4,000)[12]	(1,113)[10]	Nov	(4,000)
Sites of national importance in Great Britain							
Loch Ryan	1,047	1,654	705	800[12]	885	Dec	1,018
Inner Loch Indaal	810[21]	870[21]		485	110	Oct	569
Inner Moray and Inverness Firth	690	148	493	386	410	Feb	425
Cromarty Firth	401	(516)	363	262	510	Jan	410
Loch of Stenness	429	259	276	197	173	Feb	267
Loch of Harray	306	67	(67)	149	223	Oct	186
Dornoch Firth	222	280	108	174	37	Feb	164
Auchenharvie Golf Course	98	120	105	73	63	Mar	92
Montrose Basin	28	35	120	62	77	Nov	64
Sites of all-Ireland importance in Northern Ireland							
Belfast Lough	849[10]	1,895	1,334[10]	1,950	(1,130)	Nov	1,507
Carlingford Lough	225	177	85	62	57	Jan	121
Strangford Lough	70	90	103[10]	2	1	Oct	53
Sites no longer meeting table qualifying levels in WeBS-Year 2010/2011							
No data: Firth of Clyde and Loch Ryan offshore							
Sites below table qualifying levels but exceeding threshold in WeBS-Year 2010/11 in Great Britain							
Dee Estuary (England and Wales)	2	3	0	39	70	Dec	23

Lesser Scaup
Aythya affinis

Vagrant
Native Range: N America

First recorded by WeBS in 1992/93, Lesser Scaup has featured in the annual report in virtually every year since then. In 2010/11, singles were seen at four sites: Cosmeston Lakes (Jan-Mar), Dozmary Pool (Jan), Slimbridge, Severn Estuary (Jan-Apr) and Frampton Pools (Mar).

Common Eider
Somateria mollissima mollissima

International threshold (N Europe population):		10,300
Great Britain threshold:		550
All-Ireland threshold:		30

GB max:	17,258	Mar
NI max:	3,088	Mar

Common Eiders in Shetland form a closely related group with those from the Faeroes and southern Iceland (subspecies *faeroensis*) (Furness *et al.* 2010). As a result, birds from this population are listed separately in the subsequent account, whereas Common Eider at other sites in Britain and Northern Ireland are documented here.

The British trend for Common Eider over the course of the last twenty years has shown a consistent decline. Elsewhere in northern Europe, a large decline has also been observed in the Baltic/Wadden Sea flyway (Ekroos *et al.* 2012). A wide range of theories have been suggested to explain changes in abundance of this species in northern Europe, ranging from diminishing food supplies (Coulson 2010), climate change (Lehikoinen *et al.* 2006, D'Alba *et al.* 2010) and thiamine deficiency (Balk *et al.* 2009).

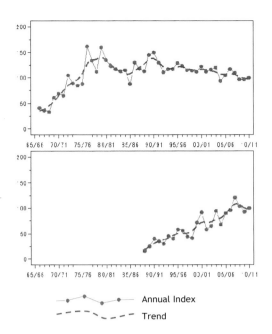

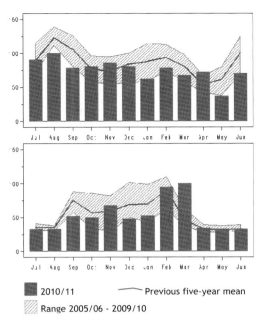

| Annual Index | 2010/11 | Previous five-year mean |
| Trend | Range 2005/06 - 2009/10 | |

Figure 29.a, Annual indices & trend for Eider (non Shetland) in GB (above) & NI (below).

Figure 29.b, Monthly indices for Eider (non Shetland) in GB (above) & NI (below).

	06/07	07/08	08/09	09/10	10/11	Mon	Mean
Sites of national importance in Great Britain							
Firth of Clyde	9,590 [14]	9,521 [14]	9,271 [14]	7,573 [14]	6,734 [14]	Sep	8,538
Tay Estuary	(9,164)	(7,500)	4,000	5,100	(1,450)	Nov	6,441
Aberdeen Bay offshore	6,269 [39]						6,269
Inner Firth of Clyde	7,274	6,918	5,700	4,078	4,736	Sep	5,741
Forth Estuary	5,646	4,571	5,925	(4,210)	5,065	Aug	5,302
Morecambe Bay	3,374	(2,138)	5,534	4,248	6,151	Dec	4,827
Ythan Estuary	(3,607)	(3,140)	3,351	3,079	2,326	May	3,101
Gare Loch	2,782 [14]						2,782
Montrose Basin	2,584	2,321	1,099	1,555	1,983	Jul	1,908
Dee Estuary (Scotland)	1,229	1,411	539	(1,417)	983	Jul	1,116
The Wash	491	125	1,438	2,970	519	Jan	1,109
Lindisfarne	(469)	619	(501)	1,074	962	Jun	885
Inner Loch Fyne	817 [14]						817
Loch Long and Loch Goil	796 [14]						796
Loch Ryan	(385)	772	429	1,025	937	Dec	791
Gourock to Largs	755 [14]						755
Don Mouth to Ythan Mouth	538	(111)	(132)	(794)	(133)	May	666
Holy Loch to Toward Point	634 [14]						634
Moray Coast (Consolidated)	603	683	939	303	(223)	Dec	632
Duddon Estuary	(715)	513	525	480	725	Oct	592
Sites of all-Ireland importance in Northern Ireland							
Belfast Lough	1,482	2,675	2,062 [10]	2,352 [10]	2,372	Mar	2,189
Outer Ards Shoreline	976	1,255	491	252	792	Jan	753
Strangford Lough	728	551 [10]	784	613	463	Sep	628
Lough Foyle	528	37	407	452	206	Sep	326
Larne Lough	76	48	106	86	70	Mar	77
Sites below table qualifying levels but exceeding threshold in WeBS-Year 2010/11 in Great Britain							
Lochs Beg and Scridain (East End)	270		240	(0)	638	Sep	383

Numbers reported from the two most important British sites provide continued cause for concern, for differing reasons. The Firth of Clyde held a peak of over 17,500 birds just ten years ago, but the population has since crashed; reasons for the decline are being investigated but have not yet been confirmed (C. Waltho, pers. comm.). Meanwhile, it is important that incomplete coverage of Tay Estuary does not allow another possible crash in numbers to occur undetected. Elsewhere in Scotland, peaks in 2010/11 were reasonably close to the recent average at most of the sites with complete coverage. An exception was the Ythan Estuary, where the peak of 2,326 (May) was the lowest since 2005/06. Further south, in England, the maximum recorded at The Wash (519, Jan) was typical for that site following the higher peak counts in both 2008/09 and 2009/10.

Common Eider (Shetland)
Somateria mollisima faeroensis

International threshold (Shetland):	85
Great Britain threshold:	55
All-Ireland threshold:	-

Furness et al. (2010) showed that Common Eiders from Shetland form a closely related group with those from the Faeroes and southern Iceland; subspecies *faeroensis*. Therefore, since Calbrade et al. (2010), the WeBS annual report has listed the two discrete populations present in the UK separately.

Sites on Shetland that are monitored routinely through WeBS (most of which are small lochs rather than open shoreline) support relatively few Common Eiders, with a monthly peak of just 28 birds (in July) noted during WeBS counts in 2010/11. Thus, for a more representative picture of their status, the table below largely comprises coordinated counts undertaken by SOTEAG during the winter.

Shetland's Common Eider population has declined during the last forty or so years (Pennington et al. 2004, Heubeck & Mellor 2012), although causes are unclear.

	06/07	07/08	08/09	09/10	10/11	Mon	Mean
Sites of international importance in the UK							
Bluemull & Colgrave Sounds	558 [9]	1,232 [9]		1,074 [9]			955
Burra, Trondra & Scalloway Islands		1,014 [9]		830 [9]			922
South Unst	601 [9]	450 [9]					526
Whiteness to Skelda Ness	179 [9]	178 [9]		201 [9]	169 [9]	Jan	186
Rova Head to Kirkabister	158 [9]	136 [9]	163 [9]	204 [9]	125 [9]	Jan	157
Sites of national importance in Great Britain							
South Yell Sound	54 [9]	35 [9]	68 [9]	70 [9]			57

King Eider
Somateria spectabilis

Vagrant	
Native range: Arctic	

King Eiders at Moray Coast (Jan) and Ythan Estuary (May-Jun) were somewhat more typical records than the bird which lingered off Minsmere earlier in the WeBS-year (Sep-Nov).

Long-tailed Duck
Clangula hyemalis

International threshold	
(W Siberia & N Europe population):	16,000
Great Britain threshold:	110
All-Ireland threshold:	+[†]

GB max:	1,011	Oct
NI max:	15	Mar

Following a huge reduction in the number wintering in the Baltic Sea, Long-tailed Duck is now listed as Vulnerable on the IUCN Red List of Threatened Species (Skov et al. 2011, Birdlife International 2012) and the international population estimate has been revised downwards by 20% (Wetlands International 2012). This trend mirrors the large declines also noted at key UK sites such as the Moray Firth.

Overall, the species was recorded at 100 sites around the UK in 2010/11, a typical total following a slight drop during the previous year.

The largest count, another low peak compared to just a few years ago, was again reported from Moray Firth. The precise extent to which the recent drop in numbers may be a result of reduced coverage, or the influence of sea conditions affecting visibility and location of birds on the Core count dates, remains unclear. However, given the situation in the Baltic, it seems increasingly likely that this is a genuine decline.

Elsewhere, the highest counts were both in March; 174 at Forth Estuary and 250 at The Ouse/Lairo Water, the latter an indication of the numbers potentially present along the extensive stretches of the Scottish coast that are not regularly counted for WeBS. Away from Scotland, the highest counts were 33 at Lindisfarne (Jan) and 14 at North Norfolk Coast (Dec).

Ground-based counts are not ideal for this species as it has a tendency to remain some distance from the coast, hence the drawing of meaningful conclusions from the totals listed below tends to be fraught with difficulties and probably best avoided. Despite these caveats, there is little doubt that Long-tailed Ducks have declined markedly in the UK since peaking approximately twenty years ago. This has occurred at the same time as numbers using traditional sites elsewhere in the species' European range have also fallen; for example the population within the Baltic Sea declined by 65% between 1992/93 and 2007/09 (Skov et al. 2011). Although a genuine decline in the species' overall population size is likely to be a contributory factor in these observations, some degree of shift in range in response to climatic

amelioration might also be involved – but there is no current evidence for this. However, the effects of climatic conditions on seaduck distributions in Arctic waters can be profound (e.g. Grebmeier et al. 2006, Zipkin et al. 2010).

Glyn Sellors

There has probably never been a greater need for regular and comprehensive surveys of wintering seaducks, divers and grebes around the UK's coast. Such surveys would both assist in the estimation of abundance (e.g. Musgrove et al. 2011) and provide detail on spatial and temporal distribution. In order to ensure that priority activities are clearly set out, a review of key knowledge gaps and information needs in the UK is being undertaken; this will incorporate recommendations for priority monitoring and conservation research. For a concise review of the situation and pressures faced by Long-tailed Duck and other seaducks in the Baltic Sea, see Gotland University (2012); available via http://seaducks.hgo.se/?q=node/14.

	06/07	07/08	08/09	09/10	10/11	Mon	Mean
Sites with mean peak counts of 50 or more birds in Great Britain[†]							
Moray Firth	10,878	1,904	(690)	(759)	(561)	Oct	6,391
Loch Branahuie (Lewis)				430 [39]			430
Forth Estuary	220	163	146	(195)	174	Mar	180
Melbost Sands (Lewis)	121	144	1	610	18	Jan	179
Quendale to Virkie		201 [9]		152 [9]			177
Don Mouth to Ythan Mouth	0	(8)	(25)	(574)	(139)	Nov	149
South Yell Sound		100 [9]	164 [9]				132
Burra and Trondra		126 [9]					126
Rova Head to Wadbister Ness		69 [9]	91 [9]	145 [9]	98 [9]	Jan	101
Rubha Ardvule to Ardivachar (South Uist)					97	Dec	97
Loch of Stenness	107	130	89	50	77	Nov	91
The Ouse and Lairo Water	5	32	78	28	250	Mar	79
Burghead Bay From Burghead to Findhorn		15	70	62	136	Oct	71
Thurso Bay	200	30	26	20	32	Jan	62
Sites below table qualifying levels but exceeding threshold in WeBS-Year 2010/11 in Great Britain							
Water Sound	51	36	25	31	68	Feb	42

[†]as few sites surpass the British threshold, sites with mean peak counts of 50+ are listed.

Common Scoter
Melanitta nigra

International threshold (W Siberia & N Europe population): **5,500**
Great Britain threshold: **1,000**[†]
All-Ireland threshold: **230**

GB max: 19,588 Mar
NI max: 13 Nov

50 is normally used as a minimum threshold

The UK's Common Scoter population is relatively poorly monitored by WeBS. The total derived through WeBS Core counts is highly dependent on weather and the associated viewing conditions at the key sites at the time of the count. In addition, apparent increases or decreases at some sites may also be at least partly attributable to changes in counting effort. Therefore, in order to supplement information provided by WeBS, in this report we collate as much supplementary data (generally from aerial surveys) as possible. An extensive programme of aerial surveys in the last decade proved to be fundamental in improving the understanding of numbers and distribution of Common Scoter in UK waters.

The highest WeBS count in 2010/11 was an exceptional 15,000 Common Scoter present in The Wash in March, considerably greater than the previous maximum recorded at that site through WeBS (4,089 in December 1985). This is presumably the same flock that tends to reside off the North Norfolk Coast, where the historical WeBS peak relates to a count of 8,008 in January 2002. Four other sites surpassed the threshold for national importance (currently 1,000 birds), including Carmarthen Bay, which is also of international importance and classified as a marine SPA due to the presence of such large numbers of this species.

Typically, there were also a small number of records of this species from scattered inland sites. These included three birds at both Haweswater Reservoir (Sep) and Hanningfield Reservoir (Apr).

	06/07	07/08	08/09	09/10	10/11	Mon	Mean
Sites of international importance in the UK							
Carmarthen Bay	14,412[28]	6,189[28]	22,930[29]	43,000[29]	34,049[29]	Mar	24,116
Sites of national importance in Great Britain							
North Norfolk Coast	4,960	3,530	2,040	6,679	(5,379)	Jan	4,518
The Wash	1,810	207	(641)	711	15,147	Mar	4,469
Towyn to Llanddulas	1,800	1,600	(23)	2,076	6,170	Feb	2,912
Alt Estuary	3,288	850	310	2,920	1,171	Nov	1,708
Forth Estuary	623	936	1,103	2,808	462	Jun	1,186
Sites with mean peak counts of 500+ birds in Great Britain[†]							
Don Mouth to Ythan Mouth	(36)	500	300	590	1,086	Sep	619
Dee Estuary (England and Wales)	2,009	297	141	168	400	Apr	603
Sites of all-Ireland importance in Northern Ireland							
Dundrum Bay			1,637				1,637
Glyne Gap	(533)	544	(480)	610[12]	(440)	Dec	577

[†]*as few sites surpass the British threshold, sites with mean peak counts of 500+ are also listed.*

Black Scoter
Melanitta americana

Vagrant
Native Range: N America

One was present between Seahouses and Budle Point (Northumberland) in April. This is the first WeBS record since a drake was recorded off Lavan Sands in three consecutive winters in the mid 2000s.

Surf Scoter
Melanitta perspicillata

Vagrant
Native Range: N America

Four WeBS sites hosted Surf Scoters in 2010/11: Fishguard Harbour (Nov), Dawlish Warren (Jan), Forth Estuary (Mar, May) and Loch Dhrombaig (May).

Velvet Scoter
Melanitta fusca

International threshold:	4,500
Great Britain threshold:	25
All-Ireland threshold:	+[†]

GB max:	783	Jan
NI max:	1	Oct

*50 is normally used as a minimum threshold

As is typical for most seaducks, numbers of Velvet Scoter can be difficult to monitor with results often dependent on sea conditions. Furthermore, monitoring of this species undoubtedly suffers from the relatively poor coverage along some parts of the Scottish coastline.

However, WeBS counts in recent years provide a clear indication that the wintering population of Velvet Scoters in the UK has declined. This is in keeping with large decreases observed elsewhere in the wintering range, particularly within the Baltic Sea (Skov *et al.* 2011). As a consequence, the international population estimate for Velvet Scoter was recently revised significantly downwards, by 55% (Wetlands International 2012), and the species is now classified as Endangered on the IUCN Red List of Threatened Species (Birdlife International 2012).

During 2010/11, Velvet Scoters were noted at 31 WeBS sites in the UK. The monthly peak of 783 in December represents a small increase compared to the previous year, but is still only approximately one third of the estimated British winter population (Musgrove *et al.* 2011). The maximum recorded during the year was 338 at Forth Estuary in March, typifying the decline noted there since successive peak counts of 1000+ during the early 2000s. The only other three-figure count received was 135 at Burghead Bay (Jan). A low total was reported from Moray Firth, where as recently as 2002/03 over 4,000 were counted.

Typically, relatively few were seen away from the Scottish coast. However, a count of 67 at The Wash in May represents the most at the site since 1993/94. The historical maximum there dates back fifty years; 185 birds in February 1961. There were six inland records of Velvet Scoter between November and April, four of which involved singles at reservoirs in the Greater London area.

gray-images.co.uk

Improved monitoring of Moray Firth and other sites which have traditionally been used by this and other seaduck species , is required in order to be able to effectively assess the respective species' statuses in the UK. This is likely to be one of the key recommendations in a review of seaducks in Britain currently being undertaken.

	06/07	07/08	08/09	09/10	10/11	Mon	Mean
Sites of national importance in Great Britain							
Moray Firth	743	(74)	(17)	(62)	(11)	Feb	743
Forth Estuary	928	372	728	457	338	Mar	565
Lunan Bay	2	100	(240)	(40)	67 [12]	Nov	102
Burghead Bay		7	(0)	150	135	Jan	97
Aberdeen Bay offshore	28 [39]						28
Sites below table qualifying levels but exceeding threshold in WeBS-Year 2010/11 in Great Britain							
The Wash	2	(0)	2	(0)	67	May	24

Common Goldeneye

Bucephala clangula

GB max:	12,564	Feb
NI max:	3,829	Feb

International threshold (NW & C Europe population):	11,400
Great Britain threshold:	200
All-Ireland threshold:	95

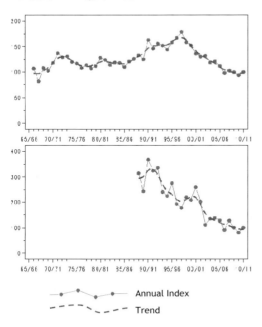

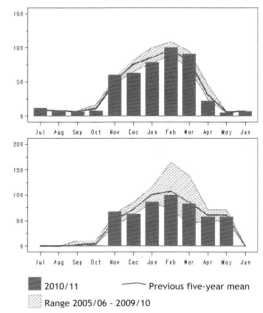

Figure 30.a, Annual indices & trend for Goldeneye in GB (above) & NI (below).

Figure 30.b, Monthly indices for Goldeneye in GB (above) & NI (below).

In light of the steady decline in Common Goldeneye wintering in Britain, the population estimate was revised downwards by 20% to 20,000 birds in 2011 (Musgrove *et al.* 2011). As with some other diving waterfowl of largely Scandinavian breeding origin, recent milder winters have led to a north-east directional shift in the core wintering range (Lehikoinen *et al.* in prep.). For example in Sweden, the estimated winter population rose from 18,800 birds in 1971 to 75,000 by 2004 (Nilsson 2008).

The monthly indices for Britain illustrate two distinct phases within the winter for this species. After below average numbers in December and January, there was evidence of an influx in February (perhaps associated with redistribution of birds following the freezing conditions prevalent over much of central and northern Europe in the midwinter period). Above-average numbers remained in Britain into March.

The steep decline in Northern Ireland has taken place since the initiation of routine monitoring through WeBS. In keeping with the recent trend, numbers at the key site, Loughs Neagh & Beg, were below average; the monthly maximum of 3,388 (Feb) was the third lowest annual peak of the last ten years. Loughs Neagh & Beg were formerly of international importance for this species, but the long term decline there, with annual peaks of more than 13,500 in the early 1990s decreasing to the recent five-year mean of under 4,000 birds, means this is no longer the case. The decline of this and other diving species at the site has been well studied and seems most likely to be attributable to the effects of eutrophication (Maclean *et al.* 2006), and may well also involve impacts of climate change, as outlined above.

Away from Loughs Neagh & Beg, the maximum count during 2010/11 was 771 (Jan) at Forth Estuary. The historic maximum at that site is 5,063 in January 1973, where there was 4,864 as relatively recently as 1997/98. At other sites of national importance, peaks were close to or below recent averages, with the most marked declines at Firth of Clyde and Humber Estuary.

	06/07	07/08	08/09	09/10	10/11	Mon	Mean
Sites of national importance in Great Britain							
Forth Estuary	331	533	431	1,340	771	Jan	681
Loch Leven	517	302	683	415	692	Nov	522
Abberton Reservoir	478	332	299	413	556	Mar	416
Rutland Water	356	349	442	390	509	Feb	409
Humber Estuary	401	577	302	232	274	Jan	357
Tweed Estuary	174	246	245	182	306	Mar	231 ▲
Morecambe Bay	191	(133)	290	242	196	Dec	230
Inner Firth of Clyde	249	452 [12]	148	130	136	Dec	223
Loch of Strathbeg	334	146	159	217	244	Nov	220
Sites of all-Ireland importance in Northern Ireland							
Loughs Neagh and Beg	2,780	4,648	3,684	3,004	3,388	Feb	3,501
Belfast Lough	(108)	226	233	(383)	184	Jan	257
Strangford Lough	83 [10]	237	181	139	471	Mar	222
Lower Lough Erne	169	267	(134)	(110)	(101)	Jan	218
Larne Lough	97	89	84	(116)	114	Feb	100
Sites no longer meeting table qualifying levels in WeBS-Year 2010/2011							
Loch of Skene	128	204	223	188	244	Feb	197
Windermere	271 [12]	242	223 [12]	103	86	Feb	185
Sites below table qualifying levels but exceeding threshold in WeBS-Year 2010/11 in Great Britain							
Loch Ryan	97	95	137	175	302	Dec	161
Loch of Skene	128	204	223	188	244	Feb	197
River Eden - Grinsdale to Sandsfield	75	111	91	131	221	Dec	126
Grafham Water	57	140	96	102	220	Dec	123
Blackwater Estuary	96	64	160	(119)	(203)	Nov	128

Hooded Merganser

Lophodytes cucullatus

Escape and potential vagrant
Native Range: N America

The long-staying drake was at Radipole (Fleet & Wey) throughout the winter.

Smew

Mergellus albellus

GB max: 232   Jan
NI max: 3   Feb

International threshold
(NW & C Europe population):   400
Great Britain threshold: 2
All-Ireland threshold: +[†]

*50 is normally used as a minimum threshold

The cold spell of weather in December 2010 to January 2011 led to an increased number of Smew in the UK, as birds fled even harsher conditions on the continent. Smew were seen across the UK at 103 WeBS sites, with typically the majority in England. Of course, it is worth noting that many WeBS sites will themselves have been frozen during the coldest period.

Several locations across Britain were graced by the species for the first time during WeBS counts. Sites in Cambridgeshire and the Midlands fared particularly well, with several holding all-time WeBS peaks. For the third year in a row, the highest count of the year was at Ouse Fen & Pits (33, Feb).

This cold-weather influx contradicts the recent situation, which up until 2009/10 had seen a reduction in the number of Smew wintering at sites in the UK. This has probably been in response to climatic amelioration and the trend for milder winters, during which period several species of diving duck have extended their wintering distributions in a north-easterly direction. This has taken place in response to newly ice-free areas of the Baltic Sea (Lehikoinen *et al.* in prep.); for example, in Sweden, wintering Smew increased from an approximate 400 birds in 1971 to 3,800 in 2004 (Nilsson 2008).

	06/07	07/08	08/09	09/10	10/11	Mon	Mean	
Sites of national importance in Great Britain								
Wraysbury Gravel Pits	19	16	(10)[12]	(8)[12]	(8)[12]	Jan	18	
Ouse Fen and Pits	0	12	14	27	33	Feb	17	
Cotswold Water Park (West)	13	19	16[12]	18	16	Jan	16	
Dungeness and Rye Bay	18	21	11	(14)	10	Jan	15	
Little Paxton Gravel Pits	4	12	2	17	23	Jan	12	
Rutland Water	5	2	12	18	23	Dec	12	
Lee Valley Gravel Pits	7	7	4	12	17	Jan	9	
Pitsford Reservoir	4	(2)	5	7	15	Jan	8	
Fen Drayton Gravel Pits	3	2	1	19[12]	15	Dec	8	
Eyebrook Reservoir	4	6	7	5	19	Jan	8	
Abberton Reservoir	2	5	8	8	8	Dec	6	
Thorpe Water Park	3	3		8	5	Jan	5	
Longham Lakes					5	Jan	5	
Wraysbury Reservoir					5	Dec	5	
Bedfont and Ashford GPs	1	6	1	(8)	10	Feb	5	
Blackwater Estuary	3	2	(1)	6	(3)[10]	Dec	4	
Sonning Eye & Henley Road GP	2		4	1	8	Jan	4	
Ravensthorpe Reservoir	1	0	1	3	14	Feb	4	
Minsmere	1	1	3	6	8	Feb	4	
Nar Valley Fisheries Lakes				3	5	Feb	4	
Tophill Low Reservoirs	5[12]	6[12]	3[12]	(2)	2	Jan	4	
Seaton Gravel Pits	1	6	3	(3)	(0)		3	
Walthamstow Reservoirs	10	0	0				3	
Colne Valley Gravel Pits	8	4	1	1	2	Dec	3	
Grafham Water	0	3	3	2	7	Dec	3	
Longtown Ponds and River	1	0	3	5	6	Dec	3	
Somerset Levels	0	0	1	4	3	Jan	2	▲
Twyford Gravel Pits	0	0	0	2	4	Mar	2	▲
Thrapston Gravel Pits				(2)	1	Mar	2	
Stanwick Gravel Pits				(2)	(2)	Jan	(2)	
Stewartby Lake			0	(3)			2	
Meadow Lane Gravel Pits	0			1	4	Dec	2	▲
Pentney Gravel Pit				0	3	Jan	2	▲
Covenham Reservoir				(0)	2	Oct	2	▲
Swithland Reservoir	0	3	2	1	2	Jan	2	▲
Holme Pierrepont GPs	1	0	5	3	2	Feb	2	
Coombe Country Park			2[12]				2	
Tindale Tarn	2	0	1	2	3	Jan	2	▲
Castle Loch, Lochmaben	1	2[12]	3	(0)	(0)		2	
Loch Leven	6	0	1[12]	2	2	Nov	2	

Sites below table qualifying levels but exceeding threshold in WeBS-Year 2010/11 in Great Britain

Dorchester Gravel Pits (5, Jan), Lower Windrush Valley GPs (4, Feb), R.Avon (Fordingbridge to Ringwood) (3, Jan), Leybourne & New Hythe GPs (3, Jan), Hanningfield Reservoir (3, Dec), Ditchford Gravel Pits (3, Jan), Waterbeach Gravel Pits (3, Jan), Buckden & Stirtloe Pits (3, Feb), Yare Valley (Markingford to Bawburgh) (3, Jan), Tattershall Pits (3, Jan), R.Eden (Grinsdale to Stansfield (3, Dec), Southampton Water (2, Dec), Ruislip Lido (2, Feb), Colne Fen GPs (2, Feb), Ouse Washes (2, Mar), Deben Estuary (2, Dec), North Norfolk Coast (2, Jan), Besthorpe & Girton GPs (2, Mar), Sutton & Lound GPs (2, Mar), Draycote Water (2, Feb), Crockfoot Reservoir (2, Nov), Whittledene Reservoirs (2, Mar), Lochwinnoch (2, Mar), Kilmardinny Loch (2, Feb), Burghfield GPs (2, Dec), Langford Lowfield GPs (2, Dec)

Edmund Fellowes

Neil Calbrade

Red-breasted Merganser

Mergus serrator

International threshold (NW & C Europe population): 1,700
Great Britain threshold: 84
All-Ireland threshold: 35*

GB max:	3,252	Mar
NI max:	417	Nov

*50 is normally used as a minimum threshold

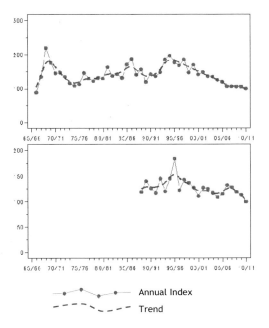

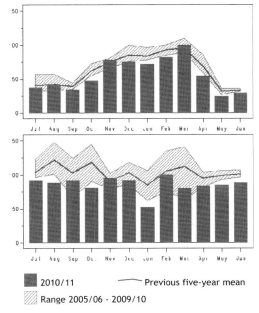

● —— Annual Index
- - - - Trend

■ 2010/11   —— Previous five-year mean
▨ Range 2005/06 - 2009/10

Figure 31.a, Annual indices & trend for Red-breasted Merganser in GB (above) & NI (below).

Figure 31.b, Monthly indices for Red-breasted Merganser in GB (above) & NI (below).

The steady decline in numbers of Red-breasted Merganser, which has been evident from the WeBS trend since the mid 1990s, has slowed in the last five years; following four years of stability in the period 2006/07 to 2009/10, the annual index dropped very slightly in 2010/11. It remains to be seen what will transpire for this species in the years ahead, as there appear to be contrasting trends to the east of the UK.

In the last thirty to forty years, wintering numbers have increased steadily in some areas, for example in Sweden (Nilsson 2008) and The Netherlands (Hornman *et al.* 2012). This is suggestive of a range shift perhaps induced by climate change. However, it is now clear that a large decrease has occurred in the Baltic Sea (Skov *et al.* 2011), implying a drop in overall population size.

The decline of this species, and other seaducks, in the UK and elsewhere has developed into an issue of real concern and therefore should become a higher priority issue for researchers and conservationists.

For the first time, Fleet & Wey became the most important WeBS site in Britain for this species. Peak numbers have been largely stable there in recent years, and that site's promotion is just as much related to the decline that has taken place at Forth Estuary in recent years. The maximum there in 2010/11, of just 223 in March, somewhat pales into insignificance when compared to counts from the past; the historic peak is an exceptional 4,290 in January 1969, while 750+ were noted as recently as March 2004. Peak counts at most other sites which surpass the threshold for national importance were close to or below average, a notable exception being Blackwater Estuary where 142 (Mar) represents the most ever recorded.

Numbers at sites in Northern Ireland in 2010/11 were also disappointing, with most of the principal sites hosting maxima that were below average.

	06/07	07/08	08/09	09/10	10/11	Mon	Mean
Sites of national importance in Great Britain							
Fleet and Wey	284	307	341	233	289	Jan	291
Forth Estuary	347	(261)	267	(316)	223	Mar	288
Moray Firth	211	366	(195)	(246)	(50)	Dec	288
Poole Harbour	(213)	(117)	(241)	(120)	(145)	Jan	(241)
Chichester Harbour	217	211	157	253	213	Dec	210
Morecambe Bay	(118)	(239)	188	176	171	Nov	194
Inner Firth of Clyde	153	145	138	158	199	Aug	159
Langstone Harbour	159	169	114	180 [10]	137	Mar	152
Whiteness to Skelda Ness	134 [9]	192 [9]		156 [9]	83 [9]	Jan	141
Montrose Basin	135	99	113	192	(75)	Apr	135
Sound of Gigha			57 [10]	(178)	(150)	Aug	128
Loch Ryan	106	100	101	136	184	Nov	125
Rova Head to Wadbister Ness		72 [9]	157 [9]	117 [9]	116 [9]	Jan	116
Jersey Shore	126	90			127	Feb	114
Duddon Estuary	106	123	92	141	102	Mar	113
The Wash	70	(53)	(136)	(73)	126	Mar	111 ▲
Piltanton and Luce Estuaries				104	118	Feb	111
Exe Estuary	139	79	140	86	84	Feb	106
North Norfolk Coast	92	131	94	107	85	Mar	102
Blackwater Estuary	72	84	97	108	142	Mar	101
Lavan Sands	81	110	68	131	111	Mar	100
Stour Estuary	85	80	88 [10]	106 [10]	118	Mar	95
Sites of all-Ireland importance in Northern Ireland							
Strangford Lough	390 [10]	(282)	(198)	257	213	Nov	287
Larne Lough	196	142	252	145	140	Feb	175
Belfast Lough	110	183	160	191	120	Oct	153
Lough Foyle	(35)	99	125	101	120	Mar	111
Carlingford Lough	171	106	29	24	(35)	Oct	83
Outer Ards Shoreline	108	38	45	14	22	Mar	45
Sites no longer meeting table qualifying levels in WeBS-Year 2010/2011							
Portsmouth Harbour	97	78	(89)	90	59	Feb	83
Loch Lomond	8	54	240	68	42	Jul	82
Tay Estuary	57 [10]	103	(47)	75	34	Sep	67
Sites below table qualifying levels but exceeding threshold in WeBS-Year 2010/11 in Great Britain							
Lindisfarne	29	34	(55)	71	149	Aug	71
Inner Loch Indaal				37	114	Oct	76

Goosander

Mergus merganser

International threshold
(NW & C Europe population): 2,700
Great Britain threshold: 120[†]
All-Ireland threshold: +[†]

GB max: 4,643 Jan
NI max: 4 Feb

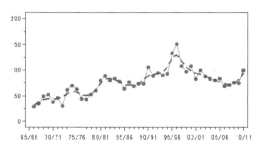

Figure 32.a, Annual indices & trend for Goosander in GB.

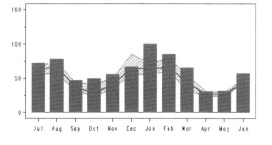

Figure 32.b, Monthly indices for Goosander in GB.

Goosanders that winter in Britain are considered to be largely derived from the breeding population, although some in south-east England are likely to originate from overseas. This is likely to be particularly the case during cold weather on the continent when influxes can occur; as experienced during the winter 2010/11 and evidenced by an associated increase in the national index value for Britain. The monthly indices illustrate elegantly an influx of Goosander into Britain in January, with numbers remaining above average thereafter for the rest of the winter. A positive showing is again apparent in the summer months; evidence of the increasing British breeding population (Baillie *et al.* 2012).

The high supplementary count of 547 birds at Solway Estuary in January is presumably linked, at least in part, to cold weather displacement from frozen water bodies inland. This count represents the highest number reported at a single site through WeBS since 550+ were at Inner Moray Firth in 1994/95 and 1995/96. Further south, in lowland England where winter counts are more likely to relate to continental immigrants, counts at some sites provided

evidence of an influx. After an exceptional peak of 238 at River Avon (Fordingbridge to Ringwood) in November, a number of further above-average counts were registered at sites in January and February. These included 238 at Stretton Sugwas Sand Pit, 152 at Hartleton Water, 53 at Chelmarsh Reservoir and 51 at Abberton Reservoir.

Tommy Holden

As ever, the submission of roost counts of Goosanders from all sites, in order to supplement Core counts, is welcomed.

	06/07	07/08	08/09	09/10	10/11	Mon	Mean
Sites of national importance in Great Britain							
Solway Estuary	(29)	(25)	50	(64)	547 [12]	Jan	299
Tay Estuary	313	(155)	232	(205)	(152)	Aug	273
Forth Estuary	(119)	(108)	(68)	(184)	225	Jun	225
Loch Lomond	261	36	217	161	153	Oct	166
Tyninghame Estuary	157	107	68	171	223	Jul	145
Tweed Estuary	123	42	85	205	186	Oct	128
Additional sites with mean peak counts of 70 or more birds in Great Britain[†]							
River Avon - Fordingbridge to Ringwood	53	43	92	101	238	Nov	105
Castle Loch Lochmaben	85	120	116	118 [12]	64	Jan	101
Montrose Basin	57	59	116	131	85	Jul	90
Loch Leven	39	151	68 [12]	97	83	Jan	88
River Tweed - Kelso to Coldstream	74	90	49	111	102	Oct	85
River Tweed - A1 Bypass to Horncliffe					84	Apr	84
Blithfield Reservoir		51	96 [11]	76 [11]	(100) [11]	Nov	81
Eccup Reservoir	82	70	60	41	135	Jan	78
Acre Nook Sand Quarry	47 [11]	77 [11]	85 [11]	122 [11]	36	Jan	73
Inchgarth Reservoir	0	48	47	149	122 [11]	Oct	73
Other sites surpassing national importance qualifying levels in Winter 2010/2011 in Great Britain							
Stretton Sugwas Sand Pit	0	18	20	28	160	Jan	45
Hartleton Water		0	0	9	152 [12]	Feb	40

[†] *as few sites surpass the British threshold and no All-Ireland threshold has been set, sites with mean peak counts of 70+ are listed.*

Ruddy Duck

Oxyura jamaicensis

Naturalised introduction
Native Range: America

GB max: 121 Oct
NI max: 11 Oct

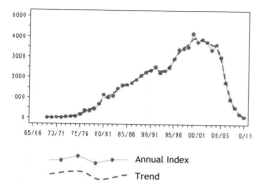

Annual Index

Trend

Figure 33.a, Annual indices & trend for Ruddy Duck in GB.

The Ruddy Duck has been the focus of a coordinated international programme to eradicate the species in Europe, as part of the conservation of the White-headed Duck (*Oxyura leucocephala*).

Despite maintaining a reasonably widespread distribution, the British index has inevitably dropped sharply in recent years. In January 2011, there were estimated to be 150 Ruddy Ducks remaining in Britain (I. Henderson pers. comm., in Musgrove *et al.* (2011)). The peaks counts during the year were at Rutland Water (23, Dec) and Dungeness & Rye Bay (16, Jan), the latter one of a small number of sites where the maxima was higher than that of 2009/10.

Sites with mean peak counts of 30 or more birds in Great Britain	06/07	07/08	08/09	09/10	10/11	Mon	Mean
Abberton Reservoir	261 [30]	49	96	24	11	Oct	88
Staines Reservoirs	277	72	69	10	9	Dec	87
Hilfield Park Reservoir	263	83	31	12	4	Jan	79
Hanningfield Reservoir	276	45	36	9	9	Jul	75
Dungeness and Rye Bay	193	73	31	6	16	Jan	64
Carsington Water	101	132	17	25	9	Jan	57
Thoresby Lake	52 [30]						52
Chew Valley Lake	(130)	17	65	19	11	Feb	48
Attenborough Gravel Pits	40	44	(56)	(31)	(8)	Jan	47
Blagdon Lake	85	103	36	4	4	Nov	46
Mersey Estuary		85	6				46
Thames Estuary	79	73	40	22	10	Jan	45
Clumber Park Lake	66	82	22	8	(1)	Jul	45
Pitsford Reservoir	102	41	40	24	7	Dec	43
Tophill Low Reservoirs	85 [30]	63	38	15	2	Sep	41
Wigan Flashes	73 [30]	55	22	6	(1)	Oct	39
Brent Reservoir	85	46	30	12	15	Oct	38
Tees Estuary	111	13	36	8	0		34
Llyn Alaw	92	18	10	11			33
Holme Pierrepont Gravel Pits	106	38	8	0	2	Feb	31
Humber Estuary	59 [30]	(31)	(14)	3	(1)	Feb	31

Red-throated Diver

Gavia stellata

International threshold: 2,600
Great Britain threshold: 170
All-Ireland threshold: 20*

GB max: 638 Mar
NI max: 48 Jan

*50 is normally used as a minimum threshold

Although a localised breeder in northern Scotland (Dillon *et al.* 2009), Red-throated Divers are widespread at coastal sites throughout the UK during the winter, with an estimated population of 17,000 in British waters (O'Brien *et al.* 2008).

In 2010/11, the species was noted at 150 WeBS sites, a typical showing, of which three currently qualify as being nationally important. However, large numbers occur further offshore, but surveys in these areas are not annual. For example, significant concentrations can be reported from coastal areas of southern Britain, depending on prevailing foraging conditions; indeed the Outer Thames Estuary was designated an SPA due to its wintering numbers of Red-throated Divers. This aggregation is largely missed during WeBS counts, although large numbers sometimes occur within sight of land off Suffolk, Essex and Kent, depending on conditions. The importance of south-east England was evidenced in 2010/11 by high counts noted at Glyne Gap (Sussex) and Pegwell Bay (Kent). Further north, numbers at sites in Scotland appear to be largely as expected.

There were no inland records away from northern Scotland during 2010/11.

	06/07	07/08	08/09	09/10	10/11	Mon	Mean
Sites of national importance in Great Britain							
Glyne Gap	126	(109)	(343)	223	(181)	Jan	218
Pegwell Bay	12	11	517	83	338	Jan	192 ▲
Aberdeen Bay offshore	175						175
Sites of all-Ireland importance in Northern Ireland							
Lough Foyle	13	53	81	128	19	Mar	59
Belfast Lough	22	67	20	(34)	21	Nov	33
Outer Ards Shoreline	64	22	12	27	31	Jan	31
Sites below table qualifying levels but exceeding threshold in WeBS-Year 2010/11 in Great Britain							
Minsmere	56	143	10	3	200	Mar	82

Black-throated Diver
Gavia arctica

International threshold: 3,500
Great Britain threshold: 6*
All-Ireland threshold: ?[†]

GB max: 78 Mar
NI max: 0

50 is normally used as a minimum threshold

Black-throated Divers were recorded at 50 sites in the UK during WeBS Core counts. Fourteen of these qualified as being nationally important. The premier WeBS site for wintering Black-throated Divers in UK continues to be Gerrans Bay (Cornwall); after an impressive peak of 124 birds noted there in 2009/10, this year's maximum of 58, in March, was more typical.

As usual, most sightings of Black-throated Divers were in Scotland. The peak Scottish WeBS Core counts this year, all during October-December, were 19 between Bay of Sandoyne and Holme Sound (Orkney), 15 off Arran, and 15 from Girvan to Turnberry. Improved coverage of the coastline of north-west Scotland in particular (such as that undertaken voluntarily by the RAF Ornithological Society each winter) would inevitably derive a truer picture of this species' winter status in northern Britain.

	06/07	07/08	08/09	09/10	10/11	Mon	Mean
Sites of national importance in Great Britain							
Gerrans Bay	60	53	55	124	58	Mar	70
Loch Ewe	40	(11)	(11)	(33)	(0)		40
Sound of Gigha			19 [12]	15	(8)	Apr	17
Bay of Sandoyne to Holme Sound				15	19	Oct	17
Loch Slapin	28 [26]	13 [26]	1	18 [26]	14	Dec	15
Girvan to Turnberry	1	7	16	25	15	Dec	13
Loch Gairloch	14	(14)	(10)	12	(4)	Jan	13
Arran	1	(3)	(4)	13	15	Nov	10
Little Loch Broom	13	(16)	5	0	(0)		9
Glyne Gap	(9)	(9)	(10)	5	(3) [12]	Jan	8
Applecross Bay	2	13	9	7			8
Red Point to Port Henderson	8	(1)	6	(0)	(0)		7
Gruinard Bay	6	8	4	13	2	Feb	7
Kilfinan Bay		11	5	3	4 [12]	Nov	6
Sites no longer meeting table qualifying levels in WeBS-Year 2010/2011							
Sand Bay	4	6	6				5
Sites with mean peak counts of 2 or more birds in Northern Ireland[†]							
Strangford Lough	3 [12]	0	4 [12]	5 [10]	0		2

[†] as no All-Ireland threshold has been set, a threshold of 2 has been selected for presentation in this report.

Pacific Diver
Gavia pacifica

Vagrant
Native Range: N America

One was seen during the WeBS Core count at Gerrans Bay in November. It, or another, was present off Cornwall throughout the 2010/11 winter (*per* birdguides.com).

Great Northern Diver
Gavia immer

International threshold: **50**
Great Britain threshold: **25***
All-Ireland threshold: **?** [†]

| GB max: | 215 | Nov |
| NI max: | 9 | Mar |

*50 is normally used as a minimum threshold

Great Northern Divers were recorded at 114 WeBS sites, a lower total than previous years. Following 2010/11, just two areas of the Scottish west coast monitored through WeBS (Sound of Gigha and Loch Na Keal) now surpass the threshold of international importance for Great Northern Divers.

Hence, further count data from sites along this stronghold of the Scottish coast are needed in order for WeBS to be able to illustrate the true status of this species within UK waters. It has long been true that dedicated surveys are required to effectively monitor wintering divers and grebes around the Scottish coastline, but it is clear that this has never more been the case than now. At sites on the west coast of Scotland, this species can form significant aggregations at sites used for roosting (D. Shackleton, pers. comm.). Surveys at dusk therefore represent an opportunity to gather additional data for this species.

The peak counts received from Scottish waters during 2010/11 was 64 at Loch Na Keal. Elsewhere, the maximum in England was 20 at Gerrans Bay in February, another good showing for that location, comparable to those of recent winters.

	06/07	07/08	08/09	09/10	10/11	Mon	Mean	
Sites of international importance in the UK								
Sound of Gigha			217[6]	19 [6]	29 [6]	Oct	88	
Rova Head to Wadbister Ness		36 [9]	31[9]	113 [9]	45 [9]	Jan	56	▲
Sites of national importance in Great Britain								
Loch Ewe	53	58	28	47	(15)	Jan	47	
Loch Na Keal	(0)	27	29	55	64	Feb	44	
Kirkabister to Wadbister Ness		33 [9]	48[9]				41	
Outer Loch Indaal					40	Nov	40	▼
Loch Eriboll	36	66	16	36	(2)	Feb	39	
Gruinard Bay	37	68	29	35	21	Feb	38	
Caernarfon Bay		68	8	40	28	Dec	36	
Traigh Luskentyre	58	6					32	
Quendale to Virkie		27[9]		30 [9]			29	
Loch Slapin	39	24	27	39	13	Dec	28	
West Loch Tarbert					27	Nov	27	▲
Lochs Beg and Scridain (East End)	8	17	25	37	36	Mar	25	▲
Sites no longer meeting table qualifying levels in WeBS-Year 2010/2011								
Broadford Bay	15	19	16	48	13	Dec	22	

No data since 2006/07: Luce Bay offshore; Coll, Tiree & west Mull offshore; Scarp to Vatersay offshore; Scapa Flow

Sites below table qualifying levels but exceeding threshold in WeBS-Year 2010/11 in Great Britain								
Whiteness to Skelda Ness	14 [9]	23 [9]		15 [9]	26 [9]	Jan	20	
Loch Buie	11	7	13	25	30	Mar	17	
Sites with mean peak counts of 5 or more birds in Northern Ireland [†]								
Lough Foyle	17	29	7	55	9	Mar	23	
Carlingford Lough	(4)	1	15	7	(0)		8	

[†] *as no All-Ireland threshold has been set, a threshold of 5 has been selected for presentation in this report.*

Great Cormorant
Phalacrocorax carbo

International threshold (NW Europe): **1,200**
Great Britain threshold: **350**
All-Ireland threshold: **140**

GB max: **17,591** Oct
NI max: **1,862** Nov

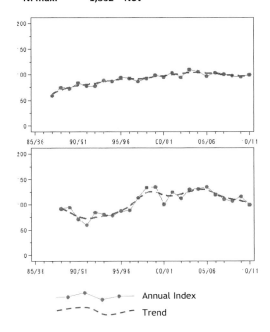

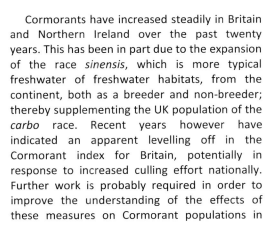

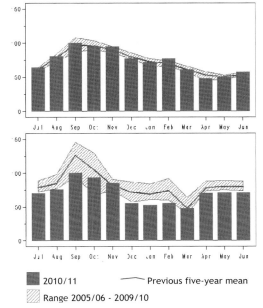

- ● — Annual Index
- - - - Trend

■ 2010/11 ⟋⟋⟋ Previous five-year mean
▨ Range 2005/06 - 2009/10

Figure 34.a, Annual indices & trend for Cormorant in GB (above) & NI (below).

Figure 34.b, Monthly indices for Cormorant in GB (above) & NI (below).

Cormorants have increased steadily in Britain and Northern Ireland over the past twenty years. This has been in part due to the expansion of the race *sinensis*, which is more typical freshwater of freshwater habitats, from the continent, both as a breeder and non-breeder; thereby supplementing the UK population of the *carbo* race. Recent years however have indicated an apparent levelling off in the Cormorant index for Britain, potentially in response to increased culling effort nationally. Further work is probably required in order to improve the understanding of the effects of these measures on Cormorant populations in the UK. In Northern Ireland, the trend over the course of the last five years is a shallow decline.

In 2010/11, the peak from Dee Estuary surpassed that from Loughs Neagh & Beg for the third year in a row, and in doing so joined the Northern Irish site as one of international importance. The highest count of the year was from Alt Estuary, where the 1,459 noted in February is the most ever recorded there. Given the proximity of the sites, there may be some degree of exchange of Cormorants between the Dee and Alt Estuaries. Elsewhere, the 1,000+ threshold was surpassed at Morecambe Bay for the first time since September 2000.

	06/07	07/08	08/09	09/10	10/11	Mon	Mean
Sites of international importance in the UK							
Loughs Neagh and Beg	1,665	1,396	990	1,297	1,192	Sep	1,308
Dee Estuary (England and Wales)	1,003	1,133	1,160	1,323	1,399	Dec	1,204 ▲
Sites of national importance in Great Britain							
Alt Estuary	1,168	937	1,142	762 [12]	1,459	Feb	1,094
Morecambe Bay	641	937	669	814	1,047	Sep	822
Abberton Reservoir	342	639	1,157	565	854	Sep	711
Dungeness and Rye Bay	717	684	616	581	658	Jan	651
Ribble Estuary	316	504	600	515 [10]	928	Nov	573
Forth Estuary	653	477	(507)	(483)	462	Sep	531

	06/07	07/08	08/09	09/10	10/11	Mon	Mean
Rutland Water	918	396	326	470	393	Sep	501
Ranworth and Cockshoot Broads	348 [11]	287 [11]	582 [11]	629 [11]	613 [11]	Mar	492
Solway Estuary	530	497	(406)	(486)	442	Aug	490
Poole Harbour	374	254	(349)	457	(630)	Oct	429
Walthamstow Reservoirs	640	433	395		247	May	429
Alde Complex	206	226	421	415	822	Feb	418 ▲
The Wash	467	453	495	370	304	Aug	418
South Yell Sound		464 [9]	335 [9]				400
Thames Estuary	434	(211)	398	344	(268)	Oct	392
Hanningfield Reservoir	500	215	600	245	279	Sep	368
Blackwater Estuary	200	279	(674)	380	237	Oct	354
Queen Mary Reservoir	88	295	211	406	(750)	Dec	350 ▲
Sites of all-Ireland importance in Northern Ireland							
Strangford Lough	422	286	(443)	359	265	Sep	355
Belfast Lough	350	312	267	286	302	Oct	303
Carlingford Lough	230	142	98	381	(91)	Nov	213
Outer Ards Shoreline	397	177	153	105	223	Nov	211
Sites no longer meeting table qualifying levels in WeBS-Year 2010/2011							
Tees Estuary	329	378	306	284	241	Aug	308
Inner Firth of Clyde	875 [11]	104	229	112	131	Sep	290
Sites below table qualifying levels but exceeding threshold in WeBS-Year 2010/11 in Great Britain							
River Avon - Fordingbridge to Ringwood	(198)	135	184	217	529	Dec	266
River Avon - Ringwood to Christchurch	(67)	73	52	(45)	461	Jan	195
Rostherne Mere	273	328	317	333	398	Jun	330
Ouse Washes	454 [12]	294	189 [12]	157 [11]	398 [11]	Mar	298
North Norfolk Coast	265	300 [11]	298	274	386	Jul	305

European Shag

Phalacrocorax aristotelis

International threshold: **2,000**
Great Britain threshold: **1,100**[†]
All-Ireland threshold: **?**[†]

GB max:	**2,777**	**Nov**
NI max:	**479**	**Nov**

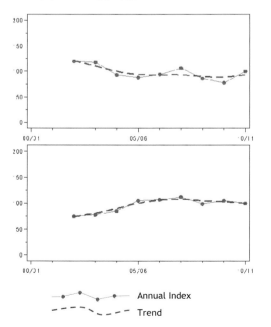

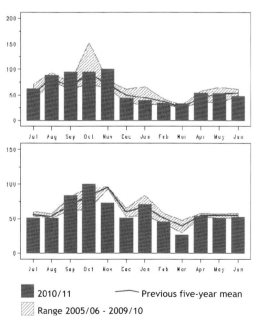

●——● Annual Index
---- Trend

■ 2010/11   ⌒ Previous five-year mean
▨ Range 2005/06 - 2009/10

Figure 35.a, Annual indices & trend for Shag in GB (above) & NI (below).

Figure 35.b, Monthly indices for Shag in GB (above) & NI (below).

In 2010/11, the largest WeBS counts of Shags were in autumn/early winter; 496 at Forth Estuary and 400 Widewall Bay. In Northern Ireland, the peak count was 353 at Outer Ards Shoreline in January. In England, numbers on the coast were close to average, and there were a small number of scattered inland records.

The UK's breeding population of Shags is well-monitored by the JNCC Seabird Monitoring Programme, results of which have shown a decline of 15% between 2000 and 2010 (JNCC 2011). However, wintering numbers are relatively poorly monitored; currently the table below is largely populated with data collected by SOTEAG in Shetland.

In contrast to the breeding trend, analysis of winter numbers based on WeBS data (presented here for the first time) indicates stability at WeBS sites in both Britain and Northern Ireland. Distribution of Shags in winter can affect subsequent breeding phenology (e.g. Daunt et al. 2006), it being a species highly dependent on a particular food resource; the lesser sandeel (Ammodytes tobianus). The application of improved knowledge of winter distribution and enhanced robustness of the winter trends, both potentially attainable through improved WeBS coverage, could therefore be of conservation value.

	06/07	07/08	08/09	09/10	10/11	Mon	Mean
Sites with mean peak counts of 120 or more birds in Great Britain†							
South Yell Sound		1,065 [9]	886 [9]				976
Forth Estuary	719	(384)	(456)	(424)	(496)	Sep	719
Rova Head to Wadbister Ness		253 [9]	377 [9]	507 [9]	327 [9]	Jan	366
Widewall Bay	390	800	70	50	400	Nov	342
Burra and Trondra		332 [9]					332
Island of Egilsay	230		286	161	(380)	Nov	264
Quendale to Virkie		102 [9]		418 [9]			260
Scalloway Islands		221 [9]					221
Sullom Voe		219 [9]	145 [9]				182
Kirkabister to Wadbister Ness		183 [9]	166 [9]				175
Island of Papa Westray	232	160	146	(190)	131	Oct	172
Moray Coast (Consolidated)	193	347	(132)	42	17	Dec	150
Loch Ewe	261	(98)	76	82	(75)	Jan	140
Inner Firth of Clyde	(150) [11]	104	108	108	150	Sep	124
Thurso Bay	170	70	262 [12]	106	5	Jan	123
Gerrans Bay	86	328	128	28	28	Sep	120
Sites with mean peak counts of 120 or more birds in Northern Ireland†							
Outer Ards Shoreline	284	317	437	334	353	Jan	345
Strangford Lough	(291)	(156)	247	(277)	(265)	Sep	270
Belfast Lough	191 [10]	107	90 [10]	139 [10]	116	Oct	129
Sites below table qualifying levels but exceeding threshold in WeBS-Year 2010/11 in Great Britain†							
Kingsbridge Estuary	45	93	132		197	Oct	117
Winterfield to Catcraig	120	98	128	70	160	Sep	115
Anstruther Bay	73	40	55	25	137	Sep	66
Exe Estuary	5 [10]	40	0	0	125	Nov	34

† as few sites surpass the GB threshold and no All-Ireland threshold has been set, a threshold of 120 has been chosen to select sites for presentation in this report.

Great Bittern
Botaurus stellaris

International threshold: 65
Great Britain threshold: 6

Bitterns were recorded at a record 99 WeBS sites in 2010/11, and a high monthly maximum of 92 birds in December was probably largely attributable to increased visibility of Bitterns when foraging for food away from frozen reedbeds. There may also have been an influx of continental immigrants. This total is set against the background of an increasing UK breeding population (Brown et al. 2011), and would also tend to suggest the number actually present in the UK during winter 2010/11 may have been higher than the estimate of a minimum of 600 individuals (Wotton et al. 2011). Singles were widespread, while several sites also hosted multiple birds. The site maximum was an impressive 18 at Dungeness & Rye Bay (Dec). Elsewhere, at least four were recorded in winter at Testwood Lakes, Godmanchester GP, London Wetland Centre and Kenfig Pool; all sites that are traditionally favoured by Bitterns in winter.

Black-crowned Night Heron
Nycticorax nycticorax

Vagrant and escape
Native Range: Europe & Africa

Three were recorded in spring; at Thames Estuary, Earlswood Lakes and Bainton Pits. This represents the most ever in a WeBS-year.

Squacco Heron
Ardeola ralloides

Vagrant
Native Range: Worldwide

One lingered at Cleddau Estuary from October into November; the sixth WeBS record and first since October 2004.

Cattle Egret
Bubulcus ibis

Vagrant
Native Range: Worldwide

Cattle Egrets were recorded at six WeBS sites in southern England during 2010/11: Colne Fen Gravel Pits (Aug), Dungeness & Rye Bay (Aug), Severn Estuary (Oct), Kingsbridge Estuary (Nov), Ouse Washes (Nov) and Somerset Levels (Feb).

Little Egret
Egretta garzetta

International threshold
(W Europe & NW Africa): 1,300
Great Britain threshold: 45
All-Ireland threshold: ?[+]

GB max: 4,423 Oct
NI max: 63 Oct

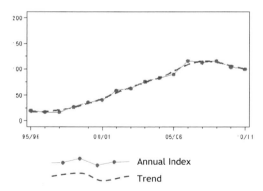

Figure 36.a, Annual indices & trend for Little Egret in GB.

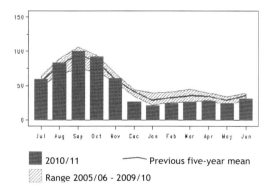

Figure 36.b, Monthly indices for Little Egret in GB.

Having expanded both in terms of numbers and range, the Little Egret is now a familiar sight at wetlands, both coastal and inland, throughout the southern half of Britain. Since 2006/07 the trend has reached a plateau, and the number of Little Egrets at WeBS sites appears to have levelled off and may now be even dropping slightly. At other sites in the wider countryside the species continues to expand, as indicated by data collected for Bird Atlas 2007-11 (D. Balmer, pers. comm.).

The WeBS monthly indices show a negative response to the onset of freezing conditions in December, which affected the numbers present in subsequent months. The cold weather may have directly increased mortality and/or may have resulted in redistribution of birds to milder areas.

At regularly counted sites, the September maximum at The Wash of 543 birds is in keeping with the recent average there, but somewhat lower than the last two years. The gradual expansion away from southern coasts continues; exemplified by promotion of the Ribble Estuary to a site of national importance where it joins others in north-west England such as Dee Estuary and Morecambe Bay.

In Northern Ireland, where the species now breeds (S. Wolsey, pers. comm.), the maximum count in 2010/11 was 51 at Strangford Lough in October.

	06/07	07/08	08/09	09/10	10/11	Mon	Mean
Sites of national importance in Great Britain							
The Wash	323	(319)	633	618	543	Sep	529
Thames Estuary	316	277	421	383	326	Oct	345
Dee Estuary (England & Wales)	132 [12]	163	258 [12]	315 [12]	303 [12]	Aug	251
North Norfolk Coast	193	272 [12]	258	281 [12]	245	Sep	250
Chichester Harbour	192	264	267	198	219	Oct	228
Blackwater Estuary	(58)	245	221	(213)	(167)	Oct	193
Poole Harbour	(84)	(79)	(136)	(146)	(115)	Sep	(146)
Stour Estuary	143	102	102	184	166	Oct	139
Swale Estuary	(72)	(100)	(109)	139	127	Oct	133
Jersey Shore	98	156			118	Jan	124
Exe Estuary	116	135	103	137	122	Sep	123
Lavan Sands	133	131	107	136	101	Sep	122
Crouch-Roach Estuary	102	100	83	104	170	Sep	112
Tamar Complex	97	(126)	125	70	97	Sep	103
Burry Inlet	86	87	156	99	79	Oct	101
Taw-Torridge Estuary	78	(121)	92	108	74	Aug	99
Severn Estuary	74	105	103	84	121	Aug	98
Hamford Water	135	95	70	(115)	74	Oct	98
Langstone Harbour	77	76	112	135	84	Oct	97
Breydon Water & Berney Marshes	71 [12]	126 [12]	114 [12]	81 [12]	85 [12]	Oct	95
Morecambe Bay	28	(24)	56	69	149	Sep	91
Cleddau Estuary	(68)	120	(104)	69	61	Oct	89
Kingsbridge Estuary	89	67	91	90	90	Aug	85
Southampton Water	80	(24)	(40)	(67)	(52)	Aug	80
Carmarthen Bay	57	106	64	106	66	Sep	80
Portsmouth Harbour	96	111	49 [11]	51	(81)	Oct	78
Somerset Levels	64	73	90	90	68	Feb	77
Pagham Harbour	90	63	67	95	70	Oct	77
Camel Estuary	80	74	88	83	57	Aug	76
Medway Estuary	(32)	(71)	(75)	(37)	(69)	Sep	(75)
Fal Complex	82	79	84	71	50	Sep	73
Humber Estuary	(36)	41	95	51	68	Aug	66
Fleet and Wey	59	67	66	58	(39)	Jul	63
North West Solent	53	56	61	52	69	Oct	60
Ribble Estuary	(21)	31	50	86	(73)	Sep	60 ▲
Pegwell Bay	71	33	79	62	45 [12]	Sep	58
Grouville Marsh	165		4	1			57
Alde Complex	56	66	50	51	62	Nov	57
Dengie Flats	51	58	63	59	43	Oct	55
Newtown Estuary	52	41	41	71 [12]	(25)	Sep	52
Colne Estuary	34	64 [11]	53	(51)	(62)	Nov	49
Deben Estuary	42	56	37	42	68	Sep	49 ▲
Avon Valley: Salisbury-Fordingbridge	57	46	41	40	53	Jan	47
Guernsey Shore	42	41	49	53	(39)	Dec	46
Dungeness and Rye Bay	45	28	91	33	29	Sep	45 ▲
Sites below table qualifying levels but exceeding threshold in WeBS-Year 2010/11 in Great Britain							
Ouse Washes	5	29	55	12	113 [11]	Mar	43
Leighton Moss	1	14	26	52	71	Aug	33
Orwell Estuary	54	(41)	28	29	64	Oct	44
Christchurch Harbour	46	32	(28)	43	47	Sep	42

Great White Egret
Ardea alba

Scarce
Native Range: S Europe, Africa, Asia, N & C America

Great White Egrets were reported from 18 WeBS sites; one fewer than the previous year. A monthly peak of ten birds was seen in January. During 2010/11, all records were from England and most involved singles, although up to five were reported from Somerset Levels during the winter period.

Grey Heron
Ardea cinerea

International threshold (N & W Europe):		2,700
Great Britain threshold:		610
All-Ireland threshold:		30

GB max:	4,178	Oct
NI max:	398	Nov

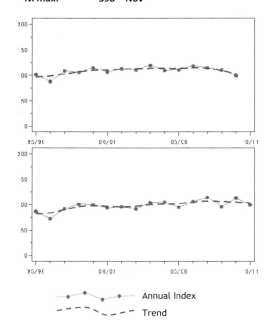

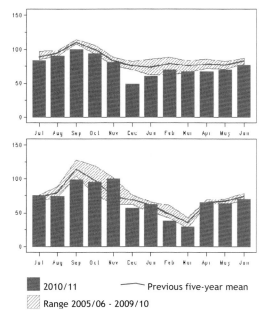

Figure 37.a, Annual indices & trend for Grey Heron in GB (above) & NI (below).

Figure 37.b, Monthly indices for Grey Heron in GB (above) & NI (below).

Although increasing slowly in terms of the breeding population (Baillie *et al.* 2012), national WeBS indices for Grey Heron in both Britain and Northern Ireland tend to show very little in the way of variation from year to year. However, there was a pronounced drop in the monthly index value for December in response to the frozen conditions, when potentially there may have been an increase in mortality rates.

In 2010/11, the monthly peaks in both Britain and Northern Ireland occurred during the autumn/early winter months of October and November, respectively, typical of recent years. Five sites held monthly peaks in excess of 100 birds, including the year's largest count; 194 at Loughs Neagh & Beg. In Britain, the maximum of 167 at River Avon (Fordingbridge to Ringwood) represents the most ever there.

	06/07	07/08	08/09	09/10	10/11	Mon	Mean
Sites of all-Ireland importance in Northern Ireland							
Loughs Neagh and Beg	225	173	147	208	194	Nov	189
Strangford Lough	95 [10]	138 [10]	92	111	89 [10]	Nov	102
Carlingford Lough	51	62	(34)	(12)	14	Feb	39
Lough Foyle	42	44	42	30	36	Oct	39
Dundrum Inner Bay	36	41	27	34	40	Jul	36

	06/07	07/08	08/09	09/10	10/11	Mon	Mean
Belfast Lough	(32)	43	35	39	24	Oct	35
Outer Ards Shoreline	35	24	18	31	52	Nov	32
Sites with mean peak counts of 70+ birds in Great Britain[†]							
Somerset Levels	143	135	161	122	112	Nov	135
River Avon: Fordingbridge to Ringwood	83	82	109	181	167	Sep	124
Avon Valley - Salisbury to Fordingbridge	114	144	92	118	97	Mar	113
Ouse Washes	55 [12]	143	199	39	123 [12]	Mar	112
Morecambe Bay	105	(38)	107	115	109	Jul	110
Forth Estuary	111	125	102	99	93	Oct	106
Thames Estuary	89	(91)	(63)	(110)	(81)	Aug	97
Coombe Country Park	107	106	81	50	78	May	84
Dee Estuary (England and Wales)	(66)	73	67	97	61	Nov	75
Walthamstow Reservoirs	75	76	62		(23)	Jan	71

[†] *as few sites surpass the British threshold, sites with mean peak counts of 70+ are also listed.*

Purple Heron

Ardea purpurea

Vagrant
Native Range: Worldwide

Four is the most ever in a WeBS-year, and comprised singles at Dungeness & Rye Bay (Jul-Aug), College Reservoir (Apr), Mount Castle Quarry (Apr) and Wellington Gravel Pits (Jun).

White Stork

Ciconia ciconia

Vagrant and escape
Native Range: Europe, Africa, Asia

One was at Pegwell Bay in September.

Glossy Ibis

Plegadis falcinellus

Vagrant
Native Range: S Europe, Africa, Asia, Australia, N & C America

Several Glossy Ibis featured during 2010/11, continuing the recent positive trend. During the period of September to November, birds were seen at Avon Estuary (Devon), Otter Estuary, Christchurch Harbour, Loughs Neagh & Beg, Cotswold Water Park and Ouse Washes. Later in the winter, one was at Dungeness & Rye Bay in January.

Eurasian Spoonbill

Platalea leucorodia

International threshold
(W Europe & W Africa): 110
Great Britain threshold: 1

Spoonbills continue to slowly expand in the UK and were recorded at 29 sites during WeBS Core counts, with a monthly peak of 47 in August. All records were in England with the exception of four at Ythan Estuary (Scotland) in July and one on the Welsh side of the Severn Estuary in June. Most counts were of one to four birds, notable exceptions being maxima of 31 at North Norfolk Coast (Aug), 14 at The Wash (Aug) and 14 at Poole Harbour (Nov). The only inland record was one at Blithfield Reservoir in June (a WeBS-first for Staffordshire).

Greater Flamingo

Phoenicopterus ruber

Escape and possible vagrant
Native Range: S Europe, Africa & SW Asia

One resided at Minsmere from April to June, with presumably the same bird having been seen at Dunstable Wetland in January. These are the fourth and fifth WeBS records, and the first since March 2004.

Pied-billed Grebe

Podilymbus podiceps

Vagrant
Native Range: America

One at Hollingworth Lake in November is the ninth WeBS record. The previous eight were all during the 1990s, most recently in Norfolk in April 1999.

Little Grebe

Tachybaptus ruficollis

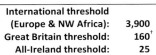

International threshold	
(Europe & NW Africa):	3,900
Great Britain threshold:	160[†]
All-Ireland threshold:	25

GB max: 5,276   Sep
NI max: 544   Oct

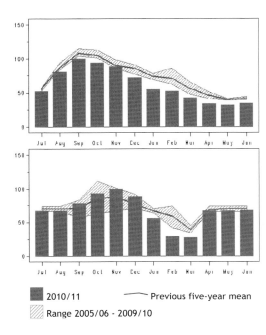

Annual Index

Trend

2010/11

Previous five-year mean

Range 2005/06 - 2009/10

Figure 38.a, Annual indices & trend for Little Grebe in GB (above) & NI (below).

Figure 38.b, Monthly indices for Little Grebe in GB (above) & NI (below).

Little Grebes are widely dispersed on small water bodies, canals and riverine habitats throughout much of the UK. Thus, WeBS monitors a relatively small proportion of the total population and care should be taken if attempting to interpret national trends based on WeBS data alone.

Little Grebes slowly, but steadily, increased in Britain from the mid 1990s, soon after the species was first routinely monitored. Interestingly, this coincided with a similar trend in the Netherlands (Hornman *et al.* 2012). However, as evidenced by the annual index, there was a pronounced drop in numbers in Britain in 2010/11. Reasons for this may be linked to the frozen conditions which will have forced diving species away from traditional sites.

The cold conditions may also have increased mortality; pertinently, the monthly indices for both Britain and Northern Ireland initially dropped during the frozen conditions in January, and they appear not to have recovered by the spring implying negative effects on the local breeding populations.

The Thames Estuary is the only site to surpass the threshold of national importance in Britain. The monthly peak there (402, Dec) was similar to the longer-term average, but numbers at twelve further sites with a five-year mean of 80+ birds showed no clear pattern. In general, coastal sites held higher peaks than inland sites which is probably to be expected given the cold winter.

	06/07	07/08	08/09	09/10	10/11	Mon	Mean
Sites of national importance in Great Britain							
Thames Estuary	499	315	474	369	(402)	Dec	414
Sites of all-Ireland importance in Northern Ireland							
Loughs Neagh and Beg	278	396	318	410	391	Oct	359
Upper Lough Erne	106	53	78	46	120	Dec	81
Strangford Lough	80	79	76 [10]	94	73	Jan	80
Lower Lough Erne	78	50	(23)	(50)	(94)	Jan	74
Lough Money	40	51					46
Portavo Lake					45	Oct	45 ▲
Lough Foyle	28	28	26	35	16	Sep	27
Sites no longer meeting table qualifying levels in WeBS-Year 2010/2011							
Larne Lough	20	27	16	23	10	Nov	19
Sites with mean peak counts of 80 or more birds in Great Britain[†]							
Humber Estuary	94	(150)	(91)	102	(42)	Nov	115
Chew Valley Lake	80	80	70	180	150	Sep	112
Rutland Water	67	93	116	164	120	Sep	112
Dungeness and Rye Bay	97	90	124	152	92	Sep	111
Crouch-Roach Estuary	44	81	115	146	152	Aug	108
Portsmouth Harbour	(69)	(69)	104	(68)	(64)	Feb	104
Hamford Water	87	84	119	120	97	Dec	101
Pitsford Reservoir	96	72	78	104	105	Oct	91
Cameron Reservoir	133	122	56	68	71 [12]	Aug	90
Severn Estuary	86	91	87	80	87	Sep	86
Blackwater Estuary	54	74	94	113	96	Oct	86
The Wash	88	113	66	62	(65)	Nov	82
Sites below table qualifying levels but exceeding threshold in WeBS-Year 2010/11 in Great Britain							
Deben Estuary	82	50	60	64	102	Dec	72
Colne Fen Gravel Pits	24	42	64	91 [12]	80 [12]	Sep	60

[†] *as few sites surpass the GB threshold, a threshold of 80 has been chosen to select sites for presentation in this report.*

Great Crested Grebe

Podiceps cristatus

International threshold (NW & W Europe):	3,500	
Great Britain threshold:	190	
All-Ireland threshold:	55	

GB max:	9,312	Sep
NI max:	1,324	Oct

*50 is normally used as a minimum threshold

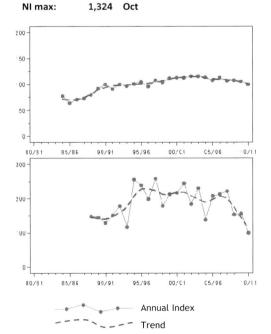

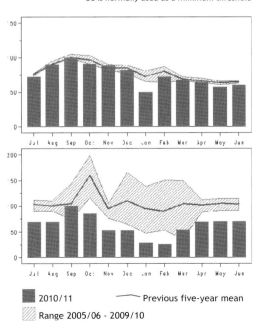

● Annual Index	◼ 2010/11	— Previous five-year mean
--- Trend	▨ Range 2005/06 - 2009/10	

Figure 39.a, Annual indices & trend for Great Crested Grebe in GB (above) & NI (below).

Figure 39.b, Monthly indices for Great Crested Grebe in GB (above) & NI (below).

During the winter, Great Crested Grebes are found at both inland and coastal wetlands. At the latter, birds are often difficult to monitor accurately particularly when frequenting open sea and/or in unsuitable weather conditions.

Amy Lewis

After a slow increase in Britain up to 2003/04, recent indices and associated trend show a shallow decline, mirroring the situation in the Netherlands (Hornman *et al.* 2012).

In 2010/11, Dungeness & Rye Bay hosted the largest aggregation during the year. A total of 1,739 in February is the highest number ever recorded there, thereby just surpassing similarly high totals of recent years. It is possible that some of this group may have been forced on to the sea from frozen freshwater bodies in the area. However, this again provides evidence of the potentially increasing importance of the rich foraging available in the shallow waters at the east end of the English Channel, both for this species and others such as Red-throated Diver and Common Scoter. Also in south-east England, two very high counts were noted at reservoirs in the Greater London area in December; 611 at Wraysbury Reservoir and 676 at Queen Mary Reservoir, both WeBS maxima for these sites.

In 2010/11, Great Crested Grebes fared very poorly in Northern Ireland, where the two other most important UK sites for the species are to be found. Although the maximum at Loughs Neagh & Beg was fairly typical, that reported from Belfast Lough was very low. It is not known the extent to which this apparent decline and those at a number of sites in the region were attributable to the cold winter.

	06/07	07/08	08/09	09/10	10/11	Mon	Mean	
Sites of national importance in Great Britain								
Dungeness and Rye Bay	880 [12]	(653)	1,492	(1,735)	1,739	Feb	1,462	
Rutland Water	655	441	584	970	727	Nov	675	
Wraysbury Reservoir					611	Dec	611	▲
Dee Estuary (England and Wales)	378 [12]	458 [12]	435 [12]	455 [12]	1,195 [12]	Jan	584	
Chew Valley Lake	430	665	690	665	440	Aug	578	
Grafham Water	471	132	471	525	486	Dec	417	
Cotswold Water Park (West)	284	309	317	365	360	Sep	327	
Pegwell Bay	48	110	300	585 [12]	585 [12]	Jan	326	
Glyne Gap	213	(206)	515	224	(294)[12]	Jan	317	
Stour Estuary	124	232	708 [10]	327 [10]	171	Nov	312	
Queen Mary Reservoir	130	208	98	362	(676)	Dec	295	▲
Swansea Bay	84	102	327	425	440	Dec	276	
Southampton Water	(47)	(216)	375	206	220	Dec	267	
Minsmere	57	1,210 [12]	5	4	15	Nov	258	
Pitsford Reservoir	267	312	186	267	247	Dec	256	
Bewl Water	188	183	224	195	274	Jul	213	
Lavan Sands	329	260	124	106	236 [12]	Jan	211	▲
Stewartby Lake					207	Dec	207	▲
Loch Leven	198	141	157 [12]	266	190	Sep	190	▲
Sites of all-Ireland importance in Northern Ireland								
Belfast Lough	1,482	2,150	(1,156)	1,175	363	Nov	1,293	
Loughs Neagh and Beg	959	1,191	752	959	1,035	Oct	979	
Upper Lough Erne	206	171	197	174	69	Feb	163	
Carlingford Lough	116	93	146	186	110	Dec	130	
Strangford Lough	65	137	145	87	108	Nov	108	
Lough Foyle	116	116	49	160	37	Oct	96	
Larne Lough	84	105	81	61	37	Sep	74	
Lower Lough Erne	123	55	(23)	(34)	21	Oct	66	
Sites below table qualifying levels but exceeding threshold in WeBS-Year 2010/11 in Great Britain								
Hanningfield Reservoir	200	30	128	118	221	Oct	139	
Abberton Reservoir	41	95	111	91	219	Oct	111	
Inner Firth of Clyde	120	135	190	(130)	207	Feb	163	

Red-necked Grebe

Podiceps grisegena

International threshold (NW Europe):	500
Great Britain threshold:	1*[†]
All-Ireland threshold:	?

GB max: 9   Dec

NI max: 0

50 is normally used as a minimum threshold

Red-necked Grebes were recorded at 29 WeBS sites in Britain during 2010/11. Despite the cold winter, a peak monthly total of just nine birds was recorded in both December and January.

The fall in numbers of this species registered by WeBS in recent years is largely attributable to a long-term decline on the Forth Estuary, the principal site in Britain. The WeBS peak there this year was just four in September; as recently as 1994/95 up to 100 birds were noted there in winter. Although it appears likely that the wintering population has indeed decreased on the Forth, it is also probable that WeBS counts do not effectively monitor the size of this population.

Elsewhere, all counts related to one or two birds at a scattering of sites, mainly in the south and east. The species featured at eight inland sites during the course of the year, including long-staying birds at Grafham Water, King George VI Reservoir and Avon Valley.

	06/07	07/08	08/09	09/10	10/11	Mon	Mean
Sites with mean peak counts of 2 or more birds in Great Britain[†]							
Forth Estuary	(4)	12	10	51 [47]	4	Sep	19
Glyne Gap	(2)	(3)	4 [12]	2	(2) [12]	Dec	3
Sites below table qualifying levels but exceeding threshold in WeBS-Year 2010/11 in Great Britain[†]							
Seahouses to Budle Point	(1)	0	0	2	2	Jan	1
Avon Valley - Salisbury to Fordingbridge	0	0	0	0	2	Apr	0

[†] *a qualifying level of 2 has been chosen to select sites for presentation in this report.*

Slavonian Grebe

Podiceps auritus

International threshold (NW Europe):	55
Great Britain threshold:	11*
All-Ireland threshold:	?[†]

GB max: 252   Feb

NI max: 11   Mar

50 is normally used as a minimum threshold

Slavonian Grebes were recorded at 103 WeBS sites in the UK, including two in Northern Ireland. The British wintering population is now estimated to be in the order of 1,100 birds (Musgrove *et al.* 2011), hence all sites with five-year means of 11+ birds surpass the 1% threshold for national importance.

The count of 84 Slavonian Grebes at Inner Firth of Clyde represents the most ever reported there, and promotes that particular site to one of international importance for this species in the UK, alongside the stretch of the Shetland coast between Whiteness and Skelda Ness. The trend noted on the Clyde is probably associated with the increase in the number of Slavonian Grebes of Icelandic origin now wintering in UK waters, which has also led to higher numbers wintering around Shetland and Orkney in the last decade (Harvey & Heubeck, in prep.). In contrast, numbers wintering on the south and east coasts of England have declined during the same period, probably linked to a decline in the number of birds of Continental origin wintering there, either due to a shift in distribution or overall population decrease. In England, the highest count of the year in 2010/11 was 10 at Gerrans Bay in December.

Inland, there was a typical scattering of birds on gravel pits and reservoirs during the course of the year.

	06/07	07/08	08/09	09/10	10/11	Mon	Mean
Sites of international importance in the UK							
Whiteness to Skelda Ness				77 [9]	73 [9]	Jan	75
Inner Firth of Clyde	40	73 [12]	49 [12]	47 [12]	84	Feb	59 ▲
Sites of national importance in Great Britain							
Sound of Gigha			89 [12]	27	43	Oct	53
Rova Head to Wadbister Ness			36 [9]	49 [9]	61 [9]	Jan	49

	06/07	07/08	08/09	09/10	10/11	Mon	Mean
Moray Firth	50	41	(23)	(6)	(8)	Dec	46
Loch of Harray	16	52	23	45	53	Oct	38
Loch Ryan	39	19	40	46[12]	31	Nov	35
Scapa Flow				37	30	Dec	34
Loch Na Keal	(0)	40[10]	20	30	41[12]	Feb	33
Ulva			26[9]				26
Forth Estuary	25[10]	18	29	25	16	Mar	23
Burghead Bay (Burghead to Findhorn)		5	(0)	26	26	Feb	19
Inner Loch Indaal				16	12	Nov	14
Broadford Bay	13	17	7	17[12]	14	Dec	14
Loch Eriboll	4	21	5	20	(2)	Feb	13 ▲
Sites no longer meeting table qualifying levels in WeBS-Year 2010/2011							
Gerrans Bay	5	4	13	20	10	Dec	10
Loch Ewe	18	7	(5)	6	(1)	Jan	10
Loch of Swannay	15	14	11	9	3	Nov	10
Lindisfarne	(18)	4	9	7	7	Nov	9
Kirkabister to Wadbister Ness			7[9]				7
Sites with mean peak counts of 4 or more birds in Northern Ireland[†]							
Lough Foyle	4	11	31	60	11	Mar	23
Strangford Lough	0	(0)	22[12]	22[10]	0		11
Sites below table qualifying levels but exceeding threshold in WeBS-Year 2010/11 in Great Britain							
Jersey Shore	4	10			17	Feb	10
Pagham Harbour	3	13	11	3	15	Feb	9
Loch Leven	1	1	3	2	13	Nov	4
Loch of Stenness	11	12	7	5	11	Mar	9

[†] as no All-Ireland threshold has been set, a threshold of 4 has been selected for presentation in this report.

Black-necked Grebe
Podiceps nigricollis

International threshold (Europe & N Africa):	2,100
Great Britain threshold:	1*[†]
All-Ireland threshold:	?[†]

GB max:	71	Dec
NI max:	0	

*50 is normally used as a minimum threshold

During 2010/11, Black-necked Grebes were seen at 65 sites in the UK, representing an increase in sites of more than 25% compared to the previous year. These included four sites in Scotland (where this species is traditionally very scarce), two in Wales and two in Channel Islands.

Two of the locations featured in the key sites table below have been kept confidential following advice from the *Rare Breeding Birds Panel* and/or local counters.

Each winter, birds can be reliably seen in relatively consistent numbers at favoured sites on the English coast from Cornwall to Hampshire. This is in contrast to the situation in the Netherlands, where marked increases have taken place since the 1990s (Hornman *et al.* 2011). In 2010/11, higher than average numbers were present at Studland Bay and Fal Complex; the supplementary count of 80 at the former site may represent the largest aggregation of Black-necked Grebes ever seen in the UK. It represents what has been a slow but steady recovery for this species in that area, following a major oiling incident in Poole Harbour in 1964 which more than halved the wintering population of approximately 50 individuals at the time (Green 2004).

Unfortunately, no WeBS Core count data were received for William Girling Reservoir during the winter period, but supplementary data from there indicate that it continues to be the most important inland site for wintering Black-necked Grebes. Double figure counts were reported from a further three sites, two of which were inland and probably featured breeding birds.

Away from the principal inland locations, counts of five Black-necked Grebes at both Sutton & Lound Gravel Pits (Oct) and Rutland Water (Dec) were notable.

	06/07	07/08	08/09	09/10	10/11	Mon	Mean
Sites with mean peak counts of 5 or more birds in Great Britain[†]							
Studland Bay	20 [47]	23 [47]	37 [47]	38 [47]	80 [47]	Jan	40
Fal Complex	(4)	5	32	17[47]	52 [47]	Dec	27
William Girling Reservoir	26	32	26	28	25 [47]	Oct	27
Woolston Eyes	(35)	17	26	22	11	Apr	22
Tor Bay					18	Jan	18
Langstone Harbour	24 [12]	5	16	22	12	Dec	16
Confidential Hertfordshire Site	9	12	18	14	21	Apr	15
Thames Estuary	4	4	4	38	0		10
Staines Reservoirs	9	9	7	11	3	Aug	8
Confidential Northumberland Site	10	8	6	0	9	Jun	7
Sites below table qualifying levels but exceeding threshold in WeBS-Year 2010/11 in Great Britain[†]							
Fleet and Wey	3	0	1	8	5	Dec	3
Rutland Water	1	2	3	5	5	Dec	3
Sutton and Lound Gravel Pits	0	2	2	2	5	Oct	2

[†] a qualifying level of 5 has been chosen to select sites for presentation in this report.

Water Rail
Rallus aquaticus

International threshold (Europe & N Africa): 10,000
Great Britain threshold: ?[†]
All-Ireland threshold: ?[†]

GB max: 575 Nov
NI max: 4 Oct

Water Rails were recorded during WeBS Core counts at 337 sites across the UK in 2010/11, a decrease of 12% compared to the previous year. However, the monthly maximum of 575 in November was considerably more than the peak of the previous year. Favoured sites tend to be those with reedbeds and/or an extensive network of ditches. The species is inevitably under-recorded due to its secretive, generally unobtrusive, behaviour, and as a result any attempts to derive population estimates for this species are notoriously difficult (see Musgrove *et al.* 2011). However, the species can often become more conspicuous during periods of freezing weather such as that experienced in the UK in January 2011. WeBS maxima this year were 39 at Somerset Levels and 30 at Malltraeth RSPB, both in November, and presumably only represent a relatively small fraction of the total numbers present at both sites.

	06/07	07/08	08/09	09/10	10/11	Mon	Mean
Sites with mean peak counts of 10 or more birds in Great Britain[†]							
Somerset Levels	58	62	38	(33)	40	Nov	50
Thames Estuary	19	8	47	(25)	(25)	Nov	25
Grouville Marsh	(10)		15	20			18
Severn Estuary	13	23	(26)	19	11	Nov	18
Malltraeth RSPB	11	15	10	25	30	Nov	18
Longueville Marsh	(10)		15	12			14
Chew Valley Lake	5	22	31	8	5	Nov	14
Southampton Water	10	(20)	19	9	14	Dec	14
Rutland Water	10	10	24	12	10	Jul	13
Chichester Harbour	15	10	12	7	16	Dec	12
London Wetland Centre	17	16	12	10	4	Nov	12
Stanwick Gravel Pits Consolidated			(16)	(12)	8	Jul	12
Doxey Marshes SSSI	2	14	10	17	15	Nov	12
Dee Estuary (England and Wales)	8	(24)	13	7	9	Jan	12
Dungeness and Rye Bay	10	7	8	14	14	Nov	11
Lower Derwent Ings	8	9	15	10	12	Jan	11
Sites below table qualifying levels but exceeding threshold in WeBS-Year 2010/11 in Great Britain[†]							
Kinnordy Loch	(0)	(0)	(0)	5	12	Dec	9
Langford Lowfields Gravel Pits	1	1	1	2	12	Nov	3
Ingrebourne Valley				8	10	Nov	9
Llangorse Lake	6	8	6	6	10	Nov	7
Lakenheath Fen	6	4	(1)	2	10	Nov	6

[†] as no British or All-Ireland thresholds have been set, a qualifying level of 10 has been chosen to select sites for presentation in this report.

Spotted Crake

Scarce

Porzana porzana

Two were at Stodmarsh in August.

Corncrake

Scarce

Crex crex

Corncrakes were noted at two sites on the Western Isles.

Moorhen

Gallinula chloropus

International threshold (Europe & N Africa):	20,000**	
Great Britain threshold:	3,200[†]	
All-Ireland threshold:	?[†]	

GB max:	12,503	Nov
NI max:	274	Oct

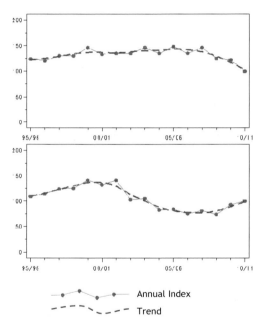

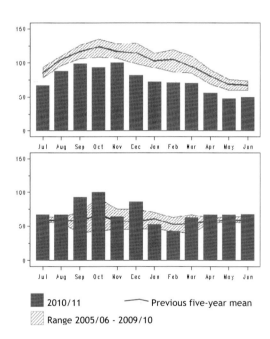

- Annual Index
- - - Trend

█ 2010/11   ⌐ Previous five-year mean

▨ Range 2005/06 - 2009/10

Figure 40.a, Annual indices & trend for Moorhen in GB (above) & NI (below).

Figure 40.b, Monthly indices for Moorhen in GB (above) & NI (below).

Moorhens are widespread across the UK and occur in a wide variety of wetland habitats. The species is poorly monitored by WeBS, and it would require significantly improved coverage of habitats within the wider countryside to be able to evaluate it's status in winter more accurately.

The WeBS trend indicates that numbers at WeBS sites in Britain have dropped off in the last couple of years. This is presumably associated with two cold winters, and only time will tell if this apparent decline continues in the years ahead. However, it is indicative of an overall decline rather than mere displacement, and hence implies reduced survival.

Most of the site peaks in 2010/11 were in November, prior to the onset of the frozen conditions in December. Maxima were 322 at Severn Estuary (Oct) and 292 at North Norfolk Coast (Dec). Numbers at most of the main sites were below their respective five-year means, notable exceptions being the peaks at North Norfolk Coast and River Wandle.

	06/07	07/08	08/09	09/10	10/11	Mon	Mean
Sites with mean peak counts of 130 or more birds in Great Britain[†]							
Severn Estuary	546	1,003	(473)	359	322	Oct	558
Thames Estuary	367	(300)	(406)	(355)	(205)	Dec	387
WWT Martin Mere	438	485	(375)	330	172	Jan	360
Lower Derwent Ings	321	268	341	256	280	Mar	293
Ouse Washes	201	557 [12]	(420)	163	115 [12]	Dec	291
Somerset Levels	430	392	156	(281)	133	Oct	278
Pitsford Reservoir	389	241	126	304	213	Aug	255
Lee Valley Gravel Pits	(300)	296	244	180	203	Sep	245
North Norfolk Coast	223	230	203	253	292	Dec	240
London Wetland Centre	218	203	229	200	180	Nov	206
Arun Valley	246	(195)	164	190	(165)	Nov	200
River Wandle: Carshalton to Wandsworth	193	186	180	191	248	Dec	200
Rutland Water	157	219	152	285	186	Sep	200
Dungeness and Rye Bay	166	181	192	167	136	Dec	168
Medway Estuary	131	180	144	130	(27)[12]	Dec	146
Grand Western Canal	178	134	124	146	128	Aug	142
Stanwick Gravel Pits Consolidated			(63)	(147)	120	Feb	134
Cotswold Water Park (West)	117	(144)	(116)	151	115	Nov	132
Sutton and Lound Gravel Pits	158	128	141	105	130	Nov	132
Sites with mean peak counts of 30 or more birds in Northern Ireland[†]							
Loughs Neagh and Beg	98	118	96	181	209	Oct	140
Upper Lough Erne	75	40	18	36	89	Dec	52
Belfast Lough	43	42	49	43 [10]	39	Dec	43
Sites below table qualifying levels but exceeding threshold in WeBS-Year 2010/11 in Great Britain[†]							
Southampton Water	81	(114)	127	(86)	135	Dec	114

[†] *as no sites exceed the British threshold and no All-Ireland threshold has been set, qualifying levels of 130 and 30, respectively, have been chosen to select sites for presentation in this report.*

Common Coot
Fulica atra

International threshold (NW Europe):	17,500
Great Britain threshold:	1,800
All-Ireland threshold:	330

GB max:	114,436	Nov
NI max:	3,182	Jan

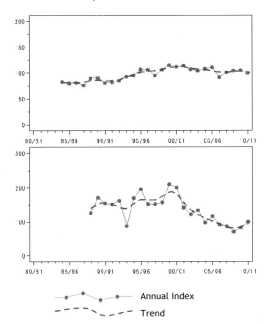

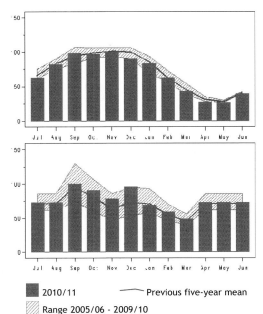

Figure 41.a, Annual indices & trend for Coot in GB (above) & NI (below).

Figure 41.b, Monthly indices for Coot in GB (above) & NI (below).

Coots wintering in the UK comprise residents and immigrants from other parts of northwest Europe, forming a population of approximately 180,000 birds (Musgrove et al. 2011). 2010/11 provided further evidence of stability in this population, although there was a negative response to the frozen weather during the midwinter period. In contrast to the situation in Britain, numbers in Northern Ireland have declined markedly over the course of the last fifteen years.

Hence, when evaluated together, these trends are suggestive of a possible shift in distribution in response to climate, but this requires further study. In The Netherlands, the trend for Coot, although prone to fluctuations, has essentially been stable for thirty years (Hornman et al. 2012). Moreover, numbers have been increasing in other parts of northern Europe (e.g. Nilsson 2008), often in response to ice-free conditions during winter (e.g. Lehikoinen et al. in prep.). Such changes in the distribution of diving waterfowl in north-west Europe are probably linked to climate change which has led to ice-free conditions in parts

In Britain, several sites held above-average peaks in 2010/11. These included Loch Leven, Lee Valley Gravel Pits, Pitsford Reservoir and Grafham Water, the latter now surpassing the threshold for national importance. The traditional autumn peak at Abberton Reservoir reached 9,911 birds, which is slightly lower than the five-year site average and represents a drop of 19% compared to the maximum recorded in 2009/10.

In Northern Ireland, the monthly maximum at Loughs Neagh & Beg was the most since 2006/07, but still considerably less than the historical peak count of 8,848 birds in December 1992. In common with most other diving waterfowl at the site, numbers of Coot have dropped steeply at the site in recent winters. Similarly, the peak at Upper Lough Erne (the other site of All-Ireland importance) was higher than in recent years; a further indication that this year's increases were probably associated with the frozen condition further east in Europe, and therefore evidence of the species' potential to respond to climatic variation.

	06/07	07/08	08/09	09/10	10/11	Mon	Mean
Sites of national importance in Great Britain							
Abberton Reservoir	(2,088)	10,046	9,270	12,188	9,911	Oct	10,354
Rutland Water	6,233	4,284	4,792	6,277	5,570	Dec	5,431
Cotswold Water Park (West)	4,001	4,013	4,803	5,330	5,074	Nov	4,644
Ouse Washes	1,834	6,229	5,865 [12]	4,053	3,810	Feb	4,358
Cheddar Reservoir	3,380	3,324	2,222	2,977	4,178	Dec	3,216
Loch Leven	2,820	1,317	3,350	3,560	4,642	Nov	3,138
Lee Valley Gravel Pits	2,417	2,979	3,331	3,318	3,507	Nov	3,110
Fleet and Wey	2,650	2,337	2,291	2,397	3,680	Jan	2,671
Dungeness and Rye Bay	2,421	2,280	2,162	3,123	2,964	Sep	2,590
Pitsford Reservoir	2,287	2,828	1,957	2,480	3,048	Sep	2,520
Chew Valley Lake	2,360	2,095	2,020	3,050	2,880	Aug	2,481
Cotswold Water Park (East)	1,835	2,134	2,248	2,050	1,820	Jan	2,017
Carsington Water	2,136	1,880	2,175	1,770	1,783	Dec	1,949
Grafham Water	1,454	1,628	1,796	2,252	2,006	Sep	1,827 ▲
Sites of all-Ireland importance in Northern Ireland							
Loughs Neagh and Beg	2,371	1,813	1,236	1,546	2,281	Sep	1,849
Upper Lough Erne	1,696	1,072	1,093	1,051	2,077	Dec	1,398
Sites no longer meeting table qualifying levels in WeBS-Year 2010/2011							
Blagdon Lake	1,400	2,323	1,403	970	678	Jul	1,355
Sites below table qualifying levels but exceeding threshold in WeBS-Year 2010/11 in Great Britain							
Chichester Gravel Pits	601	1,016	(624)	1,288	2,177	Jan	1,271
River Avon - Fordingbridge to Ringwood	2,012	1,607	1,453	1,757	2,051	Dec	1,776
Stodmarsh	904	1,369	1,350	2,310	1,969	Oct	1,580
Other sites surpassing table qualifying levels in Winter 2010/2011 in Northern Ireland							
Lower Lough Erne	326	406	3	(34)	(415)	Jan	288

Common Crane
Grus grus

Cranes were recorded at five WeBS sites in 2010/11, with a maximum of five birds reported from two sites in Fenland. Elsewhere, singles were at North Norfolk Coast (Aug), Montrose Basin (Aug) and Arun Valley (Apr).

Eurasian Oystercatcher
Haematopus ostralegus

	International threshold	
(Europe & NW Africa):	8,200
Great Britain threshold:	3,200
All-Ireland threshold:	680

GB max:	246,014	Oct
NI max:	14,130	Jan

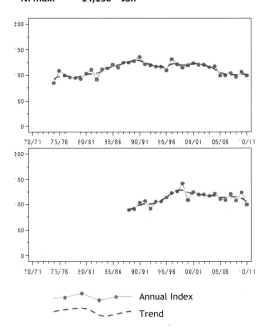

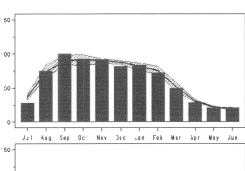

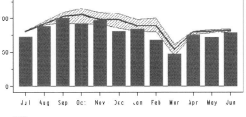

- ●— Annual Index
- - - - Trend

■ 2010/11 ——— Previous five-year mean
▨ Range 2005/06 - 2009/10

Figure 42.a, Annual indices & trend for Oystercatcher in GB (above) & NI (below).

Figure 42.b, Monthly indices for Oystercatcher in GB (above) & NI (below).

Oystercatchers in the UK form part of a population of the nominate race *ostralegus*, which breeds in north and west Europe, and winters in west Europe southwards to west Africa. Up until six years ago, the British trend for Oystercatcher was largely stable. However, since then it has become evident that this species is declining very slowly, mirroring the situation across the North Sea in The Netherlands, where Oystercatchers have declined at a faster rate (Hornman *et al.* 2012). The decline is especially pronounced at Scottish sites, and a slow decline seems to also now be apparent in Northern Ireland. In keeping with these trends, the estimated size of the *ostralegus* population internationally was recently revised downwards by 20% (Wetlands International 2012).

There are eight sites in Britain where numbers of Oystercatchers surpass the threshold for international importance, and a further ten sites of national importance. A number of stories stand out from the table below. At Morecambe Bay, an exceptional peak of 82,288 was present in September 2010, representing the highest count of all time at a site in the UK (and some 13% more than the previous maximum of 72,653 there in October 2002). A notable count also occurred at The Wash during the frozen conditions in January; the total of 26,028 contrasting with a recent decline associated with human over-exploitation of the shellfishery (Atkinson *et al.* 2010). In Wales, Carmarthen Bay consolidated its position among the top sites for Oystercatcher with a peak Core count of 11,912 birds in November. The maxima at Solway Estuary and Thames Estuary were both below average, peaking prior to the onset of the cold weather in December – at which point the monthly indices suggest a reduction in the numbers of birds present in both Britain and Northern Ireland.

In Northern Ireland, the two most important sites (Strangford Lough and Belfast Lough) both registered peaks which were below average.

	06/07	07/08	08/09	09/10	10/11	Mon	Mean
Sites of international importance in the UK							
Morecambe Bay	55,874	(41,199)	60,323	58,596	82,288	Sep	64,270
Solway Estuary	35,571	(31,091)	(25,417)	23,890	21,323	Nov	27,969
Thames Estuary	27,836	26,905	33,659	24,278	20,494	Oct	26,634
Dee Estuary (England and Wales)	15,808	20,922	32,820 [10]	25,886	21,993	Dec	23,486
The Wash	22,963	19,626	17,788	19,232	26,028	Jan	21,127
Burry Inlet	15,110 [12]	13,257	13,980	15,957	9,966 [10]	Jan	13,654
Ribble Estuary	10,872	13,148	(9,524)	(8,518)	(12,381)	Oct	12,134
Carmarthen Bay	10,154 [10]	10,911 [10]	10,562	13,673 [10]	11,912	Nov	11,442
Sites of national importance in Great Britain							
Forth Estuary	8,235	7,230	8,046	(5,949)	6,164	Sep	7,419
Lavan Sands	9,587	5,783	5,611	6,129	5,919	Jan	6,606
Duddon Estuary	5,758	(4,251)	(7,296)	(3,444)	(3,354)	Jan	6,527
Inner Moray and Inverness Firth	5,099	8,003	3,883	3,547	3,875	Oct	4,881
Swale Estuary	3,762	4,106	3,293	(5,425)	6,819	Nov	4,681
Humber Estuary	2,942	(3,121)	(2,746)	4,503	(6,104)	Nov	4,516
Medway Estuary	(1,005)	(2,535)	(4,160)	(991)	(2,285)	Oct	(4,160) ▲
North Norfolk Coast	3,238	3,954	5,111	3,936	4,271	Nov	4,102
Inner Firth of Clyde	4,144	4,663	3,450	3,866	4,165	Oct	4,058
Swansea Bay	4,430 [12]	3,150	3,743	(3,850)	2,650	Oct	3,565
Sites of all-Ireland importance in Northern Ireland							
Strangford Lough	6,842	8,689	9,575	8,513	7,910	Sep	8,306
Belfast Lough	(4,411)	3,580	3,624	3,798	3,374 [10]	Nov	3,757
Lough Foyle	(2,347)	2,837	3,629	3,647	2,792	Oct	3,226
Outer Ards Shoreline	1,825	1,515	1,622	1,569	1,712	Jan	1,649
Dundrum Inner Bay	1,027	1,700	1,497	(1,635)	2,261	Feb	1,624
Carlingford Lough	1,552	(1,446)	1,529	839	(710)	Jan	1,342
Newcastle Shore			1,331				1,331
Sites below table qualifying levels but exceeding threshold in WeBS-Year 2010/11 in Great Britain							
Wigtown Bay	2,058	2,363	(3,335)	2,407	3,379	Jan	2,708

Jill Pakenham

Pied Avocet
Recurvirostra avosetta

International threshold (W Europe & NW Africa): **730**
Great Britain threshold: **75**

GB max:	**7,183**	**Oct**
NI max:	**0**	

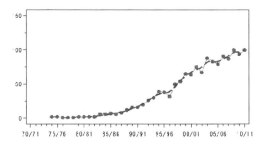

Annual Index
Trend

Figure 43.a, Annual indices & trend for Avocet in GB.

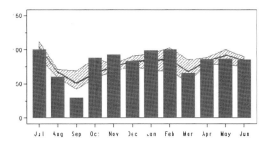

2010/11
Range 2005/06 - 2009/10
Previous five-year mean

Figure 43.b, Monthly indices for Avocet in GB.

The wintering population of Avocets in Britain comprises an increasing proportion of resident breeders with additional birds from the nearby Low Countries. The WeBS trend continues to illustrate an increasing population and the index value for 2010/11 equalled the high point reached two years previously.

Avocets were recorded at 70 WeBS sites in 2010/11, the most ever in a WeBS-year. These were all in England, including the Dee and Severn estuaries bordering England and Wales, with the exception of a single bird seen at Carmarthen Bay. There appears to have been no marked change in wintering numbers or distribution in response to the coldest winter for 35 years. Prior to the onset of the cold conditions, reasons for the drop in the monthly index for September are unclear.

Peaks at the six sites of international importance were above recent respective averages, most notably at Alde Complex where the 1,946 (Feb) represents the highest monthly site count ever submitted through WeBS. This count surpasses the previous maximum of 1,893 at Poole Harbour in February 2002. Humber Estuary now surpasses the threshold for international importance for this species, following high numbers in the autumn/early winter period for the second year in succession.

Jill Pakenham

An additional fifteen sites support nationally important numbers of Avocet; the majority of these are in East Anglia, apart from Exe Estuary, Tamar Complex, and Ribble Estuary. At Tamar Complex, the annual peaks have been revised slightly (P. Reay, pers. comm.), in order to account for probable double-counting of mobile flocks of this species at the site (Reay & Kent 2011).

At Ribble Estuary, Avocet has been an annual feature since 2002/03; a strong illustration of the steady range expansion of this species in England in the last decade. This expansion has yet to include Scotland, where there have only ever been approximately ten WeBS records of Avocet, most recently in 2007/08.

	06/07	07/08	08/09	09/10	10/11	Mon	Mean
Sites of international importance in the UK							
Thames Estuary	1,578	1,633	1,689	(1,702)	(1,728)	Jan	1,666
Alde Complex	1,383	1,465	1,419	1,373	1,946	Feb	1,517
Poole Harbour	(1,303)	1,068	(1,131)	(1,553)	(1,361)	Nov	1,283
Medway Estuary	(1,027)	(453)	(791)	(604)	(1,048)	Oct	(1,048)
Breydon Water and Berney Marshes	706	896 [12]	897 [12]	1,017 [12]	982 [12]	Aug	900
Humber Estuary	652	595	486	1,159	910	Oct	760 ▲
Sites of national importance in Great Britain							
Hamford Water	(629)	537	729 [8]	564	851	Nov	670
Colne Estuary	720 [12]	586 [10]	750 [12]	613 [12]	450 [12]	Sep	624
Blyth Estuary	660	889	369	576	(350)	Dec	624
North Norfolk Coast	645	556	674	538	626	Apr	608
Swale Estuary	(363)	447	(586)	654	602	Oct	572
The Wash	322	850	541	493	484	Jul	538
Blackwater Estuary	367	585	(508)	422	625	Feb	501
Exe Estuary	380	358	557	(440)	626	Feb	480
Deben Estuary	315	224	342	306	306	Jan	299
Stour Estuary	428	159	112	444 [10]	204	Nov	269
Tamar Complex	300	300	245	189	274	Dec	262
Crouch-Roach Estuary	22	135 [11]	213	139	343	Jan	170
Orwell Estuary	105 [10]	134 [10]	161	(124)	(262)	Jan	166
Minsmere	190	205	164	153	114	Jun	165
Ribble Estuary	76	110	71	111	68	Jul	87
Sites below table qualifying levels but exceeding threshold in WeBS-Year 2010/11 in Great Britain							
Severn Estuary	26	(76)	27	66	120	Nov	63
Dungeness and Rye Bay	(59)	(64)	60	64	(91)	May	70
Ouse Washes	4 [12]	32	42	3	84 [12]	Mar	33

Stone Curlew

Scarce

Burhinus oedicnemus

Stone Curlews were present at both ends of the WeBS year at a site in eastern England, close to a known breeding location, with a peak of seven noted in August. In spring, one was at Clevedon to Yeo Estuary, representing the 4th WeBS record for the Severn Estuary complex.

Little Ringed Plover

Charadrius dubius

International threshold (Europe & W Africa):	2,500	
Great Britain threshold:	? [†]	
All-Ireland threshold:	? [†]	

GB max:	414	Apr
NI max:	0	

In 2010, Little Ringed Plovers were recorded at 167 sites during WeBS Core counts, including four sites in Scotland. The species was seen at ten sites in March, prior to a widespread distribution from April to July. Maxima occurred in July, notably 48 at Rutland Water and a supplementary count of 45 at Uttoxeter Quarry.

Both these counts are an indication of increasing breeding populations at those sites. A light autumn passage had largely concluded by the end of September, with the exception of single birds at Dearne Valley (Oct) and Blithfield Reservoir (Nov).

	2006	2007	2008	2009	2010	Mon	Mean
Sites with mean peak counts of 10 or more birds in Great Britain[†]							
Uttoxeter Quarry				16	45 [46]	Jul	31
Rutland Water	8	9	6	10	48	Jul	16
Nosterfield Gravel Pits	23	24	9	9	12	May	15
Other sites surpassing table qualifying levels in Summer 2010 in Great Britain[†]							
North Norfolk Coast	(4)	5	4	5	18	Jul	8
Belvide Reservoir	9	3	4	6	15	Jul	7

[†] *as no British or All-Ireland thresholds have been set a qualifying level of 15 has been chosen to select sites for presentation in this report*

Ringed Plover

Charadrius hiaticula

International threshold
(N Europe, Europe & N Africa): 730
Great Britain winter threshold: 340
All-Ireland threshold: 150

GB max: 15,997 May
NI max: 418 Jan

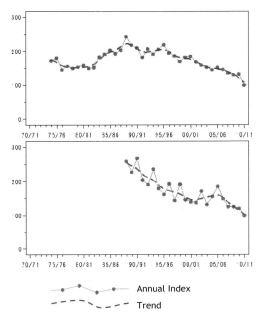

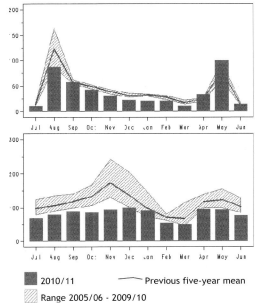

Annual Index

Trend

2010/11

Range 2005/06 - 2009/10

Previous five-year mean

Figure 44.a, Annual indices & trend for Ringed Plover in GB (above) & NI (below).

Figure 44.b, Monthly indices for Ringed Plover in GB (above) & NI (below).

Jill Pakenham

Britain and Ireland are of considerable importance for Ringed Plovers, providing winter refuges for British and continental breeders of the nominate race *hiaticula*, and passage sites for long-distance migrants of the *tundrae* race. The breeding population, comprising a large proportion of the nominate race, is in decline (Conway *et al.* 2008). The numbers of passage Ringed Plovers using UK sites in spring and autumn are much greater than those that remain in winter. Hence, virtually all the peak monthly counts from the principal sites relate to passage periods and arctic-breeding birds from Canada, Greenland, Iceland and Fennoscandia (Wernham *et al.* 2002).

The trends for wintering Ringed Plovers in both Britain and Northern Ireland have been declining steadily for over twenty years, and the current situation for the species is now somewhat depressing. Given that the decline had previously been attributed to a shift of the core wintering range (Austin & Rehfisch 2005, Maclean *et al.* 2008), one might have expected a slight upturn in fortunes during 2010/11, when birds may have been forced to the UK from continental sites such as the Wadden Sea during frozen conditions. However, the national indices for both Britain and Northern Ireland fell quite sharply, to their lowest ever levels.

As was the case in 2009/10, the maximum WeBS count during the year contrasted with this overall downward trend in terms of wintering birds. The spring count of 5,974 at Ribble Estuary surpassed the previous record of 5,432 in May 2000, and therefore stresses the importance of UK for passage Ringed Plovers.

	06/07	07/08	08/09	09/10	10/11	Mon	Mean	
Sites of international importance in the UK								
Ribble Estuary	(1,016)	1,734	(2,931)	(5,420)	5,974	May	4,376	
Humber Estuary	(783)	(1,160)	(781)	2,547	1,415	May	1,981	
North Norfolk Coast	2,046	1,023	1,814	2,758	1,310	Sep	1,790	
The Wash	(1,127)	400	1,831	2,138	1,639	May	1,502	
Solway Estuary	(644)	(402)	(936)	(1,644)	1,090	Apr	1,367	
Severn Estuary	1,453	(364)	1,457	(982)	317	Aug	1,076	
Thames Estuary	1,197	748	830	(733)	(719)	Oct	925	
Swale Estuary	(465)	(294)	(605)	(830)	(421)	Aug	(830)	
Sites of national importance in Great Britain								
Morecambe Bay	355	(428)	936	894	724	May	727	▼
Lindisfarne	581	(139)	(224)	(734)	815	May	710	
Dengie Flats	(127)	1,013	577	710	230	Aug	633	
Forth Estuary	290	502	(875)	1,080	357	Sep	621	
Blackwater Estuary	418	531	767	(689)	(434)	Aug	601	
Barnkirk Point at Annan				535 [12]			535	
West Freugh					512	Oct	512	▲
Stour Estuary	390	428	582	798	330	Sep	506	
Tay Estuary	235	(170)	658	(611)	(302)	Aug	501	
Crouch-Roach Estuary	816	594	349	419	316	Oct	499	
Alt Estuary	257	515	515	416	648	May	470	
Piltanton and Luce Estuaries				174	622	Sep	398	▲
Dee Estuary (England and Wales)	127	(551)	744	265	263	Sep	390	
South Ford	743	400	300		118	Sep	390	
Duddon Estuary	(495)	200	525	407	195	Apr	364	
Sites of all-Ireland importance in Northern Ireland								
Strangford Lough	278 [10]	227 [10]	277 [10]	288 [10]	(86)	Feb	268	
Outer Ards Shoreline	338	125	308	238	229	Jan	248	
Belfast Lough	180	253	147 [10]	187	103	Oct	174	
Carlingford Lough	247	154	(105)	54	(52)	Oct	152	
Sites no longer meeting table qualifying levels in WeBS-Year 2010/2011								
Chichester Harbour	365	233	395	422	221	May	327	
Taw-Torridge Estuary	(223)	(176)	(298)	(307)	(291)	Aug	(307)	
Sites below table qualifying levels but exceeding threshold in WeBS-Year 2010/11 in Great Britain								
Tyninghame Estuary	49	272	117	247	476	Aug	232	
Breydon Water and Berney Marshes	189	184 [12]	165 [12]	246 [12]	473 [12]	May	251	
Hamford Water	(328)	349	261	(220)	(346)	Sep	321	

Kentish Plover

Charadrius alexandrinus

Scarce

Singles were seen at Tyninghame Bay in April and at the more typical location of Pegwell Bay in April and May.

American Golden Plover

Pluvialis dominica

Vagrant
Native Range: America

One was recorded at the Exe Estuary in October; the 14th WeBS record.

Eurasian Golden Plover

Pluvialis apricaria

International threshold (Iceland, Faroes, E Atlantic coast):	9,300
Great Britain threshold:	4,000
All-Ireland threshold:	1,700

GB max:	144,916	Nov
NI max:	4,600	Nov

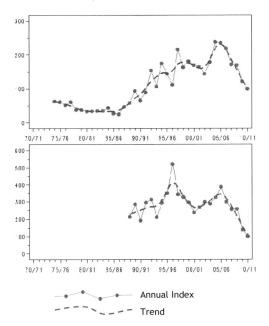

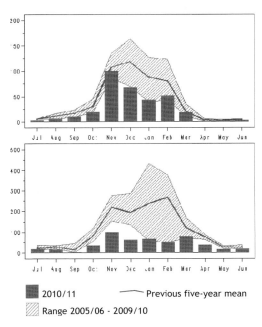

Annual Index
Trend

2010/11   Previous five-year mean
Range 2005/06 - 2009/10

Figure 45.a, Annual indices & trend for Golden Plover in GB (above) & NI (below).

Figure 45.b, Monthly indices for Golden Plover in GB (above) & NI (below).

For the second year in succession the British national index for Golden Plover fell sharply, exhibiting a profound response to a colder than average winter. Pictures are said to paint a thousand words, and the monthly indices tell the story of the winter for Golden Plovers in the UK. As in 2009/10, a typical British November for this species was followed by an entire winter period during which numbers were well below average. This was undoubtedly a consequence of cold conditions having forced birds out of northwest Europe; a similar response was recorded in The Netherlands at this time (M. Hornman, pers. comm.).

Six sites continue to surpass the threshold for international importance for Golden Plovers despite the generally low maxima at WeBS sites across Britain in 2010/11. As indicated, all these sites (as well as most of a further dozen sites of national importance) yielded their respective peaks during November. Peak numbers were lower than average at all the major sites, including Somerset Levels where, as in the previous year, the maximum was approximately one-third of the peak recorded in 2008/09.

In Northern Ireland, the fall in the national index was similarly spectacular, dropping to its lowest ever level. All the major sites held their lowest peaks for many years. Interestingly, the monthly indices also indicate that arrival of birds in November was much reduced, unlike that in Britain. The reason for this apparent difference is unknown.

	06/07	07/08	08/09	09/10	10/11	Mon	Mean
Sites of international importance in the UK							
Humber Estuary	50,188	(23,526)	(29,172)	30,352	(29,370)	Nov	40,270
The Wash	31,350	19,643	40,588	25,628	(13,569)	Nov	29,302
Breydon Water and Berney Marshes	24,930 [10]	15,790 [12]	30,800 [12]	21,900 [12]	18,100 [12]	Nov	22,304
Somerset Levels	12,054	12,422	18,467	6,874	5,917	Nov	11,147
Swale Estuary	10,520	17,327	(7,407)	6,112	8,305	Nov	10,566
Blackwater Estuary	(15,810)	5,703	(13,173)	(4,224)	(6,691)	Nov	10,344
Sites of national importance in Great Britain							
Dengie Flats	5,520	4,520	11,070	8,500	7,000	Mar	7,322
Carmarthen Bay	12,700	10,420	4,244	3,569	521	Nov	6,291
Hamford Water	(5,362)	10,228	7,234 [8]	2,284	2,050	Feb	5,449
Dearne Valley	8,700	3,000	5,000	5,000	3,000	Oct	4,940
Dungeness and Rye Bay	5,000	7,210	3,772	3,450	(2,402)	Nov	4,858
North Norfolk Coast	(4,552)	3,154	5,914	5,527	4,802	Feb	4,849
Lower Derwent Ings	10,600	5,433	2,500	4,124	976	Oct	4,727
Crouch-Roach Estuary	(2,387)	(6,696)	3,298	4,342	4,018 [10]	Nov	4,588
Ribble Estuary	(3,950)	6,610	4,307	5,815	1,476	Nov	4,552
Solway Estuary	5,746	3,761	3,223	5,428	3,313 [10]	Nov	4,294
Nene Washes	8,500	5,650	3,500	1,600	1,790	Feb	4,208
Lindisfarne	(3,236)	(2,324)	4,228	(1,470)	4,045	Nov	4,137
Pegwell Bay	4,170	(5,500)	3,500	3,150 [12]	4,000 [12]	Nov	4,064
Sites of all-Ireland importance in Northern Ireland							
Strangford Lough	8,513 [10]	8,817 [10]	11,328 [10]	7,435 [10]	2,522	Jan	7,723
Lough Foyle	9,534	9,211	8,486	5,091	2,366	Oct	6,938
Loughs Neagh and Beg	6,475	7,712	7,337	4,687	2,658	Nov	5,774
Sites no longer meeting table qualifying levels in WeBS-Year 2010/2011							
Morecambe Bay	(3,429)	(3,382)	1,716	(4,715)	2,838	Nov	3,216
Thames Estuary	4,817	4,267	2,129	2,014	1,646	Nov	2,975
Camel Estuary	(3,000)	2,501	6,000 [12]	2,100	1,100	Nov	2,940
Ouse Washes	3,312 [12]	2,427 [12]	485	6,071 [12]	2,227	Nov	2,904
Otmoor	4,670 [12]	(1,080)	(1,908)	(1,250)	500 [12]	Feb	2,585
Sites below table qualifying levels but exceeding threshold in WeBS-Year 2010/11 in Great Britain							
Deben Estuary	(1,558)	(2,073)	2,718	2,272	6,449	Jan	3,813

Jill Pakenham

Grey Plover

Pluvialis squatarola

International threshold
(W Siberia & Canada, W Europe & W Africa): 2,500
Great Britain threshold: 430
All-Ireland threshold: 65

GB max: 34,741 Jan
NI max: 83 Jan

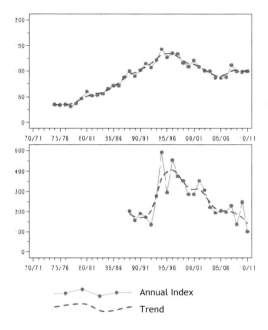

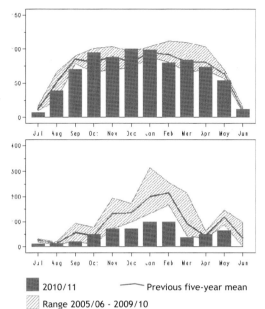

Annual Index
Trend

2010/11
Previous five-year mean
Range 2005/06 - 2009/10

Figure 46.a, Annual indices & trend for Grey Plover in GB (above) & NI (below).

Figure 46.b, Monthly indices for Grey Plover in GB (above) & NI (below).

Grey Plovers breed in the tundra zones of Eurasia and North America, with the most important wintering areas in Europe being the southern North Sea coasts, other British estuaries, and the Atlantic coast of France. Additional areas in the Mediterranean basin, and along the coasts of West Africa, the Middle East and East Africa, are also used (Delany *et al.* 2009). It appears that the number of Grey Plover using Britain may have entered a period of relative stability. This follows a decade from the mid 1990s to the mid 2000s when the species declined steadily, having previously increased at an equally consistent rate for ten years up to the mid 1990s.

The recent decline occurred at the same time as a long-term increase at sites in The Netherlands, primarily the Wadden Sea, and was therefore attributed to a north-eastward shift in wintering distribution (Maclean *et al.* 2008). Interestingly, at the same time as the current levelling of the trend in Britain, numbers have continued to increase on the Wadden Sea (Hornman *et al.* 2011), so it now seems more likely that these trends are not as closely linked as previously thought.

Seven sites surpass the threshold for international importance, one less than the previous year following the demotion of Stour Estuary, whose five-year average dropped just below the 2,500 threshold. The Wash and Dengie Flats continue to be the two most important locations for this species, and both held peaks close to recent averages. Based on the monthly maxima from the last five years of WeBS, approximately half of all Grey Plovers in Britain now occur at these two sites. Elsewhere, peaks at the other sites of international or national importance were typical, with the notable exception of the Ribble Estuary where the year's monthly maximum was one of the lowest ever. This is in stark contrast to the historical high for the site; a spring total of 16,395 in May 2000.

	06/07	07/08	08/09	09/10	10/11	Mon	Mean	
Sites of international importance in the UK								
The Wash	9,750	7,455	11,734	(15,411)	10,223	Sep	10,915	
Dengie Flats	7,239	11,940	10,669	9,550	9,058	Mar	9,691	
Blackwater Estuary	(4,819)	(5,766)	(2,083)	(4,056)	(2,186)	Nov	(5,766)	
Thames Estuary	5,700	2,970	2,801	4,734	4,286	Jan	4,098	
Ribble Estuary	3,518	3,902	2,315	(4,463)	1,272	Apr	3,094	
Humber Estuary	1,923	(3,770)	(3,530)	2,738	2,218	Aug	2,836	
Hamford Water	(2,685)	(2,658)	(2,394)	(2,246)	(1,914)	Nov	(2,685)	
Sites of national importance in Great Britain								
Stour Estuary	2,355	2,329 [10]	2,003 [10]	2,910	2,618	Oct	2,443	▼
Lindisfarne	2,171	(989)	2,058	(512)	(1,577)	Nov	2,115	
Alt Estuary	1,244	1,206	1,731	3,141	2,250	Feb	1,914	
North Norfolk Coast	1,626	1,339 [10]	1,693	2,169	2,097	Sep	1,785	
Swale Estuary	(1,415)	1,631	(1,322)	2,003	1,207	Oct	1,614	
Medway Estuary	(467)	(1,586)	(1,331)	(349)	(767)	Nov	(1,586)	
Chichester Harbour	1,592	1,604	1,416	1,960	897	Sep	1,494	
Dee Estuary (England and Wales)	1,214	762	2,033 [10]	1,160	1,388	Dec	1,311	
Pagham Harbour	902	1,269	1,059	1,329	1,215	Jan	1,155	
Morecambe Bay	(1,065)	747	994	1,073	616	Feb	899	
Langstone Harbour	702	848	989	820	825	Jan	837	
Colne Estuary	840	720	740	(726)	(305)	Oct	767	
Jersey Shore	939	373			427	Feb	580	
Beaulieu Estuary	640	545	526	519	(350)	Dec	558	
Crouch-Roach Estuary	816	292	526	474	482	Feb	518	
Eden Estuary	400	590	558	173	743	Feb	493	
Deben Estuary	342	(574)	509	516	482	Mar	485	
Tay Estuary	215	381	520	340	903	Oct	472	▲
North West Solent	457	431	448	403	470	Nov	442	▲
Sites of all-Ireland importance in Northern Ireland								
Strangford Lough	141	118	84	204	44	Feb	118	
Sites below table qualifying levels but exceeding threshold in WeBS-Year 2010/11 in Great Britain								
Loch of Strathbeg	1,200	0	0	0	500	Nov	340	
Pegwell Bay	360	(170)	269	400 [12]	466 [12]	Feb	374	

Northern Lapwing

Vanellus vanellus

International threshold:	20,000**
Great Britain threshold:	6,200
All-Ireland threshold:	2,100

GB max:	268,020	Jan
NI max:	11,902	Jan

There was considerable variation in the maxima recorded at the three sites in the UK which are internationally important for Lapwing. The January total of 72,319 at Somerset Levels is the most ever there, and presumably represents a redistribution of birds from elsewhere during the harshest of the frozen midwinter conditions. The general assertion is that waders are forced towards the coast, at least initially, during freezing conditions. Therefore, the presence of such high numbers at Somerset Levels at this time was perhaps unexpected, although the area is not too far from parts of the Severn Estuary such as Bridgwater Bay.

Numbers wintering in the UK are known to vary in response to temperatures both here and particularly in continental Europe, as the population is supplemented by the arrival of birds from Scandinavia, eastern Europe and Russia (Wernham et al. 2002). Hence, a marked response to the cold winter experienced across central Europe in 2010/11 was probably to be expected.

Although the monthly indices for Britain show a slight reduction in numbers during the onset of the cold weather in December, though by January numbers had recovered and were actually slightly above average. Did the birds depart from Britain and return, or were they temporarily displaced from WeBS sites to locations in Britain not monitored by the survey? Or does the increase in January represent a net influx of new birds from continental Europe; perhaps from The Netherlands where the trend for Lapwing has been stable over the last thirty years (Hornman et al. 2012)? Whatever the reason, the contrast between the monthly indices for Lapwing and Golden Plover is striking.

The latter species underwent a marked exodus from the UK during the frozen midwinter period in 2010/11, but in contrast, many of the major sites for Lapwing listed below actually yielded their maxima for the year during the coldest period of the winter. Interestingly, in keeping with the exceptional inland aggregation at Somerset Levels, two other inland sites – Ouse Washes and Nene Washes – both recorded notable maxima at this time.

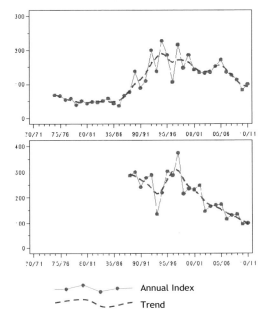

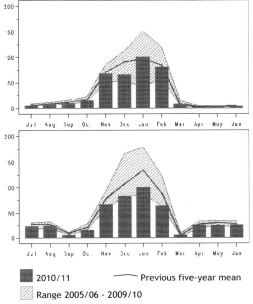

Figure 47.a, Annual indices & trend for Lapwing in GB (above) & NI (below).

Figure 47.b, Monthly indices for Lapwing in GB (above) & NI (below).

	06/07	07/08	08/09	09/10	10/11	Mon	Mean
Sites of international importance in the UK							
Somerset Levels	38,388	44,457	31,928	19,683	72,319	Jan	41,355
The Wash	36,998	11,186	24,543	21,265	(14,490)	Feb	23,498
Breydon Water and Berney Marshes	17,620 [12]	19,700 [12]	38,700 [12]	19,820 [12]	16,955 [10]	Jan	22,559
Sites of national importance in Great Britain							
Morecambe Bay	13,484	(10,683)	(17,535)	(18,225)	19,079	Nov	17,081
Ribble Estuary	13,821	18,066	16,777	19,517	15,213	Nov	16,679
Humber Estuary	(19,403)	16,500	11,700 [12]	13,581	(6,494)	Feb	15,296
Swale Estuary	(10,840)	23,479	(9,996)	8,744	9,009	Feb	13,744
Ouse Washes	13,026	11,222	(7,343)	7,340 [12]	19,530	Feb	12,780
Thames Estuary	17,270	8,728	(8,101)	9,246	(8,782)	Jan	11,748
Pegwell Bay	17,000	12,000	8,260 [10]	10,000 [12]	7,740 [12]	Jan	11,000
North Norfolk Coast	(11,560)	11,185	10,419	9,462	9,366	Jan	10,398
Severn Estuary	9,895	11,035	11,951	7,967	(4,455)	Jan	10,212
Dungeness and Rye Bay	9,936	12,758	5,320	7,553	(3,992)	Nov	8,892
Blackwater Estuary	(8,160)	8,503	10,129	5,166	(5,954)	Nov	7,990
Crouch-Roach Estuary	8,438	(9,255)	8,002	7,101	5,857 [10]	Nov	7,731
Fiddlers Ferry Power Station Lagoons	4,000	10,000					7,000 ▲
Medway Estuary	(5,184)	6,805	(5,325)	(1,011)	(5,110)	Feb	6,805
Nene Washes	4,720	10,575	6,353	1,996	9,354	Feb	6,600 ▲
Sites of all-Ireland importance in Northern Ireland							
Loughs Neagh and Beg	5,421	(7,720)	6,263	2,550	4,013	Feb	5,193
Strangford Lough	5,154 [10]	3,906 [10]	5,198 [10]	5,110	4,976	Jan	4,869
Lough Foyle	2,543	1,816	2,945	2,663	1,130	Jan	2,219
Sites no longer meeting table qualifying levels in WeBS-Year 2010/2011							
Dee Estuary (England and Wales)	5,319	9,526	4,402	5,641	4,568	Jan	5,891
Solway Estuary	(7,622)	(5,128)	5,023	5,504	3,838	Nov	5,423

Legend:
- ● Annual Index
- ┈ Trend
- ■ 2010/11
- ▬ Previous five-year mean
- ▨ Range 2005/06 - 2009/10

Red Knot
Calidris canutus

International threshold (W Europe): **4,500**
Great Britain threshold: **3,200**
All-Ireland threshold: **190**

GB max: **261,164** Oct
NI max: **1,898** Feb

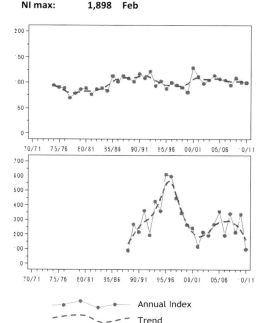

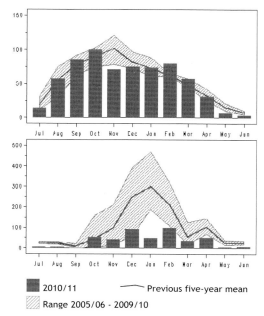

Legend:
■ 2010/11   ⎯ Previous five-year mean
▨ Range 2005/06 - 2009/10

Legend:
●—● Annual Index
- - - Trend

Figure 48.a, Annual indices & trend for Knot in GB (above) & NI (below).

Figure 48.b, Monthly indices for Knot in GB (above) & NI (below).

Although two sub-populations of Knot may pass through the UK, *canutus* (breeding in Taimyr) and *islandica* (breeding in northeast Canada and Greenland), it is assumed that all birds wintering in western Europe are *islandica* while the nominate race winters in Africa.

The British trend has been stable over the course of the last 25 years. Each year, numbers of Knot in Britain peak between September and December, following a general westerly movement of birds that have moulted at the Wadden Sea (which supports approximately 75% of staging birds (Wernham *et al.* 2002). WeBS-year 2010/11 was typical in that respect; the monthly indices illustrating a build-up during the autumn, culminating with peaks at both The Wash and Norfolk Coast in October. Thereafter, numbers during the main winter period were below average, probably in response to the cold weather conditions which may have forced birds out of Britain to sites further south in the wintering range, perhaps on the French coast for example. Numbers also fell in Northern Ireland, including a marked drop at Strangford Lough.

A recent recovery in Knot numbers on The Wash has followed a period of steady decline, and an overall change in waterbird assemblage, which arose from over-exploitation of the shellfishery stock and increased nutrient input (Atkinson *et al.* 2010). There were mixed fortunes with respect to maxima at the other 11 sites of international importance. Numbers at Morecambe Bay, Dengie Flats and Dee Estuary were more or less as expected, but below average numbers were reported from Thames Estuary. At the latter, however, the peak did represent a marked improvement on the low number noted there in 2009/10 (the lowest since 1985/86). At Ribble Estuary, the peak of 16,626 is the lowest annual maximum ever recorded at the site, and represents the low point of a long-term downward trend there; a historical maximum at Ribble Estuary dates back to September 1973 when over 102,205 Knots were logged. In contrast, the peak from Alt Estuary of 48,301 (Jan) represents significantly more than is typical there. The previous five-year average was just over 15,000 birds, although 51,000 have been recorded in the past (January 1990). It is likely that there is significant exchange of birds between these two adjacent sites (and the Dee Estuary), and the site trends may therefore be linked.

Nine further sites surpassed the threshold for national importance, including Carmarthen Bay for the first time. Typically, there can be considerable inter-annual variation in terms of annual peaks at some of the smaller estuaries, but the counts of 5,249 at Chichester Harbour and 2,024 at Eden Estuary, both in February, are perhaps two of the most noteworthy; the former being the most ever at that site.

	06/07	07/08	08/09	09/10	10/11	Mon	Mean
Sites of international importance in the UK							
The Wash	135,889	(162,724)	93,957	180,572	119,192	Oct	138,467
North Norfolk Coast	22,928	11,239	84,812	83,003	73,662	Oct	55,129
Morecambe Bay	(19,635)	(24,544)	42,671	60,719	41,194	Feb	48,195
Humber Estuary	(33,529)	41,772	(17,552)	(37,088)	(20,620)	Sep	41,772
Thames Estuary	83,716	45,162	28,203	17,861	30,725	Jan	41,133
Ribble Estuary	(41,681)	30,136	(45,400)	(25,000)[12]	16,626	Apr	31,769
Alt Estuary	15,011	12,900	19,602	15,250	48,301	Jan	22,213
Dengie Flats	30,500	17,375	10,200	(18,960)	18,000	Jan	19,019
Dee Estuary (England and Wales)	12,937	11,212	20,850 [10]	10,465	20,572	Dec	15,207
Solway Estuary	(8,910)	(14,385)	(13,364)	6,006	(13,963)	Dec	11,326
Strangford Lough	5,380 [10]	7,360 [10]	6,376 [10]	7,452	2,807 [8]	Dec	5,875
Stour Estuary	3,028	6,660	4,357 [10]	7,455 [10]	3,466	Nov	4,993
Blackwater Estuary	2,610	(3,492)	(8,630)	(4,032)	(3,800)	Dec	4,513
Sites of national importance in Great Britain							
Medway Estuary	(550)	(2,940)	4,304	(400)	(4,485)	Dec	4,395
Hamford Water	3,550	2,200	4,263 [10]	(6,250)	4,681	Nov	4,189
Swale Estuary	4,506	5,002	3,528	1,650	5,151	Feb	3,967
Severn Estuary	(966)	(5,510)	4,081	1,182	(1,021)	Dec	3,591
Lindisfarne	1,475	(4,111)	(4,150)	(1,125)	4,330	Sep	3,517
Forth Estuary	(3,542)	3,298	4,088	2,934	(3,558)	Dec	3,484
Inner Moray and Inverness Firth	2,762	2,485	5,952	3,027	3,020	Jan	3,449
Burry Inlet	4,300	7,100	2,830	1,302 [10]	690	Nov	3,244
Carmarthen Bay	1,722 [10]	6,486 [10]	1,470 [10]	2,184 [10]	4,343	Dec	3,241
Sites of all-Ireland importance in Northern Ireland							
Dundrum Inner Bay	100	2,560	1,023	1,200	22	Jan	981
Tyrella			(495)				(495)
Lough Foyle	225	501	400	38	350	Mar	303
Sites below table qualifying levels but exceeding threshold in WeBS-Year 2010/11 in Great Britain							
Chichester Harbour	1,060	2,709	1,036	2,180	5,249	Feb	2,447
Dornoch Firth	1,400	2,500	1,731	4,315	4,772	Jan	2,944

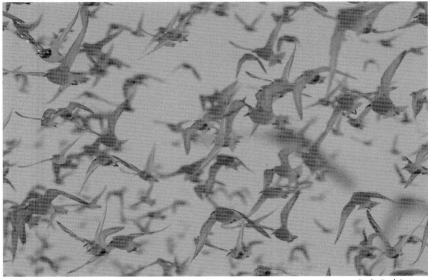

Rob Robinson

Sanderling

Calidris alba

International threshold (W Europe, W & S Africa): 1,200
Great Britain winter threshold: 160
All-Ireland threshold: 65

GB max: 11,827 Sep
NI max: 538 Oct

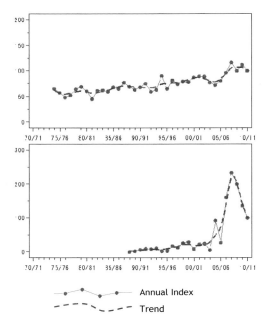

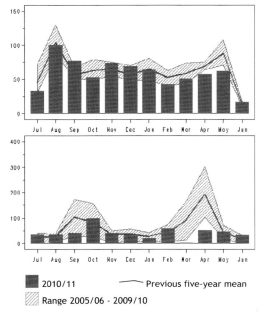

Annual Index
Trend

2010/11
Range 2005/06 - 2009/10
Previous five-year mean

Figure 49.a, Annual indices & trend for Sanderling in GB (above) & NI (below).

Figure 49.b, Monthly indices for Sanderling in GB (above) & NI (below).

Sanderling breed in the high Arctic and birds from both the Siberian and Greenland populations migrate south from northwest Europe.

In 2010/11, the British index fell slightly compared to the previous year, but the long-term trend remains positive. The increase in number of Sanderlings in Britain has occurred at the same time as a more rapid rise experienced in The Netherlands (Hornman *et al.* 2012). Similarly, following an unprecedented peak in 2007/08, the index for Northern Ireland has been at a high level in six of the last seven years. Lough Foyle again supported Northern Ireland's largest aggregation of the year. The reasons behind these changes in national trends remain poorly understood, but may be linked to the temporal changes in the use of a network of key sites in northwest Europe (Reneerkens *et al.* (2009).

Four British sites again surpassed the threshold for international importance based on the use of monthly maxima from throughout the WeBS-year. For the second year in a row, the largest count was from The Wash, where 3,469 (Sep) although considerably down on the 2009/10 all-time maximum, was still above average. The peak totals from Alt Estuary (2,523, Apr) and Carmarthen Bay (1,824, Nov) were typical, but that at Ribble Estuary (1,870, Mar) was the lowest maximum reported from there for over 20 years. The all-time spring and autumn peaks in the UK are both from Ribble Estuary, and relate to 8,737 in May 1992 and 9,450 in July 1972, respectively.

	06/07	07/08	08/09	09/10	10/11	Mon	Mean
Sites of international importance in the UK							
Ribble Estuary	(4,690)	4,700	(4,800)	(2,444)	1,870	Mar	4,015
The Wash	1,504	(1,430)	1,420	5,794	3,469	Sep	3,047
Alt Estuary	3,090	2,171	1,833	3,629	2,523	Apr	2,649
Carmarthen Bay	2,370 [10]	1,955 [10]	1,812	2,224	1,824	Nov	2,037

	06/07	07/08	08/09	09/10	10/11	Mon	Mean
Sites of national importance in Great Britain							
North Norfolk Coast	973	1,200 [10]	927	1,307	1,073	Sep	1,096
Humber Estuary	(362)	(706)	(662)	1,194	419	May	807
Thames Estuary	870	689	951	587	897	Oct	799
Jersey Shore	831	739			720	Mar	763
Scuthvie Bay	(110)	705	810	530			682
Morecambe Bay	332	(477)	532	624	705	May	548
Dee Estuary (England and Wales)	370	762	778	280	474	Dec	533
North Bay (South Uist)	318	650	780		382	Mar	533
Lindisfarne	509	467	480	(433)	(352)	Nov	485
Duddon Estuary	623 [12]	(450)[12]	241	(490)	(527)	Jan	466
Solway Estuary	501	(455)	189	(450)	(540)	Nov	427
Thanet Coast	322	431	282	499	380	Dec	383
Swansea Bay	440 [10]	(279)	327	154	475	Dec	349
Rubha Ardvule to Ardivachar (South Uist)					346	Dec	346 ▲
Severn Estuary	(140)	(29)	324	(45)	(70)	Dec	324
Forth Estuary	168	(387)	(315)	404	(181)	Nov	319
Tees Estuary	191	(193)	(351)	(353)	(425)	May	303
Ardivachar Point (South Uist)	350	267	372		184	Mar	293
Ryde Pier to Puckpool Point	200	310		292	(201)	Sep	267
South Ford	218	300	400		129	Mar	262
Chichester Harbour	324	245	242	210	212	Sep	247
Inner Moray and Inverness Firth	197	243	(106)	188	263	Mar	223
Pegwell Bay	120	110	280 [12]	386 [12]	135 [12]	Nov	206
Taw-Torridge Estuary	(183)	(150)	(176)	203 [12]	(180)	Feb	203
Dungeness and Rye Bay	183 [12]	300 [12]	234	(178)	90	Jan	202
Don Mouth to Ythan Mouth	(49)	132	(150)	(361)	126	Jul	192
Tay Estuary	303	103	160	102	(200)	Aug	174
South Hayling Seafront		150	180	140	200	Nov	168 ▲
Sites of all-Ireland importance in Northern Ireland							
Lough Foyle	(190)	879	925	488	518	Oct	703
Dundrum Bay	180	200	155	(0)	(0)		178
Bann Estuary	251	69	108	148	89	Nov	133
Tyrella			(73)				(73)
Sites no longer meeting table qualifying levels in WeBS-Year 2010/2011							
Durham Coast	(88)		(116)	(75)	(43)	Apr	(116)
Sites below table qualifying levels but exceeding threshold in WeBS-Year 2010/11 in Great Britain							
Afan Estuary and Port Talbot Harbour	0	12	240	21	246	Dec	104
Loch Gruinart	39	108	60	326	176	Nov	142
Ythan Estuary	8	(25)	173	(42)	175	Apr	119

Little Stint
Calidris minuta

International threshold (N & S Europe, N & W Africa):	3,000	
Great Britain threshold:	1 [†]	
All-Ireland threshold:	? [†]	

GB max:	76	Sep
NI max:	0	

Little Stints breed through Siberia and west into the northern extremes of Scandinavia, and typically winter around the Mediterranean and in Africa. The species was recorded at 44 WeBS sites in 2010/11, the majority between August and October. These included a maximum of 21 at The Wash in September, the highest peak

there for 15 years. The site has hosted an all-time WeBS maximum of 135 in October 1988.

A small wintering population, totalling less than ten birds, was noted at several widespread sites, including inland at Abberton Reservoir and Drakelow Gravel Pit. In spring, singles were noted at seven sites in April to June.

Sites with 4 or more birds during passage periods in 2010/11[†]

The Wash	21, Sep	Tees Estuary	6, Sep
Thames Estuary	10, Oct	Hayle Estuary	6, Oct
Severn Estuary	8, Oct	North Norfolk Coast	5, Sep
Blackwater Estuary	7, Aug	Northwest Solent	4, Sep

[†] *a qualifying level of 4 has been chosen to select sites for presentation in this report*

Temminck's Stint
Calidris temminckii

Scarce

One at Stodmarsh in August was followed by five typical spring records, all in May, at Joe's Ponds & Rainton Meadows, Tees Estuary, Wigan Flashes, The Wash and Pegwell Bay.

Baird's Sandpiper
Calidris bairdii

Vagrant
Native Range: America

One at Holland Marshes in October was the 18th WeBS record.

Pectoral Sandpiper
Calidris melanotos

Vagrant
Native Range: America, N Siberia, Australia

Pectoral Sandpipers were noted at 14 sites, typically with the majority in autumn. This total represents the most in a WeBS-year since 2003/04. Following one at The Wash in July, a total of 16 birds were recorded during September (13) and October (3). These included multiple inland occurrences at Pitsford Reservoir (3, Sep) and Little Paxton GPs (2, Sep). More unusually, two birds were noted in June, at Dee Estuary and Tees Estuary.

Curlew Sandpiper
Calidris ferruginea

International threshold (W Siberia, W Africa):	10,000
Great Britain threshold:	?[†]
All-Ireland threshold:	?[†]

GB max:	272	Sep
NI max:	6	Sep

Curlew Sandpipers are passage migrants to the UK, which breed in central Siberia with the bulk of the population wintering in central and southern Africa. They are scarce here in spring, and autumn numbers are largely dependent on the summer's breeding success. The species primarily passes to the east of the UK on passage, rendering it relatively scarce here. In contrast, a staging site on the German part of the Wadden Sea has hosted up to 27,000 birds (Delany *et al.* 2009); putting the numbers observed in the UK each autumn into context.

Records from 58 WeBS sites in Britain and two in Northern Ireland is evidence of a reasonably strong autumn period. The majority of records were in September (when juveniles tend to predominate) in what was considered to be a relatively productive breeding season for birds in many Arctic regions (Soloviev & Tomkovich 2011). The geographic spread of the main aggregations (listed below) is further evidence of relatively high numbers that are likely to have passed through Britain at that time. A small number of inland records included four at Arlington Reservoir in July.

Birds were noted at two locations during the winter (Swale Estuary and Tamar Complex) and a light return passage generated May records from four sites (Dee Estuary, Ribble Estuary, North Norfolk Coast and Pegwell Bay).

Sites with 10 or more birds during passage periods in 2010/11[†]

Severn Estuary	41, Sep	Thames Estuary	21, Sep
North Norfolk Coast	32, Sep	Morecambe Bay	17, Sep
The Wash	28, Sep	Ribble Estuary	10, Sep
Loch Leven	23, Sep	Blyth Estuary	10, Sep
Breydon Water & Berney Marshes	23, Sep	Forth Estuary	10, Sep

[†] as no British or All-Ireland thresholds have been set a qualifying level of 10 has been chosen to select sites for presentation in this report

Purple Sandpiper
Calidris maritima

International threshold (N Europe): **710**
Great Britain threshold: **130**
All-Ireland threshold: **35***

GB max: 1,516 Dec
NI max: 93 Jan

*50 is normally used as a minimum threshold

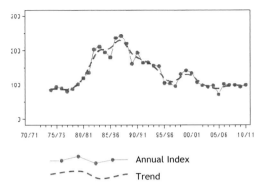

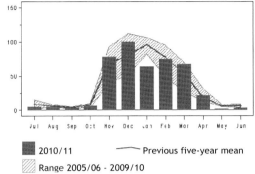

———•——— Annual Index

– – – – – – Trend

■ 2010/11 ⌒ Previous five-year mean

▨ Range 2005/06 - 2009/10

Figure 50.a, Annual indices & trend for Purple Sandpiper in GB.

Figure 50.b, Monthly indices for Purple Sandpiper in GB.

The UK's wintering population of Purple Sandpipers comprises birds which breed in eastern Canada, Scandinavia and Svalbard (the birds breeding in Iceland and much of Greenland are considered to be mainly resident). Most of those that occur in the UK are on Scotland's rocky shores which are monitored more effectively by NEWS (Non-Estuarine Waterbird survey), e.g. Austin *et al.* (2007).

Following a marked decline during the 1980s and 1990s, numbers have been relatively stable since the turn of the century. There is a suggestion of a shift in the wintering distribution of this species with the proportion of birds found in the north-western parts of the UK having increased in recent years. This indicates a shift towards Canadian breeding grounds (Rehfisch *et al.* 2004). Pertinently, a marked response to the prevailing weather conditions appears to have taken place in January 2011, with reduced numbers noted at WeBS sites in Britain. It is tempting to speculate that this decline may have involved displacement to milder shores further south and or west in the wintering range.

Some notable Core counts were received in 2010/11, the largest of which was an all-time site maximum of 436 at Papa Westray (Mar). Six other sites held peaks of 100+ Purple Sandpipers: Farne Islands, Egilsay, Forth Estuary, Seahouses to Budle Bay, St Andrews Bay, and Rubha Ardvule to Ardivachar (South Uist). Historical WeBS maxima for this species relate to a series of high counts from the Moray Coast in the late-1980s/early-1990s, the largest of which was 517 birds in February 1988.

In Northern Ireland, the peak reported from Outer Ards Shoreline (80, Jan) was typical of recent years. The most important site in Northern Ireland for this species has a historic maximum of 156 in February 1990.

	06/07	07/08	08/09	09/10	10/11	Mon	Mean
Sites of national importance in Great Britain							
Island of Papa Westray	420	413	324	298	436	Mar	378
Farne Islands	(184)	(171)	(348)	104	(263)	Oct	214
Island of Egilsay	(90)		99	160	235	Mar	165
Ardivachar Point (South Uist)	139	108	233		98	Feb	145
Forth Estuary	98	145	(114)	(147)	168	Feb	140 ▲
Rubha Ardvule to Ardivachar (South Uist)					137	Feb	137 ▲
Moray Coast (Consolidated)	67	229	199	88	77	Jan	132
Sites of all-Ireland importance in Northern Ireland							
Outer Ards Shoreline	122	66	85	45	80	Jan	80
Sites below table qualifying levels but exceeding threshold in WeBS-Year 2010/11 in Great Britain							
Seahouses to Budle Point	(65)	12	63	85	136	Dec	74

Dunlin

Calidris alpina

International threshold (W Europe & NW Africa):	13,300
Great Britain threshold:	3,500
All-Ireland threshold:	880

GB max: 309,306 Jan
NI max: 5,848 Jan

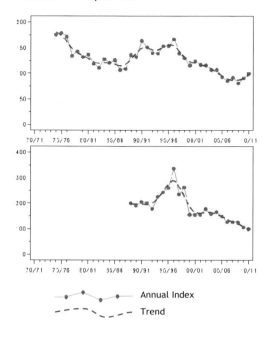

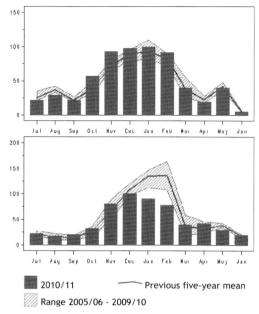

Figure 51.a, Annual indices & trend for Dunlin in GB (above) & NI (below).

Figure 51.b, Monthly indices for Dunlin in GB (above) & NI (below).

Dunlins have been in steady decline in Britain since the mid 1990s. It is perhaps pertinent therefore that two relatively cold winters (2009/10 and 2010/11) have seen improved national index values in Britain and an upturn in the associated trend. Prior to that, the decrease in the UK has been associated with an increase in The Netherlands (Hornman *et al.* 2011), implying that a larger proportion of birds from northern breeding populations were wintering on the Dutch Wadden Sea – probably as a result of climatic amelioration, as demonstrated by Maclean *et al.* (2008). Recent declines in wintering numbers of other wader species in UK, including Bar-tailed Godwit and Curlew, have also been attributed to similar shifts in their core wintering distribution. It remains to be seen whether the apparent change of fortune for Dunlin in Britain in the last two years is maintained in the years ahead.

Ten sites surpass the threshold for international importance. The peak count at

Severn Estuary of 31,397 is the highest there for several years, and is reminiscent of numbers that formerly used the site during the 1970s and 1980s when the Severn was nearer to the top of the table below. The historic maximum from the site is a startling 64,314 in January 1974. The trend at Severn Estuary since then has been downwards (Thaxter *et al.* 2010), considered attributable to a north-easterly shift in the centroid of wintering distribution (Maclean *et al.* 2008).

For the second year in succession, the highest individual site count did not relate to the spring aggregation at Ribble Estuary, where birds of the nominate race (which breeds from Scandinavia north and westwards) are joined by the *arctica* and *schinzii* races. The year's peak, 41,430 birds at Mersey Estuary in November, consolidated that site's second position in the table (following a similarly high number recorded in 2009/10). Maxima at other internationally important sites were generally close to the recent averages, although the peak at Morecambe Bay was the lowest reported there since 2004/05. Among the further twenty sites surpassing the threshold for national importance is Dengie Flats where this year's peak (16,450, Jan) is the most ever for this site.

In Northern Ireland, the recent trend is also one of decline, and despite the putative westward shift of waterbirds in response to the cold winter there was no change in abundance of Dunlin noted in 2010/11. Peaks at individual sites were generally close to or below recent averages.

	06/07	07/08	08/09	09/10	10/11	Mon	Mean
Sites of international importance in the UK							
Ribble Estuary	(33,506)	52,551	(45,662)	28,940	(39,744)	Oct	42,384
Mersey Estuary	34,600	41,270	23,115	44,030	41,430	Nov	36,889
Thames Estuary	33,335	34,941	32,123 [10]	(23,217)	(15,970)	Jan	33,466
The Wash	25,913	24,523	24,444	33,181	26,136	Oct	26,839
Morecambe Bay	(38,248)	24,409	20,289	31,084	19,942	Nov	26,794
Severn Estuary	16,625	(16,072)	27,136 [10]	21,640	31,937	Jan	24,335
Chichester Harbour	14,152	(18,759)	26,311	17,465	16,658	Jan	18,669
Humber Estuary	14,951	(18,349)	15,444	(16,124)	18,622	Nov	16,842
Blackwater Estuary	9,581	15,015	17,966	(19,606)	(17,435)	Jan	15,921
Dee Estuary (England and Wales)	15,584	12,094	16,855 [10]	9,654	18,574	Dec	14,552
Sites of national importance in Great Britain							
Langstone Harbour	12,950	15,007	8,126	13,615 [10]	12,319	Feb	12,403 ▼
Dengie Flats	(7,340)	6,116	10,650	11,570	16,450	Jan	11,197
Medway Estuary	(5,222)	(9,132)	(10,633)	(3,795)	(7,340)	Nov	(10,633)
Alt Estuary	7,630	7,652	7,819	16,004	12,826	Mar	10,386
Duddon Estuary	(6,542)	14,523	8,000 [12]	7,481	(2,206)	Jan	10,001
Swale Estuary	5,706	7,692	6,419	13,073	9,046	Jan	8,387
Stour Estuary	7,231	8,150	5,674	6,501	9,691	Nov	7,449
Solway Estuary	6,512	(7,194)	7,836	10,094	5,197	Nov	7,410
Portsmouth Harbour	(6,592)	(7,002)	(6,842)	(6,530)	(4,182)	Feb	(7,002)
Forth Estuary	5,488	4,937	6,565	(5,357)	6,988	Nov	5,995
Breydon Water and Berney Marshes	5,755 [10]	5,310 [12]	4,720 [12]	5,108 [12]	5,407 [10]	Dec	5,260
Burry Inlet	6,218 [8]	6,903	5,703	2,412	4,770	Jan	5,201
Colne Estuary	3,756	6,716 [10]	4,970	4,891	(3,960)	Nov	5,083
Lindisfarne	6,951	(5,315)	3,755	2,108	5,170	Nov	4,660
Alde Complex	3,149	5,380	4,782	4,601	3,994	Dec	4,381
Dornoch Firth	5,681	3,911	(1,050)	3,474	3,996	Jan	4,266
Crouch-Roach Estuary	3,684	(4,403)	2,930	5,209	4,242	Nov	4,094
Exe Estuary	3,091 [10]	3,975	4,005	3,559	4,885	Dec	3,903
Cleddau Estuary	2,664	4,666	3,988	3,433	4,709	Feb	3,892
Blyth Estuary	4,895	6,130	2,715	2,743	2,919	Nov	3,880
Hamford Water	(3,735)	(3,340)	3,731 [10]	(2,945)	(3,492)	Jan	3,733
North Norfolk Coast	3,321	4,088	2,811	3,830	3,873	Dec	3,585 ▲
Sites of all-Ireland importance in Northern Ireland							
Strangford Lough	3,151 [10]	4,115 [10]	4,455 [10]	2,514 [10]	4,384 [10]	Nov	3,724
Carlingford Lough	(2,185)	2,621	1,552	(1,370)	(2,210)	Dec	2,142
Lough Foyle	1,592	2,028	3,750	1,183	1,515	Jan	2,014
Dundrum Inner Bay	1,047	1,186	1,277	1,157	876	Jan	1,109
Belfast Lough	(1,712)	742	699	743	(1,116)	Feb	1,002
Outer Ards Shoreline	2,810	739	605	425	338	Jan	983
Sites no longer meeting table qualifying levels in WeBS-Year 2010/2011							
Bann Estuary	1,030	900	671	1,060	265	Nov	785
Sites below table qualifying levels but exceeding threshold in WeBS-Year 2010/11 in Great Britain							
Eden Estuary	550	3,015	4,705	1,458	3,846	Nov	2,715

Buff-breasted Sandpiper
Tryngites subruficollis

Vagrant
Native Range: America

A group of three was recorded for the second successive year; at Dungeness & Rye Bay in October. Prior to that, two had been seen in Northern Ireland, at Lough Foyle in September.

Ruff
Philomachus pugnax

International threshold (N Europe & W Africa): 12,200
Great Britain threshold: 8*
All-Ireland threshold: +†

| GB max: | 522 | Nov |
| NI max: | 2 | Aug |

50 is normally used as a minimum threshold

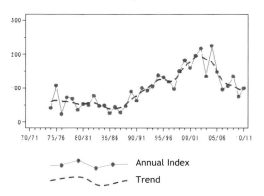

Figure 52.a, Annual indices & trend for Ruff in GB.

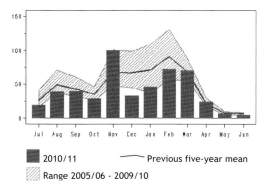

Figure 52.b, Monthly indices for Ruff in GB.

After a marked increase in Ruff at WeBS sites during the 1990s and early 2000s, the reasons for a downward trend since then are unclear. In 2010/11, the peak count of 243 at Ouse Washes in November was the most there for five years, and represented the highlight of an otherwise largely uneventful year for the species in Britain. The highest count on the coast was 131 at North Norfolk Coast, also in November. Those two counts contributed to a pronounced peak in the monthly indices during November, which was then followed by a general exodus of birds from WeBS sites during the frozen conditions in December and January when many traditionally favoured inland sites held relatively low numbers.

	06/07	07/08	08/09	09/10	10/11	Mon	Mean
Sites of national importance in Great Britain							
Ouse Washes	82 [12]	135 [12]	(115)	73 [12]	243	Nov	133
North Norfolk Coast	121	90	189	116	131	Nov	129
Lower Derwent Ings	148	129	93	78	69	Mar	103
Humber Estuary	61	62	79	37	60	Aug	60
WWT Martin Mere	76	67	48	42	48	Nov	56
Breydon Water and Berney Marshes	55 [11]	89 [12]	20	38 [12]	56 [12]	Dec	52
Overcote Marina	112 [12]		58	13	0		46
Somerset Levels	29	96	48	37	9	Jan	44
Nene Washes	4	38	76	62	3	Jan	37
Swale Estuary	49	40	14	44	32	Feb	36
Ribble Estuary	32	37	40	21	52	Oct	36
Hickling Broad	3		55	47			35
Morecambe Bay	92	3	2	3	(13)	Mar	25
Fen Drayton Gravel Pits	33	60	8	8	0		22
Middle Yare Marshes	27	21	18	12	32	Jan	22
Severn Estuary	33	14	18	9	32	Oct	21
Tees Estuary	33	15	19	22	15	Sep	21
Abberton Reservoir	(9)	21	5	26	22	Oct	19
Dungeness and Rye Bay	34	16	22	14	4	Sep	18
Rutland Water	29	15	20	12	16	Aug	18
The Wash	11	2	12	15	35	Sep	15
Loch of Strathbeg	8	6	11	17	31	Sep	15
Minsmere	20	10	9	10	17	Apr	13
Tophill Low Reservoirs	0	62 [12]	1	1	0		13
Thames Estuary	3	(4)	11	22	(10)	Sep	12
Blackwater Estuary	10	15	18	11	5	Jul	12
Dee Estuary (England and Wales)	9	11	13	(7)	(6)	Mar	11
Nosterfield Gravel Pits	23	9	14	2	7	Aug	11

	06/07	07/08	08/09	09/10	10/11	Mon	Mean
Otmoor	31[12]	3[12]	3[12]	7[12]	0		9
Sandbach Flashes	14	12	8	7	4	Aug	9
Stodmarsh	5	8	10	9	8	Aug	8
Hamford Water	5	14	7	12	3	Dec	8
Cresswell Pond	10	2	24	1	3	Oct	8
Forth Estuary	14	4	6	10[12]	4	Sep	8
Sites no longer meeting table qualifying levels in WeBS-Year 2010/2011							
Arun Valley	10	(10)	3	(9)	5	Feb	7
Holland Marshes	17	7	3	2[12]	0		6
Stour Estuary	1	1	1	1	5	Sep	2
Sites with mean peak counts of 8+ birds in Northern Ireland[†]							
Loughs Neagh and Beg	34	6	0	14	0		11
Sites below table qualifying levels but exceeding threshold in WeBS-Year 2010/11 in Great Britain							
Christchurch Harbour	1	0	(0)	0	12	Jan	3
Castlemartin Corse	0	0	(0)	0	9	Jan	2
Crouch-Roach Estuary	2	6	5[12]	2	8	Apr	5
Grindon Lough	0	1	0	0	8	Aug	2

[†] as no All-Ireland threshold has been set a qualifying level of 8 has been chosen to select sites for presentation in this report

Jack Snipe
Lymnocryptes minimus

International threshold (N, S & W Europe, W Africa):	20,000
Great Britain threshold:	1,000[†]
All-Ireland threshold:	250[†]

GB max:	87 Nov
NI max:	1 Jan

Jack Snipe is a very difficult species to census and is probably the most poorly monitored of all European waders on both breeding and wintering areas (Delany *et al.* 2009). It is difficult to draw reliable inferences from analysis of each year's WeBS counts, as the species has very low detectability and a preference for habitats poorly covered by the survey. As emphasised in previous reports, the continuation of standardised counts at WeBS sites favoured by Jack Snipes may prove valuable in assessing changes in status at the local level at least.

In 2010/11, the species was recorded at 107 WeBS sites during Core counts, 19% fewer than the previous year. The peak count was 14 at Cathkin Marsh in November, during which month the majority of maxima at the main locations were logged – ahead of the onset of frozen conditions in December.

	06/07	07/08	08/09	09/10	10/11	Mon	Mean
Sites with mean peak counts of 5 or more birds in Great Britain[†]							
Craigmarloch	15[12]	35					25
Bickershaw Colliery Area	32[19]	4[19]	21[19]				19
Chichester Harbour	37	21	8	10	2	Nov	16
Chat Moss	7[19]	6[19]	11[19]	25[19]			12
Rumworth Lodge Reservoir	21[19]	1[19]					11
Windlaw Marsh	25	12	6	3	4	Nov	10
Somerset Levels	9	9	9	(15)	2	Jan	9
Cathkin Marsh			0	12	14	Nov	9
Severn Estuary	6	12	7	14	3	Nov	8
Cainhoe Lakes			11	6	4	Mar	7
Lower Derwent Ings	14	4	7	4	5	Oct	7
Kinsham Pool	7	16	4	5	2	Mar	7
St David`s Airfield Heath SSSI		5	8				7
Dee Estuary (England and Wales)	2	18	8	2	2	Oct	6
Sites below table qualifying levels but exceeding threshold in WeBS-Year 2010/11 in Great Britain[†]							
Lindisfarne	(1)	(0)	0	(0)	(7)	Dec	2
River Kennet: Ramsbury to Chilton Foliat	6	3	3	(1)	5	Feb	4

[†] as no sites exceed the British and All-Ireland thresholds, a qualifying level of 5 has been chosen to select sites for presentation in this report

Common Snipe
Gallinago gallinago

International threshold (Europe & NW Africa): 20,000**
Great Britain threshold: 10,000[†]
All-Ireland threshold: ?[†]

GB max:	6,029	Nov
NI max:	173	Dec

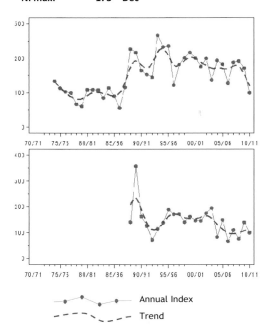

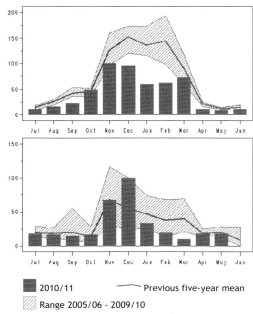

Figure 53.a, Annual indices & trend for Snipe in GB (above) & NI (below).

Figure 53.b, Monthly indices for Snipe in GB (above) & NI (below).

Snipe use a variety of habitats in winter, and the population is considered to comprise residents as well as immigrants from northwest Europe. Interpretation of national figures for this species is notoriously difficult because many favoured habitats (such as marshes and damp grassland) are relatively poorly covered through WeBS. Moreover, there are inherent difficulties in obtaining accurate estimates of numbers due to their secretive habits. Musgrove *et al.* (2011) estimate that around one million birds are present in Britain during the winter period, while although the breeding population has experienced marked declines historically, there are indications that it is now increasing (Baillie *et al.* 2012).

The indices and associated WeBS trend are included here for the first time, but should be used with caution in view of the caveats concerning interpretation of WeBS counts for this species. However, the monthly indices are undoubtedly interesting in the context of the coldest winter for 35 years. They suggest a

marked exodus of birds from Britain during the frozen conditions in December and January, and numbers had not returned to near normal there until March with the onset of spring migration. Perhaps pertinently, the monthly indices for Northern Ireland show a pronounced peak in December. This is suggestive of an initial arrival of birds from frozen Britain and the continent, before a subsequent decline as birds were presumably displaced further south in the species' wintering range. This general pattern also suggests that a usefully indicative trend can be derived from WeBS counts, though a more thorough examination of this is needed.

Snipe tend to be profoundly impacted by frozen conditions and snow cover, when they can be displaced to alien habitats such as the open coast or even urban gardens. The sites table below also portrays the effects of the frozen midwinter, with atypically, no site maxima registered in December or January (with the majority in October/November prior to displacement).

John Harding

An example of movement towards the coast during freezing conditions is provided by the supplementary counts from Southampton Water in the last two winters and a high count of 245 at Camel Estuary in January 2011.

Across all sites, the largest WeBS count in 2010/11 was 830 at Lower Derwent Ings in October, where it is worth noting that an historical maximum of 3,125 birds has been logged, in September 2004. In Northern Ireland, the peak was 119 at Belfast Lough, in December, the second highest count ever there.

	06/07	07/08	08/09	09/10	10/11	Mon	Mean
Sites with mean peak counts of 200+ birds in Great Britain[†]							
Somerset Levels	1,012	1,794	1,240	711	397	Nov	1,031
Lower Derwent Ings	567	302	1,396	765	830	Oct	772
North Norfolk Coast	96	1,225 [10]	135	217	73	Nov	349
Malltraeth RSPB	261	573	328	206	205	Oct	315
Morecambe Bay	140	107	378	276	388	Nov	258
Doxey Marshes SSSI	224	278	495	209	70	Nov	255
Dee Estuary (England and Wales)	(95)	401	245 [10]	103	130	Oct	220
Southampton Water	(66)	(74)	(138)	204 [12]	202 [12]	Feb	203
Sites with mean peak counts of 50+ birds in Northern Ireland[†]							
Loughs Neagh and Beg	33	110	23	204	37	Oct	81
Strangford Lough	38 [10]	(27)	(27)	102 [10]	(47)	Dec	70
Outer Ards Shoreline	68	13	75	88	25	Jan	54
Belfast Lough	33	57	35	20	119	Dec	53
Sites below table qualifying levels but exceeding threshold in WeBS-Year 2010/11 in Great Britain[†]							
Camel Estuary	103	53	(189)	(215)	245	Jan	161
Other sites surpassing table qualifying levels in Winter 2010/2011 in Northern Ireland[†]							
Larne Lough	0	32	3	15	83	Nov	27

[†] as no sites exceed the British threshold and no All-Ireland threshold has been set, qualifying levels of 200 and 50, respectively, have been chosen to select sites for presentation in this report

Long-billed Dowitcher
Limnodromus scolopaceus

Vagrant
Native Range: America

One was present at Lodmoor in January; the sixth consecutive winter that the species has been recorded during WeBS Core counts.

Eurasian Woodcock
Scolopax rusticola

International threshold: 20,000**
Great Britain threshold: 14,000
All-Ireland threshold: ?

GB max: 207 Dec
NI max: 1 Jan

*50 is normally used as a minimum threshold

Records of Woodcock were received from 130 WeBS sites in 2010/11; a relatively high total, which is presumably attributable to the prolonged period of frozen weather having forced birds out of typical wintering habitats. A monthly maximum of 207 birds was logged in December, a similar peak to that in 2009/10. There were several counts of multiple birds, the highest of which were during the cold midwinter period; namely 35 at Hamford Water, 13 at Hauxley Haven, 11 at Lower Derwent Ings and 10 at Cors Caron.

Black-tailed Godwit
Limosa limosa

International threshold (Iceland & W Europe):	610
Great Britain threshold:	430
All-Ireland threshold:	140

GB max: 32,799 Oct
NI max: 1,771 Mar

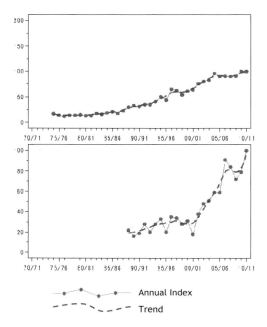

Figure 54.a, Annual indices & trend for Black-tailed Godwit in GB (above) & NI (below).

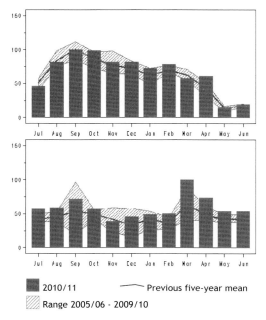

Figure 54.b, Monthly indices for Black-tailed Godwit in GB (above) & NI (below).

Most non-breeding Black-tailed Godwits that occur in Britain and Northern Ireland are of Icelandic origin, arriving in July and August and forming large moulting flocks at coastal sites that tend to peak in September. In addition, a small proportion of passage birds are of the nominate race which are mainly to be found in the south and east of England where a very small number also breed.

After a brief period of stability from 2005/06 to 2008/09, the last two years have seen a further small increase in the national index. This continues the long-term increase undergone over the last thirty years, which mirrors that of the flyway population, the estimated size of which was recently revised upwards by 30% (Wetlands International 2012). These trends are at least partly attributable to the higher breeding success achieved on Icelandic breeding grounds as well as the high quality of sites used in Portugal (Lourenco & Piersma 2008).

Twenty-nine sites surpass the threshold for international importance, and peaks at most of the principal sites were above recent average. The historical peak WeBS count for this species emanates from The Wash where 11,451 were noted in October 2002, and typically, the 2010/11 maximum was also at that site (9,843 in September). This was followed by a midwinter count from Dee Estuary (6,188, Dec), the second highest count ever there, surpassed only by 6,452 in September 2004. Hence, in combination with strong showings at Mersey Estuary and particularly Morecambe Bay, 2010/11 represented a good year for Black-tailed Godwits in northwest England. Five sites no longer qualify as being internationally important following the increase in the associated threshold (Wetlands International 2012).

In Northern Ireland, the maximum at Strangford Lough was higher than the previous year and thereby maintained the site's status as one of international importance. Elsewhere, there were also strong showings at Lough Foyle, Loughs Neagh & Beg, and Bann Estuary.

	06/07	07/08	08/09	09/10	10/11	Mon	Mean
Sites of international importance in the UK							
The Wash	8,090	(6,961)	10,839	9,925	9,843	Sep	9,674
Thames Estuary	4,893	8,081	4,709	5,783	(2,019)	Sep	5,867
Dee Estuary (England and Wales)	3,713	5,278	3,923	5,763	6,188	Dec	4,973
Ribble Estuary	5,095	3,913	3,088	5,714	(1,585)	Feb	4,453
Humber Estuary	5,323	4,554	3,828	3,981	4,069	Oct	4,351
Nene Washes	1,120	3,800	3,530	3,500	1,340	Jan	2,658
Poole Harbour	1,907	(1,413)	(2,371)	(1,926)	(2,084)	Nov	2,072
Blackwater Estuary	2,201	2,387	1,572	1,712	(2,124)	Apr	1,999
Breydon Water and Berney Marshes	1,421 [10]	2,469 [12]	2,712 [10]	1,023 [12]	2,329 [12]	Nov	1,991
Morecambe Bay	(928)	759	1,844	1,605	3,221	Apr	1,857
Ouse Washes	1,790 [12]	761	2,067 [12]	809 [12]	3,820	Feb	1,849
Stour Estuary	1,215	2,148	1,939	1,953	1,541	Jan	1,759
Swale Estuary	1,396	(1,186)	(1,545)	1,825	1,760	Jan	1,660
River Avon - Ringwood to Christchurch	(3,000)	2,000	650	2,530	45	Nov	1,645
Alde Complex	1,385	774	(840)	1,114	1,305 [10]	Feb	1,144
Medway Estuary	(1,120)	(490)	(603)	(384)	(968)	Oct	(1,120)
Mersey Estuary	420	(339)	(54)	(270)	(1,760)	Mar	1,090
Belfast Lough	(586)	708	690 [10]	1,510	(962)	Mar	969
Pagham Harbour	(764)	1,100	960	833	(806)	Nov	964
Exe Estuary	999	913	943	980	868	Oct	941
Warton Floods		600	950	570	1,200	Nov	830
North Norfolk Coast	645	1,139	804	809	606	Sep	801
River Avon - Fordingbridge to Ringwood	(1,750)	888	(920)	381	4	Nov	789
Colne Estuary	800 [12]	617 [10]	500 [12]	812 [12]	980 [12]	Apr	742
Orwell Estuary	523	845 [10]	813 [10]	816	572	Oct	714
Chichester Harbour	685	775	613	603	832	Jan	702
Deben Estuary	622	707	948	503	622	Oct	680
Crouch-Roach Estuary	(554)	754	627	764	508	Nov	663
Overcote Marina	850 [12]		1,400	373 [12]	0		656
Sites of national importance in Great Britain							
Langstone Harbour	562	674	422	574	705	Oct	587 ▼
North West Solent	353	469	525	640	656	Apr	529 ▼
Fen Drayton Gravel Pits	571	31	1,800	200	8	Jan	522 ▼
Portsmouth Harbour	(398)	371	666 [10]	(30)	(32)	Nov	519 ▼
Severn Estuary	297	221	646 [10]	382	804	Dec	470 ▲
Sites of All-Ireland importance in Northern Ireland							
Strangford Lough	535 [10]	645	707	193 [10]	455	Oct	507 ▼
Sites no longer meeting table qualifying levels in WeBS-Year 2010/2011							
Southampton Water	295	(374)	(490)	514	414	Aug	428
Hamford Water	372	441	521 [10]	(440)	190	Sep	393
Sites below table qualifying levels but exceeding threshold in WeBS-Year 2010/11 in Great Britain							
Abberton Reservoir	2	3	2	493	720	Oct	244
Burry Inlet	300 [10]	40	200 [10]	343	477	Dec	272
Other sites surpassing table qualifying levels in Winter 2010/2011 in Northern Ireland							
Lough Foyle	60	52	25	113	213	Mar	93
Loughs Neagh and Beg	104	75	143	106	204	Mar	126
Bann Estuary	22	90 [10]	15	69	180	Apr	75

Jill Pakenham

Bar-tailed Godwit
Limosa lapponica

International threshold (N & W Europe): 1,200
Great Britain threshold: 380
All-Ireland threshold: 160

GB max: 61,563 Feb
NI max: 2,124 Jan

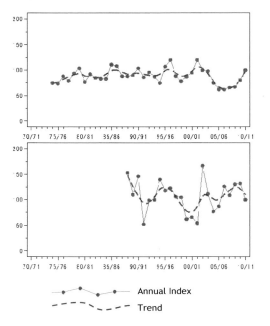

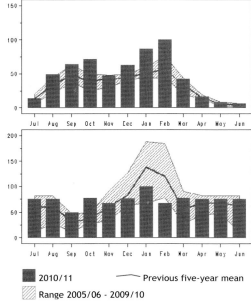

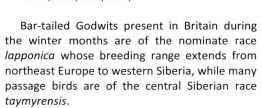

Figure 55.a, Annual indices & trend for Bar-tailed Godwit in GB (above) & NI (below).

Figure 55.b, Monthly indices for Bar-tailed Godwit in GB (above) & NI (below).

Bar-tailed Godwits present in Britain during the winter months are of the nominate race *lapponica* whose breeding range extends from northeast Europe to western Siberia, while many passage birds are of the central Siberian race *taymyrensis*.

Following a concerning dip in the British trend during the mid 2000s, there appears to have been an equally marked recovery in the last couple of years. As speculated in last year's report it remains to be seen whether this will be maintained over the longer term; the British trend for this species over the last 15 years has typically been characterised by a succession of peaks and troughs. In contrast, the Netherlands has witnessed a steady rise in wintering numbers (Hornman *et al.* 2012), indicative of an eastward shift of the population in western Europe in response to climate change (Maclean *et al.* 2008). Therefore, the relative magnitude of the rise in the British index value during the very cold winter of 2010/11 may be especially pertinent, with the monthly indices showing that above average numbers were present in Britain during the core of the winter in January and February.

Eleven sites surpass the threshold for international importance, the top four of which all registered higher than expected maxima in 2010/11 (The Wash, Alt Estuary, North Norfolk Coast and Thames Estuary). In a similar story to 2009/10, the February count from The Wash represented one of the key features of the WeBS-year for this species; the total of 21,687 is second only to the 23,751 recorded there in March 2002 in terms of peak monthly WeBS counts.

The maxima recorded at Alt Estuary and North Norfolk Coast also stand out in the table below, representing record counts for these two sites. The maximum at North Norfolk Coast was especially impressive, being some 40% greater than the previous peak (7,429 in September 2003). In Northern Ireland, a drop in the index in comparison to 2009/10 was at least in part due to a decline in numbers at Strangford Lough.

	06/07	07/08	08/09	09/10	10/11	Mon	Mean
Sites of international importance in the UK							
The Wash	11,900	10,755	15,381	15,490	21,687	Feb	15,043
Alt Estuary	4,100	2,939	8,171	5,265	12,412	Jan	6,577
Thames Estuary	8,629	3,711	3,804	7,903	8,784	Feb	6,566
North Norfolk Coast	2,990	1,783	1,382	5,010	10,455	Oct	4,324
Ribble Estuary	4,628	5,162	2,762	3,419 [10]	1,118	Sep	3,418
Humber Estuary	(1,871)	1,490	(5,926)	2,056	2,972	Aug	3,111
Dengie Flats	1,062	(1,500)	4,170	2,910	1,232	Feb	2,344
Lough Foyle	(2,672)	2,300	2,789	1,501	1,473	Oct	2,147
Lindisfarne	2,535	(2,170)	2,333	(1,398)	1,542	Oct	2,145
Morecambe Bay	(2,157)	(417)	1,331	(2,164)	2,411	Feb	2,016
Forth Estuary	1,502	921	1,270	(1,293)	(1,382)	Jan	1,274
Sites of national importance in Great Britain							
Swale Estuary	585	750	842	1,806	1,752	Jan	1,147
Cromarty Firth	803	(707)	717	1,549	1,506	Feb	1,144
Hamford Water	(1,239)	1,255	655	(622)	(1,085)	Nov	1,059
Dee Estuary (England and Wales)	187	215	4,213 [10]	65	367	Feb	1,009
Tay Estuary	1,002 [10]	(1,000)	482	815	1,495	Oct	959
Chichester Harbour	630	1,228	802	1,006	890	Jan	911
Dornoch Firth	541	301	871	749	869	Jan	666
Solway Estuary	529	473	(860)	952	499	Oct	663
Eden Estuary	555	605	682	(348)	756	Feb	650
South Ford	782	454	574		230	Feb	510
Pegwell Bay	550	240	273 [10]	193 [12]	1,240 [12]	Apr	499 ▲
Inner Moray and Inverness Firth	(785)	390	311	464	493	Feb	489
Breydon Water and Berney Marshes	653 [12]	75 [12]	10	118 [12]	1,172 [12]	May	406 ▲
Sites of all-Ireland importance in Northern Ireland							
Strangford Lough	529	(1,305)	969 [10]	1,158	436	Jan	879
Belfast Lough	(159)	212	167	(43)	(396)	Nov	258
Sites below table qualifying levels but exceeding threshold in WeBS-Year 2010/11 in Great Britain							
Ardivachar Point (South Uist)	170	314	24		460	Feb	242
Stour Estuary	259	212	500	425	(456)	Jan	370
Loch Gruinart	209	258	314	404	405	Feb	318

Whimbrel

Numenius phaeopus

		International threshold	
		(Iceland, Faroes & Scotland, W Africa):	**6,700**
		Great Britain threshold:	**1+[†]**
		All-Ireland threshold:	**+[†]**

GB max:	1,048	Aug	
NI max:	7	Jul	

The majority of Whimbrel seen in Britain are en route to and from breeding sites in Iceland, Scandinavia and western Siberia, and the main wintering areas in West Africa. In 2010/11, the species was recorded at 137 sites across the UK, including five in Northern Ireland.

The short passage period in spring generally peaks in late April and early May. Outside the mid-month Core count priority dates, this tends to mean the spring passage is relatively poorly monitored by WeBS. Therefore, additional counts for use in the table below are welcomed.

Spring passage of Whimbrel tends to have a more westerly distribution than autumn passage (Grant 2002). This is illustrated by the site maxima shown in the table below; a highest Core count in spring of 209 at Severn Estuary and an autumn peak of 275 at The Wash.

A very small number of Whimbrel winter at favoured British estuaries. In 2010/11, just two sites hosted birds during the midwinter period of December to February, which may have been linked to the cold weather experienced across the UK.

	06/07	07/08	08/09	09/10	10/11	Mon	Mean
Sites with mean peak counts of 50 or more birds in Great Britain							
Barnacre Reservoir and Grizedale Lea	477 [11]	417 [11]	372 [11]	529 [11]			449
Brockholes Quarry	210 [11]	304 [11]	246 [11]	290 [11]			263
Severn Estuary	(186)	(85)	331 [12]	226	209	May	255
The Wash	233	324	151	150	275	Aug	227
North Norfolk Coast	70	257	123	97	197	Aug	149

	06/07	07/08	08/09	09/10	10/11	Mon	Mean
Dungeness and Rye Bay	246 [11]	287 [11]	23	28	14	May	120
Chichester Harbour	31	209	83	132	113	Apr	114
Burry Inlet	223	40	94	108	8	May	95
Ribble Estuary	9	7	58	390 [11]	8	Apr	94
Taw-Torridge Estuary	(42)	(17)	93	(76)	(40)	May	93
Morecambe Bay	(53)	(17)	103	76	89	May	89
Pegwell Bay	76	19	51	191 [12]	39 [12]	May	75
Langstone Harbour	58	84	73	58	39	Jul	62
Breydon Water and Berney Marshes	40 [12]	2	1	116 [12]	148 [12]	Apr	61
Exe Estuary	109	60	51	33	35	Jul	58
Humber Estuary	78	36	57	26	58	Jul	51
Sites below table qualifying levels but exceeding threshold in WeBS-Year 2010/11 in Great Britain							
Tamar Complex	(29)	17	33	59	79	May	47
Blackwater Estuary	(14)	8	20	(22)	71	Apr	33

Eurasian Curlew

Numenius arquata

International threshold (N Europe & W Africa):	8,400
Great Britain threshold:	1,400
All-Ireland threshold:	550

GB max:	83,396	Oct
NI max:	5,272	Jan

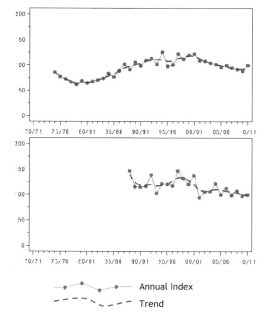

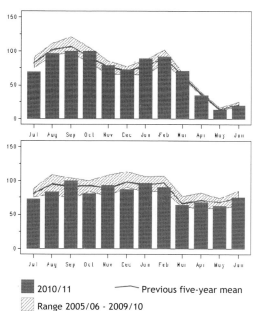

Figure 56.a, Annual indices & trend for Curlew in GB (above) & NI (below).

Figure 56.b, Monthly indices for Curlew in GB (above) & NI (below).

The wintering population of Curlew in UK comprises birds from the declining British breeding population (Baillie *et al.* 2012), augmented by birds of Scandinavian origin.

The WeBS trend indicates that numbers of wintering Curlew increased from the mid 1970s until the start of the 2000s. This was followed by a decade of consistent gradual decline, probably associated with a shift in wintering distribution (Màclean *et al.* 2008). The latter hypothesis is

supported by evidence from The Netherlands, where numbers in the winter have increased, both on The Wadden Sea and in the wider countryside (Hornman *et al.* 2012). However, the national index value rose slightly in 2010/11, thereby interrupting the recent downward trend. Only time will tell if this represents a change in the longer term, or was merely a temporary response to the coldest winter in north-west Europe for 35 years.

Morecambe Bay and The Wash maintained their status as sites which surpass the threshold for international importance; the all-time record count of Curlew relates to 22,300 at the former site in August 1973. Counts at most of the other important sites were generally either similar to their recent average or somewhat down, such as at Dee Estuary and Humber Estuary (where the peak was the lowest for seven years). An exception was Severn Estuary, where this year's maximum of 4,176 represented the most since an all-time peak there of 5,307 in February 1995.

The trend in Northern Ireland illustrates a slow decline in recent years, epitomised by low maxima at the two principal sites (Lough Foyle and Strangford Lough) in 2010/11.

	06/07	07/08	08/09	09/10	10/11	Mon	Mean
Sites of international importance in the UK							
Morecambe Bay	(14,027)	11,530	13,136	11,167	11,203	Oct	12,213
The Wash	9,710	7,664	7,548	12,811	10,475	Oct	9,642
Sites of national importance in Great Britain							
Thames Estuary	6,993	3,722	4,130	4,603	(3,618)	Oct	4,862
Dee Estuary (England and Wales)	5,565	5,346	3,608	3,590	3,747	Sep	4,371
Forth Estuary	4,567	3,568	4,023	(2,939)	(2,552)	Feb	4,053
Humber Estuary	5,180	4,355	(3,099)	3,448	3,037	Jan	4,005
Severn Estuary	(3,230)	(2,560)	3,396	3,731	4,176	Oct	3,768
Solway Estuary	4,007	(3,185)	(2,691)	2,698	2,938	Feb	3,214
North Norfolk Coast	2,190	2,884	2,318	2,293	2,109	Sep	2,359
Duddon Estuary	2,113	2,145	(2,315)	1,716	(1,576)	Nov	2,072
Lavan Sands	3,243	1,091	1,839	1,878	1,954	Feb	2,001
Lindisfarne	(1,174)	(1,441)	(1,260)	(2,102)	1,464	Jan	1,783
Cleddau Estuary	(1,869)	1,832	1,428	1,682	2,017	Jul	1,766
Inner Moray and Inverness Firth	(1,939)	1,687	1,840	1,702	1,636	Feb	1,761
Swale Estuary	(1,516)	1,357	(1,433)	1,808	2,097	Feb	1,754
Chichester Harbour	2,052	1,760	1,481	1,763	1,685	Nov	1,748
Ribble Estuary	1,497	1,419	(1,308)	1,926	(1,653)	Oct	1,624
Burry Inlet	1,413	1,370	1,689	1,488	(1,615)	Aug	1,515
Stour Estuary	1,424	1,669	1,231 [10]	1,480	1,355	Aug	1,432 ▲
Sites of all-Ireland importance in Northern Ireland							
Lough Foyle	2,681	2,510	2,588	1,834	1,656	Jan	2,254
Strangford Lough	1,918 [10]	1,552	1,571	2,040	1,504	Sep	1,717
Belfast Lough	779 [10]	821	567	824	503	Oct	699
Outer Ards Shoreline	519	238	601	721	758	Nov	567 ▲
Carlingford Lough	754	(759)	470	280	(172)	Nov	566
Sites no longer meeting table qualifying levels in WeBS-Year 2010/2011							
Blackwater Estuary	1,296	(1,267)	1,481	1,249	(1,521)	Mar	1,387
Langstone Harbour	1,343	1,279	1,228	1,469	1,506	Oct	1,365
Montrose Basin	1,115	1,734	1,822	1,094	893	Feb	1,332
Sites below table qualifying levels but exceeding threshold in WeBS-Year 2010/11 in Great Britain							
Alt Estuary	1,270	1,257	997	(810)	1,952	Oct	1,369
Mersey Estuary	1,379	(982)	1,038	1,051	(1,719)	Jan	1,297
Cromarty Firth	1,373	1,318	1,147	1,447	1,556	Dec	1,368
Blackwater Estuary	1,296	(1,267)	1,481	1,249	(1,521)	Mar	1,387
Langstone Harbour	1,343	1,279	1,228	1,469	1,506	Oct	1,365

Common Sandpiper

Actitis hypoleucos

International threshold (W & C Europe, W Africa):	17,500
Great Britain threshold:	1 [†]
All-Ireland threshold:	? [†]

GB max:	1,190	Jul
NI max:	8	Jul

For the fifth year in succession, the peak count of the year was at Pegwell Bay, an exceptional 163 in August. This equals the previous maximum noted at the site five years earlier, and is only just short of the all-time peak WeBS count of the species; 180 at Morecambe Bay in July 1988. In 2010/11, autumn passage appears to have been reasonably well spread across July and August, with the maxima at Cleddau Estuary (54), Montrose Basin (54) and Morecambe Bay (73) being particularly notable. Numbers traditionally peak at sites in Wales and Scotland in July rather than August, when they presumably attract post-breeding birds from nearby breeding areas.

A small, but slowly increasing, number of Common Sandpipers have over-wintered in Britain in recent years. Musgrove et al. (2011) estimated the total to be in the order of 75 birds, the majority typically being singles at coastal sites, primarily in the south. In 2010/11, during the mid-winter period of December to February the species was seen at 26 WeBS sites. This total is nine less than the previous year, which may be associated with the cold winter, and included a peaks of six at Severn Estuary (Jan) and five at Avon Estuary (Dec). The only inland record during this period was one at Stretton Sugwas Sand Pit (Feb).

	06/07	07/08	08/09	09/10	10/11	Mon	Mean
Sites with mean peak counts of 30 or more birds in Great Britain[†]							
Pegwell Bay	163 [10]	106	122	84	163	Aug	128
Morecambe Bay	48	(38)	21	48	73	Jul	48
Dungeness and Rye Bay	37	30	72	35	60	Aug	47
Thames Estuary	50	41	(15)	(14)	(5)	Aug	46
Humber Estuary	(14)	46	(19)	(12)	(10)	Jul	46
Severn Estuary	(12)	(20)	(40)	42	38	Aug	40
Cleddau Estuary	(47)	33	14	27	54	Jul	35
Abberton Reservoir	(41)	31	46	15	22	Aug	31
Other sites surpassing table qualifying levels in Summer 2010 in Great Britain[†]							
Montrose Basin	14	15	4	23	54	Jul	22
North Norfolk Coast	18	14	35	16	43	Aug	25

[†] as all sites exceed the British winter threshold (1) and no All-Ireland thresholds has been set, a qualifying level of 30 has been chosen to select sites for presentation in this report

---

Spotted Sandpiper
Actitis macularius

Vagrant

One was at Exe Estuary in September; the fifth successive year that the species has been recorded by WeBS.

Green Sandpiper
Tringa ochropus

International threshold (Europe & W Africa):	15,500
Great Britain threshold:	9 [†]
All-Ireland threshold:	? [†]

GB max:	768	Aug
NI max:	1	Aug

Green Sandpipers were recorded during Core counts at 287 WeBS sites in 2010/11. Widely distributed, particularly across England, during the autumn period, the monthly maximum typically fell in August when a high total of 768 was logged. The peak count of 67 at North Norfolk Coast represents the highest WeBS count ever there, almost surpassing the all-time high of 82 at Thames Estuary in August 1973.

During the November to February period, when sites with flowing freshwater such as streams and cress beds tend to be favoured, the species was noted at 128 WeBS sites. This total is 17% less than the previous year, which is presumably attributable to the frozen conditions prevalent across much of the UK during the midwinter period reducing the suitability of a number of sites.

Typifying recent years, the two top sites for wintering birds were River Avon (Salisbury to Fordingbridge) and Beddington Sewage Farm, where maxima of ten and 12 birds, respectively, were noted. Elsewhere, seven at Thorpe Water Park was also particularly noteworthy.

Sites with 20 or more birds during passage periods in 2010/11[†]

North Norfolk Coast	67, Aug	Beddington Sewage Farm	25, Jul
Rutland Water	32, Aug	William Girling Reservoir	23, Jul
Dungeness and Rye Bay	30, Aug	Swale Estuary	22, Aug
Blackwater Estuary	29, Aug	The Wash	20, Aug

[†] a qualifying level of 20 has been chosen to select sites for presentation in this report

Spotted Redshank

Tringa erythropus

International threshold (Europe, N & W Africa): 850
Great Britain threshold: 1[†]
All-Ireland threshold: +[†]

GB max: 243 Aug
NI max: 0

Spotted Redshank breed from Scandinavia through sub-arctic Russia, with most wintering in equatorial Africa and a small proportion remaining in western Europe. In general, very little is known about population trends in the species, although breeding populations appear to be stable (Delany *et al.* 2009).

In 2010/11 in the UK, typically the majority were recorded in autumn and winter, with a smaller number in spring. Overall, numbers during the course of the year were disappointing and the year was one of the poorest on record. The 64 sites where the species was recorded represents a relatively low number, but similar to that of the previous year. The British peak

monthly count was 243 in August. The peak site count of 34 at The Wash in August was only a slight improvement on the maximum recorded there in 2009/10. On a more positive note, 27 at Abberton Reservoir in October represents the most there since the end of the 1990s when a brief period of high counts of this species included a historical site maximum of 45 (in September 1997).

During the winter period, Spotted Redshank were recorded at 35 WeBS sites, with peaks of 12 at Northwest Solent (Dec) and 14 at North Norfolk Coast (Jan). There were no records from Northern Ireland during the year.

	06/07	07/08	08/09	09/10	10/11	Mon	Mean
Sites with mean peak counts of 10 or more birds in Great Britain[†]							
The Wash	86	40	48	28	34	Aug	47
North Norfolk Coast	42	29	26	18	19	Jul	27
Blackwater Estuary	8	32	26	9	23	Jul	20
Humber Estuary	25	13	13	25	19	Sep	19
Abberton Reservoir	(0)	14	4	23	27	Oct	17
Minsmere	3	6	47	23	3	Apr	16
Dee Estuary (England and Wales)	14	12	14 [10]	11	11	Apr	12
Sites below table qualifying levels but exceeding threshold in WeBS-Year 2010/11 in Great Britain[†]							
Beaulieu Estuary	10	0	(1)	14	13	Oct	9
North West Solent	6	5	4	8	12	Dec	7

[†] *a qualifying level of 10 has been chosen to select sites for presentation in this report*

Greenshank

Tringa nebularia

International threshold (Europe & W Africa): 2,300
Great Britain threshold: 6*
All-Ireland threshold: 20*

GB max: 1,470 Aug
NI max: 119 Oct

*50 is normally used as a minimum threshold

The numbers of Greenshank present during winter in Britain has increased over the last two decades, probably at least in part due to milder climatic conditions (Austin & Rehfisch 2005, Maclean *et al.* 2008), although this trend appears to have stabilised.

In 2010/11, numbers of Greenshank at most of the major sites were close to average, with the peak counts typically noted during autumn when birds migrate from their breeding grounds in northern Europe (including some sites in northern Scotland) to wintering areas in southwest Europe, and North and West Africa.

Four sites held autumn passage peaks of over 100 birds; typically The Wash, Chichester Harbour and North Norfolk Coast, and more notably Humber Estuary (for the first time since 1999).

The highest counts received during the December to February period in Britain were from Fal Complex (58, Feb), Chichester Harbour (24, Jan) and Jersey Shore (20, Feb). In Northern Ireland, where the recent upward trend has now dipped, the midwinter maxima were notably lower than recent years.

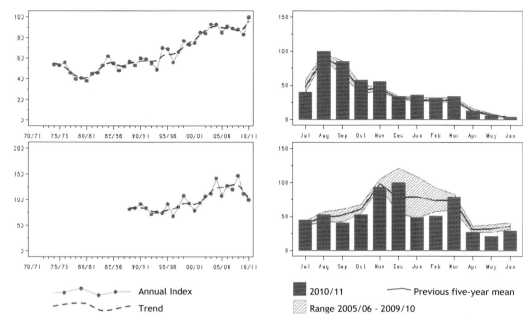

Figure 57.a, Annual indices & trend for Greenshank in GB (above) & NI (below).

Figure 57.b, Monthly indices for Greenshank in GB (above) & NI (below).

	06/07	07/08	08/09	09/10	10/11	Mon	Mean
Sites with mean peak counts of 30 or more birds in Great Britain[†]							
The Wash	201	252	301	173	179	Sep	221
Thames Estuary	196	132	130	129	(69)	Aug	147
Chichester Harbour	132	77	82	88	140	Sep	104
North Norfolk Coast	118	87	71	118	124	Aug	104
Stour Estuary	106	103	110	84	92	Sep	99
Blackwater Estuary	(73)	(119)	(86)	(59)	73	Oct	88
Fal Complex	59	66	52	67	60	Sep	61
Humber Estuary	21	(47)	52	65	106	Aug	58
Morecambe Bay	59	(28)	44	38	86	Sep	57
Exe Estuary	71	41	34	61	70	Sep	55
Medway Estuary	(10)	(9)	(4)	(50)	(9)	Aug	(50)
Pegwell Bay	42 [12]	40	64 [12]	50	31 [12]	May	45
Hamford Water	79	86	31	8	10	Oct	43
Dee Estuary (England & Wales)	32	50	67	31	28	Aug	42
Langstone Harbour	51	37	26	26	48	Aug	38
Cleddau Estuary	25	25	39	40	49	Oct	36
Montrose Basin	19	(19)	36	73	15	Jul	36
Tamar Complex	29	32	31	34	43	Sep	34
Kingsbridge Estuary	27	45	48	5	28	Mar	31
Sites of all-Ireland importance in Northern Ireland							
Strangford Lough	85	65	95	70	71	Sep	77
Lough Foyle	34	65	48	47	31	Oct	45
Carlingford Lough	40	66	(17)	(14)	(15)	Nov	34
Dundrum Inner Bay	24	20	28	26	30	Jul	26
Sites below table qualifying levels but exceeding threshold in WeBS-Year 2010/11 in Great Britain[†]							
Camel Estuary	(20)	16	19	48	30	Sep	27
Breydon Water and Berney Marshes	8	10	3	25 [12]	67 [12]	May	23
Dungeness and Rye Bay	13	10	15	21	40	Aug	20

[†] as many sites exceed the British winter threshold, a qualifying level of 30 has been used to select sites for presentation in this report

Lesser Yellowlegs
Tringa flavipes

Vagrant
Native Range: America

Two were recorded in 2010/11; a typical showing for recent years. They were at Port Meadow (Oct) and Fal Complex (Mar-Apr).

Wood Sandpiper
Tringa glareola

International threshold (NW Europe & W Africa):	10,400
Great Britain threshold:	+[†]
All-Ireland threshold:	+[†]

Wood Sandpipers were seen at 39 WeBS sites in 2010/11; almost twice as many as had featured in each of the previous two years. A monthly peak of 34 birds was noted in August. Autumn produced records from six sites in July, 16 in August and three in September. WeBS totals for this species are highly dependent on Core count dates coinciding with fluxes of passage; in autumn 2010, most sites held one or two birds with the exception of the four locations listed below. A fair spring passage produced singles at 17 sites in the April to June period, the majority in May, and all in England with the exception of one at Conwy Estuary.

Sites with 3 or more birds during passage periods in 2010/11[†]

Blackwater Estuary	6, Aug	Dungeness and Rye Bay	3, Aug
North Norfolk Coast	4, Aug	Loch of Strathbeg	3, Sep

[†] *as no British or All-Ireland thresholds have been set, a qualifying level of 3 has been chosen to select sites for presentation in this report*

Common Redshank
Tringa totanus

International threshold (Iceland & Faroes, W Europe):	2,400
Great Britain threshold:	1,200
All-Ireland threshold:	310

GB max:	88,627	Oct
NI max:	6,191	Nov

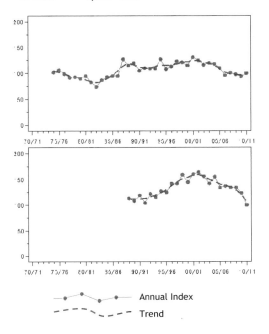

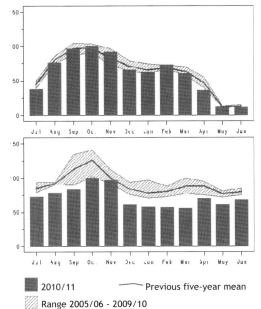

Figure 58.a, Annual indices & trend for Redshank in GB (above) & NI (below).

Figure 58.b, Monthly indices for Redshank in GB (above) & NI (below).

133

Predominantly found on the coast in the UK, the non-breeding population of Redshank is considered to comprise local breeders and birds from Iceland and nearby European populations. Maclean *et al.* (2008) demonstrated a northwesterly shift in core wintering range of Redshank in recent decades, suggestive of a degree of short-stopping towards Icelandic breeding grounds.

Redshanks wintering in both Britain and Northern Ireland have shown downward trends during the last decade, but their respective indices contrasted somewhat in 2010/11. Whereas a further decline occurred in Northern Ireland, there was a slight rise in the British index. However, it remains to be seen whether this proves to be the start of a change in fortunes for the species in Britain. The size of the *robusta* population of Redshank has been revised downwards by 14% (Wetlands International 2012). Fourteen sites surpass the associated threshold for international importance, the peaks at most of which were close to the respective five-year means, notable exceptions being Morecambe Bay and The Wash. At Morecambe Bay, the November peak of 12,979 represents the most there since over

21,000 were logged in September 1989. For the second year in succession, numbers at The Wash were considerably higher than normal in August and September, peaking at a record 10,052 in the latter month. Elsewhere, maxima at other sites were generally slightly below average, an obvious exception being the Severn Estuary where the November total was the highest ever monthly peak in winter (and just 30 birds less than a count of 3,379 in July 1974). Notably, more than 2,300 were also present during January, February and March, following the cold conditions experienced in midwinter. In Northern Ireland, the peak at the principal site, Strangford Lough, was the lowest since 2001/02.

Typically, monthly maxima at many of the other sites of importance were also in the autumn/early winter period. Scrutiny of the monthly indices suggests a clear response to the cold weather. A pronounced drop is particularly apparent in the monthly indices for Northern Ireland. In Britain, after the presence of higher numbers in November, a drop in the monthly indices during the freeze in December and January was followed by an equally marked increase to higher than typical numbers during the milder conditions in February.

Tommy Holden

	06/07	07/08	08/09	09/10	10/11	Mon	Mean
Sites of international importance in the UK							
Morecambe Bay	(8,254)	(5,802)	10,302	8,814	12,979	Nov	10,698
Dee Estuary (England and Wales)	9,384	12,994	9,576 [10]	11,235	9,494	Sep	10,537
The Wash	5,605	4,407	5,367	11,017	10,052	Sep	7,290
Forth Estuary	4,689	4,374	5,141	4,244	4,524	Sep	4,594
Strangford Lough	3,632	4,028	4,969	4,488	3,286	Nov	4,081
Humber Estuary	3,886	(4,059)	4,716	4,169	3,204	Nov	4,007
Solway Estuary	(1,822)	(3,213)	(2,739)	3,918	(2,311)	Nov	3,918
Thames Estuary	4,134	3,512	4,243	3,701	3,284	Oct	3,775
Alde Complex	1,673	9,246	1,213	2,289	2,636	Nov	3,411
Ribble Estuary	1,491	3,559	3,414	4,339	3,640	Nov	3,289
Blackwater Estuary	2,514	(3,586)	3,752	(1,926)	2,591	Oct	3,111
Severn Estuary	(2,362)	(1,962)	2,997	2,433	3,349	Nov	2,926 ▲
Duddon Estuary	3,122	2,562	3,213	2,102	2,401	Oct	2,680
Mersey Estuary	(2,455)	(2,069)	(1,228)	(1,520)	(1,108)	Jan	(2,455)
Sites of national importance in Great Britain							
Montrose Basin	1,794	(1,860)	2,198	2,770	1,951	Oct	2,178
Deben Estuary	2,710	2,080	1,856	1,992	2,064	Oct	2,140
Chichester Harbour	(2,535)	2,403	1,810	2,028	1,873	Sep	2,130
North Norfolk Coast	1,786	2,899 [10]	2,109	1,333	1,595	Aug	1,944
Stour Estuary	1,988	1,948	2,176 [10]	1,779 [10]	1,661	Nov	1,910
Crouch-Roach Estuary	1,202	1,361	2,403	1,791	2,601 [10]	Oct	1,871
Inner Moray and Inverness Firth	(1,658)	2,040	1,988	1,731	1,617	Jan	1,844
Orwell Estuary	2,075 [10]	1,375 [10]	1,908	1,737 [10]	1,996	Jan	1,818
Ythan Estuary	1,481	1,497	(2,308)	(1,706)	1,398	Aug	1,678
Cromarty Firth	1,491	1,514	(1,402)	1,613	2,061	Oct	1,670
Tees Estuary	1,865	1,383	1,471	1,331	1,646	Oct	1,539
Lindisfarne	1,267	(1,746)	1,367	(1,026)	1,459	Oct	1,460
Hamford Water	1,266	1,538	1,366	(1,127)	1,207	Mar	1,344
Lavan Sands	1,016	1,794	1,058	1,221	1,182	Feb	1,254
Breydon Water and Berney Marshes	1,310	1,405	1,117 [12]	1,189 [12]	1,160 [12]	Apr	1,236
Colne Estuary	742	1,442 [10]	730	1,107	(2,150)	Nov	1,234 ▲
Swale Estuary	1,139	(1,384)	(1,049)	910	1,375	Oct	1,202
Sites of all-Ireland importance in Northern Ireland							
Belfast Lough	(1,698)	1,303	1,432	1,769	1,377	Oct	1,516
Carlingford Lough	1,128	1,174	1,818	801	(608)	Dec	1,230
Outer Ards Shoreline	1,160	1,124	1,145	1,183	1,055	Nov	1,133
Lough Foyle	1,177	905	1,239	1,305	495	Oct	1,024
Dundrum Inner Bay	759	1,284	1,105	897	695	Jul	948
Larne Lough	379	383	397	253	355	Jan	353
Sites no longer meeting table qualifying levels in WeBS-Year 2010/2011							
Medway Estuary	(307)	(668)	(874)	(497)	(1,073)	Nov	(1,073)
Blyth Estuary	1,031	2,002	(1,012)	789	458	Nov	1,070
Bann Estuary	261	392	230	290	246	Aug	284
Sites below table qualifying levels but exceeding threshold in WeBS-Year 2010/11 in Great Britain							
Alt Estuary	1,157	805	1,025	628	(1,450)	Feb	1,013

Ruddy Turnstone

Arenaria interpres

International threshold
(NE Canada & Greenland, W Europe & NW Africa): 1,400
Great Britain threshold: 480
All-Ireland threshold: 120

GB max: 11,157 Oct
NI max: 1,628 Nov

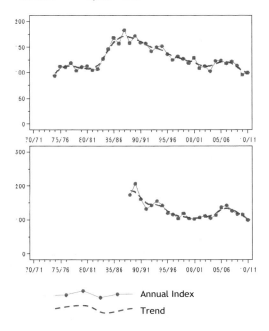

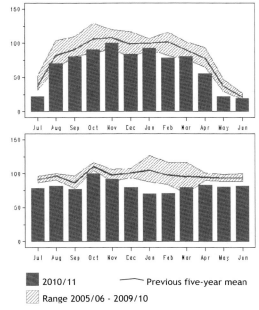

Annual Index
- - - Trend

2010/11   Previous five-year mean
Range 2005/06 - 2009/10

Figure 59.a, Annual indices & trend for Turnstone in GB (above) & NI (below).

Figure 59.b, Monthly indices for Turnstone in GB (above) & NI (below).

Turnstone from two distinct breeding populations occur in the UK. The majority of those which winter originate from Greenland and east Canada, while Siberian and Scandinavian breeders pass through in spring and autumn en route to and from wintering sites in West Africa. The UK is of considerable importance for Turnstone, supporting in excess of 50% of the flyway population during the winter (Delany *et al.* 2009).

Following a sharp drop in the British national index in 2009/10, this year proved to be little better. The downward trend that has characterised the last 25 years appears to be continuing, both in Britain and Northern Ireland. Pertinently, rocky shores and the associated specialist waders, such as Turnstone and Purple Sandpiper, are considered especially vulnerable to the effects of changing climate, both due to loss of habitat as a result of rising sea levels, as well as changes to invertebrate communities (Kendall *et al.* 2004, Rehfisch *et al.* 2004). With relatively poor coverage of the rocky shores

around the UK through WeBS, particularly in Scotland, it can be difficult to interpret WeBS trends with certainty, as any distributional shifts around the coastline may not be detectable. The species is therefore dependent on monitoring through NEWS, last undertaken in 2006/07 (Austin *et al.* 2007), to derive the most reliable picture of its status in the UK.

In 2010/11, the peak at Morecambe Bay (1,071, Dec) was close to average, but there was variation in the fortunes of this species at other sites of national importance. The maxima at two of these sites were markedly lower than their preceding five-year averages; Thanet Coast (50% lower) and Forth Estuary (37% lower). In contrast, peaks at The Wash and Stour Estuary represented the most at those sites since 2005/06 and 2000/01, respectively. Historically, The Wash has held a monthly peak of 2,596 in July 1988, but even that total compares poorly with the all-time WeBS maximum of 3,795 at Morecambe Bay in August 1972.

The peak count at Outer Ards Shoreline, consistently the most important site in Northern Ireland, exhibited a marked drop compared to preceding years. In contrast, the count at Belfast Lough was the most since 1998/99.

	06/07	07/08	08/09	09/10	10/11	Mon	Mean
Sites of national importance in Great Britain							
Morecambe Bay	1,163	(709)	973	1,394	1,071	Dec	1,150
Thanet Coast	1,477	(783)	722	624	529	Nov	838
Thames Estuary	680	1,090	1,060	382	703	Jan	783
North Norfolk Coast	678	913	774	741	746	Aug	770
Forth Estuary	(778)	(934)	(855)	(699)	553	Jan	764
Blackwater Estuary	527	676	1,102	502	(377)	Mar	702
The Wash	657	478	685	547	789	Aug	631
Stour Estuary	569	617	525	459 [10]	710	Nov	576
Humber Estuary	542	(344)	447	(553)	(379)	Oct	514
Farne Islands	(445)	556	580	349	(455)	Oct	495
Sites of all-Ireland importance in Northern Ireland							
Outer Ards Shoreline	1,292	930	937	949	742	Mar	970
Belfast Lough	436	419	503	537	612	Oct	501
Strangford Lough	382	344	589	391	406	Nov	422
Carlingford Lough	480	315	155	(150)	124	Feb	269
Sites no longer meeting table qualifying levels in WeBS-Year 2010/2011							
Langstone Harbour	450	488	550	299	415	Oct	440

Rob Robinson

Wilson's Phalarope
Phalaropus tricolor

Vagrant
Native Range: America

Singles graced Stodmarsh in September and Ouse Washes in October.

Red-necked Phalarope
Phalaropus lobatus

Scarce

A single Red-necked Phalarope was seen in 2010/11, at North Norfolk Coast in September.

Grey Phalarope
Phalaropus fulicarius

Scarce

Thirteen WeBS records of Grey Phalarope in 2010/11 represents a good annual showing. Typically all were recorded between September and November, including duos at Chew Valley Lake and North Norfolk Coast.

Neil Calbrade

Kittiwake
Rissa tridactyla

International threshold:	20,000**
Great Britain threshold:	?[†]
All-Ireland threshold:	?[†]

GB max:	682	Sep
NI max:	16	Oct

Kittiwakes were recorded at most traditional sites during WeBS counts in 2010/11, with the exception, as in the previous year, of Loch of Strathbeg. The peak monthly total of 682 birds in September is very low compared to recent years. The largest counts received were from Arran and at sites along the Northumberland and Durham coasts.

Counts of Kittiwakes at WeBS sites are probably affected by breeding productivity on stretches of coastline nearby, as well as the weather and offshore conditions. Hence, the decline in numbers recorded through WeBS in recent years is likely to be associated with the drop in the UK's breeding population and recent poor productivity (JNCC 2011).

	06/07	07/08	08/09	09/10	10/11	Mon	Mean
Sites with mean peak counts of 200 or more birds in Great Britain[†]							
Loch of Strathbeg	3,282	785	37	0	0		821
Arran	400	1,000	800	1,500	302	Sep	800
Beadnell to Seahouses	850	(460)	200	450	322	Apr	456
Durham Coast	(363)	(71)	(225)	(379)	(268)	May	(379)
Forth Estuary	(379)	(127)	(334)	(141)	(40)[12]	Nov	(379)
Glyne Gap	457	(233)	(78)	233	(41)	Dec	345

	06/07	07/08	08/09	09/10	10/11	Mon	Mean
Dee Estuary (Scotland)	175	458	183	(640)	188	Sep	329
Lunan Bay	133	67	(120)	(1,000)	42	Oct	272
Howick to Beadnell	0	0	0	(1,208)	135	Mar	269
Otter Estuary to Kingsbridge Estuary		250					250
Tay Estuary	(190)	300	(17)	155	(1)	Sep	228
Sites below table qualifying levels but exceeding threshold in WeBS-Year 2010/11 in Great Britain[†]							
Pegwell Bay	0	0	1 [12]	18 [12]	272 [12]	Jan	58

Bonaparte's Gull

Chroicocephalus philadelphia

Vagrant
Native Range: N America

One was present at Exe Estuary in May and June. It represents the 11th WeBS record, and is the third to be noted in June, following birds at the same site in 2004 and at Dee Estuary in 1994 (the first record for WeBS).

Black-headed Gull

Chroicocephalus ridibundus

International threshold: 20,000**
Great Britain threshold: 22,000
All-Ireland threshold: ?[†]

GB max: 224,169 Jan
NI max: 9,292 Mar

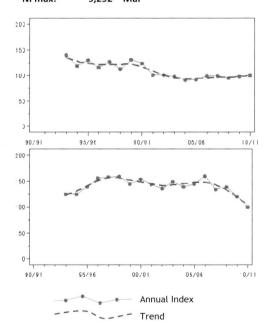

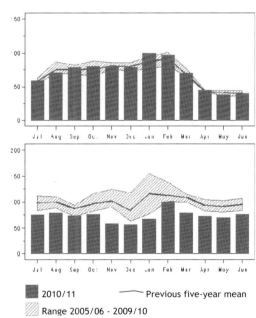

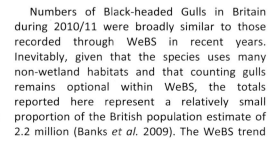

Annual Index

Trend

2010/11 — Previous five-year mean

Range 2005/06 - 2009/10

Figure 60.a, Annual indices & trend for Black-headed Gull in GB (above) & NI (below).

Figure 60.b, Monthly indices for Black-headed Gull in GB (above) & NI (below).

Numbers of Black-headed Gulls in Britain during 2010/11 were broadly similar to those recorded through WeBS in recent years. Inevitably, given that the species uses many non-wetland habitats and that counting gulls remains optional within WeBS, the totals reported here represent a relatively small proportion of the British population estimate of 2.2 million (Banks *et al.* 2009). The WeBS trend suggests a shallow decline over the course of the last 15 years. In Northern Ireland, a more pronounced drop was apparent in 2010/11.

Considering the important caveats regarding coverage through WeBS, three sites continue to be listed as surpassing the threshold for international importance; Bewl Water, Eccup Reservoir and The Wash. For the seventh year in succession, the largest count submitted related to the roost at the former site. A number of other localities of assumed importance do not feature within the tables below, owing to a lack of data submitted through WeBS since the last wintering gulls survey (WinGS, undertaken approximately on a decadal basis) in 2003/04. These include several sites formerly recognised as being used by large numbers of Black-headed Gulls, e.g. Chew Valley Lake and Humber Estuary. Moreover, many other reservoirs and wetlands across lowland Britain attract roosting gulls in significant numbers. Increased submission of counts from such sites (as demonstrated by recent data from Nosterfield GPs and Swithland Reservoir) is especially useful at helping to provide a more representative picture of the abundance and distribution of the UK's commonest gull.

	06/07	07/08	08/09	09/10	10/11	Mon	Mean
Sites of international importance in the UK							
Bewl Water	67,840[11]	48,400[11]	35,340[11]	36,400[11]	25,350[11]	Jan	42,666
The Wash	30,097	(18,679)	(20,878)	(29,615)	(15,142)	Sep	30,097
Eccup Reservoir		20,000					20,000
Sites with mean peak counts of 10,000+ birds in Great Britain[†]							
Severn Estuary	(3,589)	(4,851)	16,121[10]	(9,721)	(8,199)	Aug	16,121
Ribble Estuary	15,261	10,055	6,389	25,000[10]	(16,065)	Feb	14,554
Morecambe Bay	(15,232)	(12,153)	13,758	13,034	13,403	Sep	13,857
Nosterfield Gravel Pits	1,417	2,631	30,000[11]	1,042	30,000[11]	Mar	13,018
Rutland Water	12,000	10,000	5,000	30,000	5,000	Sep	12,400
Thames Estuary	10,712	(12,901)	(14,532)	(7,601)	(10,978)	Aug	12,281
Swithland Reservoir				12,000[11]			12,000
Lower Derwent Ings	5,321	11,600	11,200	11,000	17,000	Mar	11,224
Wintersett and Cold Hiendley Reservoirs	5,000	20,000	6,000				10,333
Sites with mean peak counts of 1,000+ birds in Northern Ireland[†]							
Belfast Lough	(6,823)	4,971	2,168[10]	4,307[10]	3,253[10]	Feb	4,304
Strangford Lough	3,889[10]	4,109[10]	5,656[10]	2,826	2,634	Oct	3,823
Outer Ards Shoreline	3,800	2,893	3,614	5,628	2,739	Jan	3,735
Loughs Neagh and Beg	(3,978)	2,610	2,989	3,599	3,915	Mar	3,418
Lough Foyle	(2,091)	3,237	3,324	2,573	2,266	Sep	2,850
Larne Lough	2,245	1,989	2,453	692	1,945	Feb	1,865
Sites below table qualifying levels but exceeding threshold in WeBS-Year 2010/11 in Great Britain[†]							
Dee Estuary (England and Wales)	(7,515)	(4,705)	6,639	(8,351)	10,372	Oct	8,506

[†] *as few sites exceed the British threshold and no All-Ireland threshold has been set, qualifying levels of 10,000 and 1,000, respectively, have been chosen to select sites for presentation in this report*

Little Gull

Hydrocoloeus minutus

	International threshold	
	(C, E & SW Europe, W Mediterranean):	**1,100**
	Great Britain threshold:	?[†]
	All-Ireland threshold:	?[†]

GB max: 88 Apr
NI max: 0

In 2010/11, Little Gulls were noted at 42 sites across Britain during WeBS Core counts. The totals recorded were largely unimpressive, with a maximum Core count in autumn of just 15 at the favoured site of Hornsea Mere, which remains the only site that surpasses the threshold for international importance for this species.

Howard Vaughan

Generally, the table below tends to be populated with count data for that site from supplementary sources. In spring, there was some evidence of passage coinciding with the Core count date in April; a scattering of inland records included notable counts of 42 at Staines Reservoirs and 24 at King George VI Reservoir.

	06/07	07/08	08/09	09/10	10/11	Mon	Mean
Sites of international importance in the UK							
Hornsea Mere	(16,000)[11]	21,500 [11]	134	610 [11]	500 [11]	Aug	7,749
Sites with mean peak counts of 10+ birds in Great Britain[†]							
Tay Estuary	206	(3)	(0)	(1)	(0)		206
Alt Estuary	162 [12]	97 [12]	75 [12]	66	100 [12]	Apr	100
Tophill Low Reservoirs	26 [11]	250 [11]	125 [12]	15 [12]	0		83
North Norfolk Coast	176	30	10	4	2	Apr	44
Staines Reservoirs	6	1	32	1	42	Apr	16
Humber Estuary	(0)	(33)	(2)	5	3	Aug	14
Morecambe Bay	14	(0)	3	23	(2)	Apr	13
Anstruther Bay	0	55	0	0	0		11
Tees Estuary	6	11	21	10	1	Aug	10
East Chevington Pools	14	7	18	9	4	Jun	10
Forth Estuary	25	9	3	(2)	1	Feb	10
Sites below table qualifying levels but exceeding threshold in WeBS-Year 2010/11 in Great Britain[†]							
King George VI Reservoir			0	0	0	24	Apr	6

[†] *as no British or All-Ireland thresholds have been set, a qualifying level of 10 has been chosen to select sites for presentation in this report*

Franklin's Gull
Larus pipixcan

Vagrant
Native Range: N America

One at Chasewater in July represents the fourth ever WeBS record and first since 2005/06.

Mediterranean Gull
Larus melanocephalus

International threshold	
(W Europe, Mediterranean, NW Africa):	770
Great Britain threshold:	18
All-Ireland threshold:	?[†]

GB max: 1,565 Sep
NI max: 3 Feb

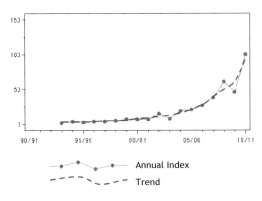

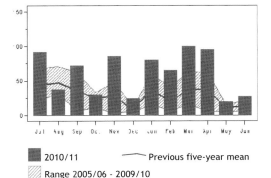

Figure 61.a, Annual indices & trend for Mediterranean Gull in GB.

Figure 61.b, Monthly indices for Mediterranean Gull in GB.

In 2010/11, Mediterranean Gulls were recorded at a record 145 WeBS sites in Britain and three in Northern Ireland, with a peak monthly total in Britain of 1,565 in September.

The table below lists the sites where counts surpass the 1% threshold for national importance, published by Musgrove *et al.* (2011). Still relatively few Mediterranean Gulls tend to be seen away from the southern counties and East Anglia.

The trend for Mediterranean Gull shows the continued increase, as illustrated by a single WeBS Core count of 628 at Southampton Water in September 2010; evidence of the expanding breeding population there (Holling *et al.* 2012). Furthermore, four of the other seven sites to hold peaks of more than 100 were either in Hampshire or the Isle of Wight, providing additional evidence of the importance of The Solent for this species. Several other south coast locations known to be favoured by this species, including Copt Point in Kent, are currently not monitored through WeBS.

	06/07	07/08	08/09	09/10	10/11	Mon	Mean	
Sites of national importance in Great Britain								
Southampton Water	(112)	(309)	(30)	(36)	628	Sep	628	
Brading Harbour	91	64	461 [12]	101	329	Oct	209	
Breydon Water and Berney Marshes		131 [12]	118 [11]	189 [11]	309 [11]	Sep	187	
Pagham Harbour	71	(124)	(118)	140	336	Feb	182	
Fleet and Wey	39	61	140	211 [10]	94	Nov	109	
North West Solent	8	29	101	41	180	Mar	72	
Newtown Estuary	56	19	53	111	119	Mar	72	
Ryde Pier to Puckpool Point	22	45		27	181	Aug	69	
Beaulieu Estuary	6	1	65	172	95	Jan	68	
Tamar Complex	34	37	45	65	41	Jul	44	
Thames Estuary	71	34	40	37	22	Nov	41	
Thorness Bay				27	52	Mar	40	
Swansea Bay	33	12	34	55	63	Aug	39	
Camel Estuary	11	6	78	33	60	Aug	38	
Chichester Harbour	12	(31)	28	(56)	(61)	Apr	38	
Wootton Creek	102	16	6	4	4	Feb	26	
Foreland	20	50		10	14	Nov	24	
Minsmere	10	11	45	33	22	May	24	
Medway Estuary	(18)	(13)	(14)	(12)	(23)	May	(23)	
Yar Estuary	0	2	4	42	55	Mar	21	▲
Aberarth		0	2		60 [12]	Sep	21	▲
North Norfolk Coast	(18)	10	(14)	(9)	27	Jul	19	▲
Gerrans Bay	0	2	22	12	52	Feb	18	▲
Portsmouth Harbour	11	(12)	29	(22)	10	Feb	18	▲
Sites below table qualifying levels but exceeding threshold in WeBS-Year 2010/11 in Great Britain								
Pegwell Bay	3	4	11	32 [12]	26 [12]	Aug	15	
Hayle Estuary	5	4	2	5	22	Nov	8	
Poole Harbour	(4)	(14)	9	(11)	(20)	Mar	14	
Fal Complex	8	7	11	16	18	Mar	12	

Common Gull
Larus canus

	International threshold (N, W & C Europe, Mediterranean):	16,400
	Great Britain threshold:	7,000[†]
	All-Ireland threshold:	?[†]

GB max:	52,115	Dec
NI max:	2,842	Feb

January 2011 saw a large count of Common Gulls roosting at Bewl Water. The total of 76,020 is the highest ever submitted, and based on the estimate of Banks *et al.* (2009), represents over 10% of the British wintering population of the species. The magnitude of this concentration may be related to the cold weather prevalent across north-west Europe at the time. Bewl Water is the largest body of inland water in southeast England, and hence parts of the surface of the reservoir are likely to have remained unfrozen, thereby attracting gulls from usual roosts elsewhere in the region.

The estimate of the size of the international population was recently revised downwards by 18% (Wetlands International 2012), and the associated drop in the threshold for international importance means that three of the sites in the table below now qualify whereas before they would not have done so. The trend based on WeBS data also indicates a decline in numbers in recent years, but Common Gulls at several important sites have not been counted since the last wintering gulls survey (WinGS) in 2003/04. Submission of count data from all sites, particularly those where the species is known to roost in significant numbers, is therefore encouraged.

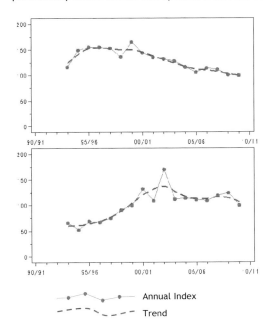

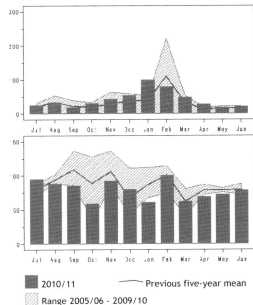

Figure 62.a, Annual indices & trend for Common Gull in GB (above) & NI (below).

Figure 62.b, Monthly indices for Common Gull in GB (above) & NI (below).

	06/07	07/08	08/09	09/10	10/11	Mon	Mean
Sites of international importance in the UK							
Bewl Water	75,500 [11]	59,650 [11]	34,200 [11]	52,000 [11]	76,020 [11]	Jan	59,474
Ribble Estuary				32,000 [10]			32,000 ▲
Haweswater Reservoir	17,185 [11]	17,560 [11]	23,565 [11]	19,612 [11]	21,320 [11]	Feb	19,848 ▲
Derwent Reservoir	18,500 [11]						18,500 ▲
Tophill Low Reservoirs	8,000 [11]	25,000 [11]	19,000 [11]				17,333 ▲
Sites no longer meeting table qualifying levels in WeBS-Year 2010/2011							
Hallington Reservoir	700 [11]						700
Sites with mean peak counts of 3,000+ birds in Great Britain[†]							
Inner Firth of Clyde	5,978	3,610 [10]	1,465	9,188	1,159	Aug	4,280
Carsebreck and Rhynd Lochs	3,000 [11]	320 [12]	6,700 [11]	3,300 [11]	2,900 [11]	Mar	3,244
Sites below table qualifying levels but exceeding threshold in WeBS-Year 2010/11 in Great Britain[†]							
Wet Sleddale Reservoir	2,020 [11]	533 [11]	2,046 [11]	3,740 [11]	6,100 [11]	Sep	2,888

[†] as few sites exceed the British threshold and no All-Ireland threshold has been set, qualifying levels of 3,000 and 1,000, respectively, have been chosen to select sites for presentation in this report

Ring-billed Gull
Larus delawarensis

Vagrant
Native Range: N America

Singles were recorded at Thames Estuary (Sep-Mar), Portsmouth Harbour (Nov-Jan), Sands Lane GP (Dec-Jan), Beaulieu Estuary (Jan) and Dunstaffnage Bay (Mar).

Lesser Black-backed Gull

Larus fuscus

GB max: 34,907 Jul
NI max: 1,143 Sep

International threshold
(W Europe, Mediterranean, W Africa): 5,500
Great Britain threshold: 1,200
All-Ireland threshold: ?[†]

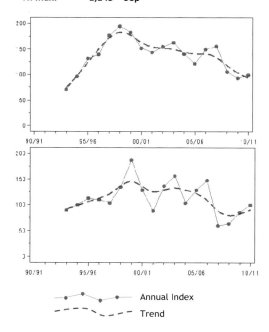

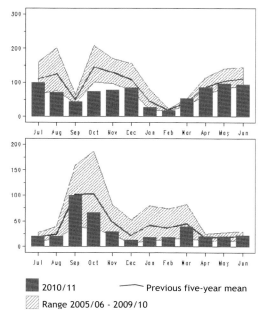

Annual Index
Trend

2010/11　　Previous five-year mean
Range 2005/06 - 2009/10

Figure 63.a, Annual indices & trend for Lesser Black-backed Gull in GB (above) & NI (below).

Figure 63.b, Monthly indices for Lesser Black-backed Gull in GB (above) & NI (below).

There are no data since the last wintering gulls survey (WinGS) in 2003/04 for a number of sites that are probably used by Lesser Black-backed Gulls in sufficient numbers to surpass the thresholds for international or national importance. Currently, three sites (Morecambe Bay, Cotswold Water Park (West) and Ribble Estuary) have a five-year mean beyond the threshold for international importance. At Ribble Estuary, the peak was the lowest noted for several years. The monthly maximum of Lesser Black-backed Gulls was significantly lower than recent years, but because the counting of gulls is optional during WeBS, the summed national maxima are likely to reflect changes in effort as much as actual numbers.

As with the other gulls, an increased submission rate for this species is encouraged, in order to improve the robustness of the WeBS indices and therefore the representativeness of the associated trend. It should be noted that of the gull species for which WeBS trends have now been derived, the trend for this species is based on a relatively small sample of monitored sites owing to the species prevalence during the summer.

	06/07	07/08	08/09	09/10	10/11	Mon	Mean
Sites of international importance in the UK							
Morecambe Bay	29,576	41,347	17,097	20,110	20,484	Jul	25,723
Cotswold Water Park (West)	6,500 [11]	9,500 [11]	4,500 [11]	4,630 [11]	4,250 [11]	Nov	5,876
Ribble Estuary	5,525	9,005	6,045	6,800 [10]	1,171	Jan	5,709
Sites of national importance in Great Britain							
Solway Estuary	4,701	(202)	(384)	(219)	5,960	Jul	5,331
River Avon - Fordingbridge to Ringwood	3,160	500	1,507	9,800 [11]	8,665 [11]	Sep	4,726
River Severn & River Vyrnwy Confluence	(144)	(401)	4,636	(242)	(215)	Feb	4,636
Hule Moss	550	(1,750)	(450)	2,900 [12]	6,550 [12]	Sep	3,333
Great Pool Westwood Park	2,000	3,500	3,000	4,500	(1,500)	Jan	3,250
Llys-y-fran Reservoir	(4,000)	700	2,000	3,000	5,800	Oct	3,100

	06/07	07/08	08/09	09/10	10/11	Mon	Mean	
Severn Estuary	(115)	(130)	2,899 [10]	(143)	(176)	Jun	2,899	
Alde Complex	2,990	453	2,775	2,609	1,336	Mar	2,033	
Calvert Brick Works	610	2,500	1,200	520	4,000	Dec	1,766	
Alt Estuary	1,980	1,063	703	2,206	1,288	Aug	1,448	
Roadford Reservoir	56	188	100	27	6,755 [11]	Nov	1,425	▲
The Wash	1,027	1,184	(1,081)	(2,052)	1,341	Jul	1,401	
Longnewton Reservoir	2,740	1,320	1,810	430	470	Sep	1,354	
Carsington Water	1,450	1,200 [11]	500	51	3,500 [11]	Nov	1,340	▲
Lower Windrush Valley Gravel Pits	2,922	(750)	852	468	687	Jan	1,232	
Eversley Cross and Yateley Gravel Pits	862	693	80	3,010 [11]	1,453 [11]	Oct	1,220	▲
Sites with mean peak counts of 500+ birds in Northern Ireland[†]								
Loughs Neagh and Beg	1,136	387	214	1,177	1,081	Sep	799	
Sites below table qualifying levels but exceeding threshold in WeBS-Year 2010/11 in Great Britain								
Hurleston Reservoir	35	50	50	50	4,000 [11]	Oct	837	
Doddington Pool	700	400 [11]	450 [9]		2,200 [11]	Nov	938	
Talybont Reservoir	0	0	1	4	1,670	Oct	335	
Rutland Water	50	2,500	100	1,500	1,500	Sep	1,130	

[†] *as no All-Ireland threshold has been set, a qualifying level of 500 has been chosen to select sites for presentation in this report*

Herring Gull
Larus argentatus

International threshold (Iceland & W Europe):	10,200
Great Britain threshold:	7,300[†]
All-Ireland threshold:	?[†]

GB max:	106,832	Jan
NI max:	2,378	Mar

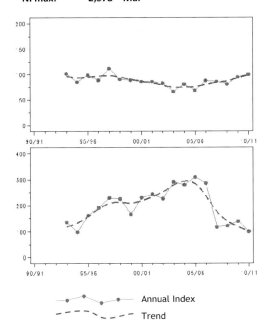

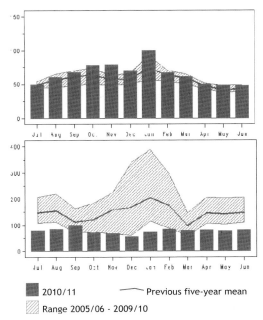

●—● Annual Index	■ 2010/11
--- Trend	◯ Previous five-year mean
	▨ Range 2005/06 - 2009/10

Figure 64.a, Annual indices & trend for Herring Gull in GB (above) & NI (below).

Figure 64.b, Monthly indices for Herring Gull in GB (above) & NI (below).

The counted British maximum of Herring Gull was greater than the total recorded in 2009/10. However, as counting of gulls remains optional in WeBS, any summed national maxima may reflect changes in effort as much as numbers.

Edmund Fellowes

The national WeBS trend indicates a slight improvement over the course of the last five or so years, in contrast to the decline in the breeding population (JNCC 2011).

In the table below, five WeBS sites continued to surpass the threshold for international importance. The count of 22,155 at Morecambe Bay in November is the highest at the site for over a decade, however peaks at most other major sites were below average.

Counting gulls at all sites, including at roost, is very much encouraged. A number of sites of known importance for this species do not feature in the tables below, having not been counted for WeBS since the last wintering gulls survey (WinGS) in 2003/04.

	06/07	07/08	08/09	09/10	10/11	Mon	Mean	
Sites of international importance in the UK								
Ribble Estuary	(25,336)	(11,086)	(19,024)	29,000 [10]	(14,427)	Jan	29,000	
Morecambe Bay	8,553	(10,258)	6,820	6,594	22,155	Nov	11,031	
Sites of national importance in Great Britain								
Glyne Gap	(2,700)	6,800 [11]	11,500 [11]	14,000 [11]	6,500 [11]	Oct	9,700	▼
The Wash	(6,212)	(5,960)	(3,455)	(8,657)	(6,836)	Mar	(8,657)	▼
Severn Estuary	(279)	(437)	6,332 [10]	(481)	(1,497)	Nov	6,332	▼
North Norfolk Coast	2,474	5,351	(3,113)	12,935	2,711	Mar	5,868	▼
Thames Estuary	4,456	6,655	(4,968)	(4,661)	(3,228)	Sep	5,556	
Guernsey Shore	5,704	4,432	7,586	3,896	4,890	Jun	5,302	
Lower Derwent Ings	1,600	1,500	1,050	1,140	17,340	Jan	4,526	▲
Sites with mean peak counts of 2,500+ birds in Great Britain[†]								
Alt Estuary	(1,005)	2,000	3,076	6,514	5,970	Oct	4,390	
Durham Coast	3,949	(300)	(629)	(983)	(1,323)	Dec	3,949	
Pegwell Bay	3,200	4,500	2,614 [10]	1,030	4,300 [12]	Oct	3,129	
Forth Estuary	(2,814)	(2,764)	(1,864)	(3,349)	2,840	Feb	3,095	
Burry Inlet	2,407	3,037 [10]	3,648	2,869	2,989	Sep	2,990	
Dungeness and Rye Bay	1,500 [12]	5,000 [12]	(1,700)	1,756	2,740	Oct	2,749	
Dee Estuary (England and Wales)	(2,613)	1,360	2,736 [10]	(1,456)	(4,035)	Jan	2,686	
Exe Estuary	2,357 [11]	2,849 [11]	2,689 [11]	2,166 [11]	2,456 [11]	Jan	2,503	
Sites with mean peak counts of 1,000+ birds in Northern Ireland[†]								
Belfast Lough	6,655 [10]	2,511	649	970 [10]	(420)	Nov	2,696	
Outer Ards Shoreline	1,602	1,053	1,520	2,306	1,185	Jan	1,533	
Sites below table qualifying levels but exceeding threshold in WeBS-Year 2010/11 in Great Britain[†]								
Bewl Water	130 [11]	1,250 [11]	3,209 [11]	2,347 [11]	3,590 [11]	Jan	2,105	
Pontsticill Reservoir (Taf Fechan)	1,109	(1,300)	1,117	2,200	3,420	Jan	1,962	
Tees Estuary	1,765	1,948	1,660	2,605	(2,813)	Jun	2,158	
Axe Estuary (Devon)	640	650	1,230	1,270	2,500	Dec	1,258	
Rutland Water	700	320	250	1,000	2,500	Dec	954	

[†] *as few sites exceed the British threshold and no All-Ireland threshold has been set, qualifying levels of 2,500 and 1,000, respectively, have been chosen to select sites for presentation in this report*

Yellow-legged Gull
Larus michahellis

International threshold: 7,000
Great Britain threshold: 11
All-Ireland threshold: ?[†]

Yellow-legged Gulls were recorded at 55 WeBS sites in England and two in Wales. Birds were noted in every month, with a peak of 52 in November. Currently, a lack of WeBS coverage during the first quarter of the WeBS-year at several important localities for Yellow-legged Gulls on the south coast of England is resulting in an unrepresentative picture of true numbers. The highest WeBS count received during 2010/11 was 21 at River Avon in December.

Caspian Gull
Larus cachinnans

International threshold:	7,000
Great Britain threshold:	?

Caspian Gulls were reported from 11 WeBS sites in 2010/11. With the exception of one in August, all records fell between October and March and included three at Minsmere (Mar) and Thames Estuary (Dec), the latter part of a total of nine recorded that month.

Iceland Gull
Larus glaucoides

International threshold:	2,000
Great Britain threshold:	?

Iceland Gulls were seen during WeBS Core counts at 17 sites in 2010/11 (ten in England, six in Scotland and one in Northern Ireland). With the exception of singles at Blyth Estuary (Aug) and Loch Connell (Oct), all were in the typical winter period of November to March. A monthly peak of eight birds occurred in January.

Glaucous Gull
Larus hyperboreus

International threshold:	10,000
Great Britain threshold:	?

2010/11 was another poor year for Glaucous Gull, with records received from just seven WeBS sites. The majority of records spanned the winter period, one exception being a long-stayer at Dungeness that lingered into June. A monthly peak of just five birds occurred in January.

Great Black-backed Gull
Larus marinus

International threshold (NW Atlantic):	4,200
Great Britain threshold:	760
All-Ireland threshold:	?[†]

GB max:	9,463	Jan
NI max:	369	Mar

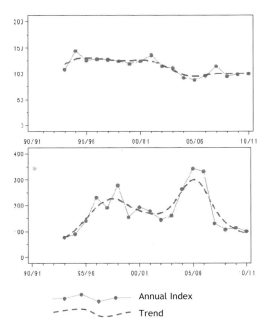

Figure 65.a, Annual indices & trend for Great Black-backed Gull in GB (above) & NI (below).

Figure 65.b, Monthly indices for Great Black-backed Gull in GB (above) & NI (below).

Counts of 1,000+ were received from four sites during the course of 2010/11, a typical showing. The highest of these was 1,860 at Lower Derwent Ings in January, while site maxima were distributed throughout the winter period, with a monthly maximum of 9,463 noted in Britain in November. The national trend shows evidence of a slight decline at WeBS sites during the course of the last decade. A number of sites of known importance for this species do not feature in the tables below, having not been counted for WeBS since the last wintering gulls survey (WinGS) in 2003/04. Submission of counts of Great Black-backed Gulls from such sites, as well as from gull roosts more generally, is therefore particularly encouraged.

	06/07	07/08	08/09	09/10	10/11	Mon	Mean
Sites of national importance in Great Britain							
The Wash	1,186	(2,131)	(1,011)	1,726	(1,538)	Oct	1,645
Humber Estuary	(20)	(165)	(176)	(1,441)	(351)	Oct	(1,441)
Thames Estuary	1,096	(2,107)	(1,236)	(1,431)	835	Sep	1,341
Lower Derwent Ings	1,030	870	1,000	1,740	1,860	Jan	1,300
Tees Estuary	1,028	668	971	1,169	1,268	Dec	1,021
Ribble Estuary	(200)	(365)	211	1,700 [10]	(223)	Jan	956
Dungeness and Rye Bay	700 [12]	1,200 [12]	(305)	(601)	510	Oct	803
Glyne Gap	655	(800)[11]	1,100 [11]	850 [11]	600 [11]	Nov	801 ▲
Pegwell Bay	700	850	821 [10]	420 [12]	1,100 [12]	Oct	778
Sites no longer meeting table qualifying levels in WeBS-Year 2010/2011							
Durham Coast	(659)	(35)	(99)	(139)	(227)	Sep	(659)
Sites below table qualifying levels but exceeding threshold in WeBS-Year 2010/11 in Great Britain							
Rutland Water	195	380	100	300	800	Dec	355

Little Tern
Sternula albifrons

International threshold (N of Mediterranean):	190
Great Britain threshold:	?[†]
All-Ireland threshold:	?[†]

GB max:	1,145	Jul
NI max:	0	

Little Terns were recorded at 38 WeBS sites in 2010, a similar showing to the previous year. Typically, most were in England, although the species was seen at nine sites in Scotland for the second year in a row. Most were in May to September, exceptions being April records at Humber Estuary and Northwest Solent, and October birds at Stour Estuary and Hamford Water. Maxima from the main sites were similar to those in 2009, with North Norfolk Coast and Dee Estuary consolidating recent strong showings. Following the revision by Wetlands International (2012), both sites now surpass the threshold for international importance .

	2006	2007	2008	2009	2010	Mon	Mean
Sites of international importance in the UK							
North Norfolk Coast	284	496	593	491	(502)	Jul	473 ▲
Dee Estuary (England and Wales)	250	251	309	300	284	Jul	279 ▲
Sites with mean peak counts of 50 or more birds in Great Britain[†]							
The Wash	83	255	(80)	153	85	Jul	144
Morecambe Bay	(4)	42	156	152	137	Jul	122
Thames Estuary	154	101	57	(125)	(0)		109
Humber Estuary	59	(8)	44	(12)	(32)	Jul	52
Other sites surpassing table qualifying levels in Summer 2010 in Great Britain[†]							
North West Solent	4	(4)	(14)	57	56	Jul	39

[†] *as no British or All-Ireland thresholds have been set, a qualifying level of 50 has been chosen to select sites*

Whiskered Tern
Chlidonias hybrida

Vagrant
Native Range: Worldwide

A juvenile was at Tees Estuary in August; the sixth WeBS record and first since May 2008.

Black Tern

Chlidonias niger

International threshold (Europe, W Asia, Africa): 7,100
Great Britain threshold: ?
All-Ireland threshold: ?

In 2010, Black Terns were seen at 40 WeBS sites. Following a dismal spring featuring just a single record, autumn was somewhat more productive, with a peak of 63 logged in September. Site maxima in autumn comprised 17 at Thames Estuary and six at Swale Estuary. Inland, four were at each of Rutland Water, Bough Beech Reservoir and Grafham Water, while 11 October records included singles at Draycote Water and Somerset Levels.

White-winged Black Tern

Chlidonias leucopterus

Vagrant
Native Range: S Europe

One was at Hornsea Mere in August; the 14th WeBS record.

Sandwich Tern

Sterna sandvicensis

International threshold (W Europe, W Africa): 1,700
Great Britain threshold: ?[†]
All-Ireland threshold: ?[†]

GB max: 6,322 Jun
NI max: 78 Jul

Sandwich Terns were recorded at 137 WeBS sites in the UK during 2010. The majority of sightings were during the period spanning April to October, although a small wintering population was also recorded. During the 2010/11 winter, Portsmouth Harbour, Pegwell Bay, Guernsey Shore and Jersey Shore hosted birds in the period of December to February; several of these winter records at re-occurring sites may relate to returning adults (although direct evidence of this through observations of colour-marked individuals is lacking).

The British monthly maximum was typical of recent years, although the top two sites in the table experienced contrasting fortunes in terms of peak counts. The maximum of 3,787 at North Norfolk Coast in July was below average, while the 1,669 at Dee Estuary in August is the most reported there since 1996.

	2006	2007	2008	2009	2010	Mon	Mean
Sites of international importance in the UK							
North Norfolk Coast	8,062	2,873	5,729	4,687	3,787	Jun	5,028
Sites with mean peak counts of 200+ birds in Great Britain[†]							
Dee Estuary (England and Wales)	(530)	1,334	953	(1,235)	1,669	Aug	1,319
Forth Estuary	(1,037)	680	(448)	(312)	(783)	Sep	833
Pegwell Bay	650 [12]	520	1,060	1,050 [12]	658 [12]	Aug	788
Humber Estuary	(957)	805	(383)	349	(92)	Aug	704
Duddon Estuary	843	460	886	877	405	Jun	694
The Wash	(164)	(338)	(498)	(213)	(602)	Jul	(602)
Tay Estuary	(377)	545	373	648	452	Aug	505
Tees Estuary	(490)	438	(108)	249	(191)	Aug	392
Eden Estuary	766	460	90	53	(55)	Jul	342
Solway Estuary	(339)	(162)	(227)	211	(88)	Sep	259
Morecambe Bay	190	(201)	216	280	332	Aug	255
Alt Estuary	207	348	112	293	210	Aug	234
Minsmere	50	24	104	847	16	Jun	208
Sites with mean peak counts of 200+ birds in Northern Ireland[†]							
Dundrum Inner Bay	311	233	276	179	40	Jul	208
Other sites surpassing table qualifying levels in Summer 2010 in Great Britain[†]							
Ribble Estuary	7	256	148	(220)[12]	351	Aug	196
Exe Estuary	155	285	165	164	200	Jul	194

[†] *as no British or All-Ireland thresholds have been set, a qualifying level of 200 has been chosen to select sites for presentation in this report*

Common Tern
Sterna hirundo

International threshold (S & W Europe):   1,800
Great Britain threshold: ?[†]
All-Ireland threshold: ?[†]

GB max: 5,712 Jul
NI max: 5 Aug

Common Terns were recorded at 347 WeBS sites in 2010. All sightings were between April and October, with the exception of a late individual reported from Jersey Shore in November. The highest Core count of the year was from Alt Estuary, where 1,000+ have been recorded for several consecutive years. The total of 1,768 represents the highest Core count since 2,010 at the same site in August 2005. Maxima at the most of the important sites were typical. As in 2009, this year saw no exceptional aggregations submitted to match recent reports at Humber Estuary (in 2008) and Breydon Water & Berney Marshes (in 2007 and 2008).

	2006	2007	2008	2009	2010	Mon	Mean
Sites of international importance in the UK							
Humber Estuary	(19)	(330)	7,000 [12]	(1,126)	(162)	Aug	7,000
Breydon Water and Berney Marshes		8,720 [12]	2,520 [11]				5,620
Sites with mean peak counts of 200+ birds in Great Britain[†]							
Alt Estuary	1,503	1,074	1,655	1,513	1,768	Jul	1,503
The Wash	(1,092)	(342)	(688)	(179)	(387)	Aug	(1,092)
Tees Estuary	869	618	558	536	798	Jul	676
North Norfolk Coast	606	894	782	385	362	May	606
Thames Estuary	(206)	(198)	514	(132)	(75)	Aug	514
Dee Estuary (England and Wales)	454	677	(327)	(249)	160	Jul	430
Pegwell Bay	5	173	474	440 [12]	692 [12]	Aug	357
Tay Estuary	(100)	600	105	410	204	Aug	330
Southampton Water	(133)	(2)	(310)	(260)	(159)	Aug	(310)
Dungeness and Rye Bay	(1)	(0)	(62)	302	(60)	Sep	302
Loch of Strathbeg	326	554	174	61	46	Jun	232

[†] *as no British or All-Ireland thresholds have been set, a qualifying level of 200 has been chosen to select sites for presentation in this report*

Roseate Tern
Sterna dougallii

Scarce

Roseate Terns were reported from ten WeBS sites during 2010, including a peak count of four at Coquet Estuary in May. Away from the typical core range of north-east England, singles were at Glyne Gap (May), Minsmere (Jun) and notably at Tamar Complex (Aug).

Arctic Tern
Sterna paradisaea

International threshold (W Eurasia):   20,000
Great Britain threshold: ?[†]
All-Ireland threshold: ?[†]

GB max: 632 Jul
NI max: 2 Jul

2010 was a stark year for counts of Arctic Terns at WeBS sites, with the British monthly maximum of 632 in July being one of the lowest ever. Of course, it should be remembered that the counting of terns remains optional during WeBS counts and hence any summed national maxima may reflect changes in effort as much as actual numbers. However, it is likely that the poor showing is a reflection of pressures faced at breeding sites in the UK (JNCC 2011). In total, birds were reported from just 67 WeBS sites, approximately 25% less than a typical showing. The majority were seen between May and September, with small numbers in both April and October (with the final sighting of the year at Dungeness). Typically, the largest counts were from sites in Scotland, but maxima at the major sites were very low, with peak counts at Forth Estuary (153, Aug) and The Houb, Whalsay (137, Jul).

	2006	2007	2008	2009	2010	Mon	Mean
Sites with mean peak counts of 50+ birds in Great Britain[†]							
Tay Estuary	(50)	1,841	1,100	200	31	Jul	793
Loch of Strathbeg	164	1,210	883	38	3	Jul	460
Eden Estuary	209	617	25	7	(5)	Jul	215
The Houb (Whalsay)	200	275	80	150	137	Jul	168
Loch of Beith	45	250	200	100			149
Morecambe Bay	(11)	(30)	123	122	82	Jun	109
Loch a` Phuill (Tiree)	37	77	101	135	103	Jun	91
Hamna Voe and Galtagarth, Yell	50	100	150	50	45		79
Ness of Sound, Yell	90	80	100	60	40	Jun	74
Peterhead Bay and Sandford Bay			130	0	(1)	Jul	65
St Andrews Bay	110	(0)	(0)		13	Jul	62
Nor Wick and Skaw	214	23	10	16	21	Jul	57
Forth Estuary	32	28	10	(4)	153	Aug	56
Loch Inver	18	0	80	120	50	May	54
Montrose Basin	21	2	90	144	0		51
Other sites surpassing table qualifying levels in Summer 2010 in Great Britain[†]							
Melbost Sands (Lewis)	2	2	30	(15)	69	May	26
Loch of North Haa & Loch of Beith				16	60	Jun	38

[†] *as no British or All-Ireland thresholds have been set, a qualifying level of 50 has been chosen to select sites for presentation in this report*

Kingfisher
Alcedo atthis

International threshold:	?
Great Britain threshold:	?[†]
All-Ireland threshold:	?[†]

GB max:	444	Nov
NI max:	3	Nov

The Kingfisher is not ideally suited to being monitored by WeBS, owing to its widespread distribution and preference for habitats that are poorly covered by the survey. Having shown a decline in breeding numbers in the UK up to the mid 1980s, the species seems to have recovered since then (Baillie *et al.* 2012).

In 2010/11, the British counted maximum of 444 in November was lower than normal, with, predictably, fewer reported during the cold period in midwinter. The site peaks noted were 16 at Somerset Levels (Nov) and nine at Ditchford Gravel Pits (Oct).

	06/07	07/08	08/09	09/10	10/11	Mon	Mean
Sites with mean peak counts of 8+ birds in Great Britain[†]							
Somerset Levels	17	22	14	15	16	Nov	17
Ditchford Gravel Pits	12	19	17	16	9	Sep	15
Wraysbury Gravel Pits	17	14					15
North Norfolk Coast	14	20 [10]	5	7	5	Nov	10
Southampton Water	(8)	(8)	(6)	(6)	(7)	Nov	(8)
Lee Valley Gravel Pits	(13)	(9)	7	6	5	Sep	8
The Wash	(0)	9	8	9	6	Oct	8

[†] *as no British or All-Ireland thresholds have been set a qualifying level of 8 has been chosen to select sites for presentation in this report*

PRINCIPAL SITES

Table 5 below lists the principal sites for non-breeding waterbirds in the UK as monitored by WeBS. All sites supporting more than 10,000 waterbirds are listed, as are all sites supporting internationally important numbers of one or more waterbird species. Naturalised species (*e.g.* Canada Goose, Ruddy Duck) and non-native species presumed to have escaped from captive collections have been excluded from the totals, as have gulls and terns since the recording of these species is optional (see *Analysis* in Methods). All Greylag Geese are included following the reclassification of the listing of populations (Holt *et al.* 2011). Table 6 lists other sites holding internationally important numbers of waterbirds, which are not routinely monitored by standard WeBS surveys, but by the Icelandic Goose Census and aerial surveys.

A total of 183 sites are listed in Tables 5 & 6, 80 of which held a five-year mean peak of 10,000 or more birds. Typically there are few changes between years to the top twenty sites listed in the principal sites table, and the order of the top ten sites tends to remain unchanged although 2010/11 saw a marked rise by Somerset Levels. Across the UK, five-year averages of sites holding 10,000 or more waterbirds were relatively similar compared to the previous year, with very few sites undergoing changes of greater than 10%.

The Wash remains the key site for waterbirds in the UK in terms of absolute numbers, and in 2010/11 it held a figure slightly below the average of the last five-years. This follows the 435,227 birds there in 2009/10 which represented the highest site total in WeBS history. Compared to recent averages, numbers at the other top 10 sites showed a high degree of variation. Notably, the peaks at the two principal inland sites, Somerset Levels and Ouse Washes, were the most ever recorded and the most for five years, respectively. Those totals at extensive inland wetlands may have been attributable to the effects of freezing conditions during the midwinter period, when exceptional numbers of dabbling ducks and Lapwing were presumably forced from smaller inland sites. The total number of non-breeding waterbirds at Morecambe Bay was the highest since 2003/04. In contrast, the peak at Humber Estuary was very low, and represents a continuation of a downward trend at that site in recent years.

The Wash supports internationally important numbers of 16 species. *Dawn Balmer*

Table 5. Total number of waterbirds at principal sites in the UK, 2006/2007 to 2010/11 (includes data from all available sources) and species occurring in internationally important numbers at each. (Species codes are provided in Table 7.)

Site	06/07	07/08	08/09	09/10	10/11	Average	Int.Imp.Species
The Wash	381,341	373,566	345,609	435,228	360,074	379,164	PG,DB,SU,PT,OC,RP,GP,GV L.,KN,SS,DN,BW,BA,CU,RK
Ribble Estuary	214,506	263,487	274,779	210,700	215,024	235,699	WS,PG,WN,T.,PT,OC,RP,GV KN,SS,DN,BW,BA,RK
Morecambe Bay	194,990	155,048	220,210	236,976	240,267	209,498	PG,SU,T.,PT,OC,KN,DN,BW, BA,CU,RK
North Norfolk Coast	217,121	144,141	209,045	204,250	220,287	198,969	PG,DB,RP,KN,BW,BA
Thames Estuary	226,590	189,813	158,941	141,275	145,940	172,512	DB,GA,SV,OC,AV,RP,GV,KN DN,BW,BA,RK
Humber Estuary	168,245	149,622	126,712	152,931	123,306	144,163	PG,DB,SU,AV,RP,GP,GV,KN DN,BW,BA,RK
Somerset Levels	108,163	114,246	104,339	74,482	181,157	116,477	MS,WN,T.,PT,SV,GP,L.
Dee Estuary (England and Wales)	103,753	104,315	124,122	103,072	118,390	110,730	SU,PT,CA,OC,KN,DN,BW,RK
Breydon Water and Berney Marshes	97,127	100,556	128,151	92,574	85,424	100,766	PG,WN,SV,AV,GP,L.,BW
Solway Estuary	118,199	89,947	88,038	93,915	112,244	100,469	PG,YS,PT,SP,OC,RP,KN,RK
Ouse Washes	73,012	67,605	78,260	68,535	104,497	78,382	MS,BS,WS,WN,GA,PT,SV, PO,BW
Strangford Lough	74,657	87,535	81,876	74,063	71,688	77,964	MS,WS,QN,SU,KN,RK
Swale Estuary	62,313	92,111	66,619	87,603	77,162	77,162	T.,RP,GP,BW
Forth Estuary	59,926	76,442	93,611	70,760	68,734	73,895	PG,SU,BA,RK
Severn Estuary	66,918	72,613	86,217	67,398	75,995	73,828	MS,BS,SU,PT,SV,RP,DN,RK
Blackwater Estuary	72,445	71,693	86,468	66,795	64,850	72,450	DB,GP,GV,KN,DN,BW,RK
Alt Estuary	50,362	40,261	48,791	60,285	107,802	61,500	PG,KN,SS,BA
Dengie Flats	61,848	53,043	58,269	64,265	61,803	59,846	DB,GV,KN,BA
Mersey Estuary	66,708	68,499	39,236	60,723	56,085	58,250	SU,DN,BW,RK
Loch of Strathbeg	51,245	52,062	61,125	67,483	46,441	55,671	WS,PG
Chichester Harbour	44,025	54,125	55,981	48,520	52,704	51,071	DB,DN,BW
Loughs Neagh and Beg	51,398	57,560	46,609	47,747	41,422	48,947	MS,WS,PO,SP,CA
Inner Moray/Inverness Firth	47,200	43,379	42,200	45,062	44,351	44,438	PG,JI
Lindisfarne	47,955	46,951	44,989	36,134	45,387	44,283	PG,YS,QS,BA
Stour Estuary	35,069	40,304	49,936	56,319	37,506	43,827	MS,KN,BW
Montrose Basin	45,569	45,842	55,216	23,030	38,383	41,608	PG
Hamford Water	34,465	45,489	49,200	35,782	41,987	41,385	DB,T.,GV
Carmarthen Bay	52,989	48,033	28,941	31,694	27,957	37,923	OC,SS
Nene Washes	30,467	37,849	30,430	45,395	41,803	37,189	BS,WS,PT,BW
Burry Inlet	44,625	44,794	42,639	29,126	23,256	36,888	PT,OC
Lower Derwent Ings	43,648	34,293	26,056	38,772	40,995	36,753	
Alde Complex	33,419	47,038	31,326	32,875	35,133	35,958	AV,BW,RK
West Water Reservoir	57,529	28,196	47,847	26,449	16,650	35,334	PG
Dungeness and Rye Bay	35,636	39,400	27,379	34,758	36,341	34,703	MS,SV
Crouch-Roach Estuary	31,943	36,223	32,184	34,121	32,202	33,335	DB,BW
Lough Foyle	36.225	34.836	39.210	29.936	21.920	32.425	WS,QN,BA
Loch Leven	34,279	19,699	44,962	29,499	33,161	32,320	MS,WS,PG,JI,T.,PT
Medway Estuary	24,672	36,478	40,126	18,270	35,664	31,042	PT,SV,AV,BW
Dornoch Firth	28,356	30,940	32,282	26,866	36,024	30,894	JI
Cromarty Firth	23,330	39,055	25,256	32,111	32,334	30,417	PG

Site	06/07	07/08	08/09	09/10	10/11	Average	Int.Imp.Species
Duddon Estuary	28,924	34,971	35,218	28,284	19,464	29,372	PT,RK
Rutland Water	30,859	23,394	27,356	31,501	26,893	28,001	MS,GA,SV
Langstone Harbour	28,041	30,784	22,066	29,053	26,778	27,344	DB
Abberton Reservoir	12,778	30,380	25,631	37,186	30,328	27,261	MS,GA,SV
WWT Martin Mere	28,857	22,659	26,507	28,043	23,666	25,946	WS,PG
Pegwell Bay	29,881	24,090	19,646	25,987	23,070	24,535	
Loch of Skene	24,337	20,619	20,403	17,967	28,725	22,410	PG
Orwell Estuary	23,996	20,511	23,934	21,009	20,245	21,939	BW
Colne Estuary	17,734	31,470	23,598	20,908	15,806	21,903	BW
Tees Estuary	23,036	23,222	17,356	23,881	19,338	21,367	
Cleddau Estuary	19,659	23,337	21,694	19,006	22,745	21,288	
Wigtown Bay	18,101	26,142	19,646	20,218	17,827	20,387	PG,YS
Deben Estuary	17,540	21,611	18,521	16,670	24,831	19,835	BW
Carsebreck and Rhynd Lochs	17,239	14,294	19,873	22,527	21,200	19,027	PG
Exe Estuary	17,825	19,278	19,570	17,076	20,379	18,826	BW
Pagham Harbour	22,679	18,438	16,672	16,912	15,470	18,034	DB,BW
Belfast Lough	18,964	19,414	16,262	18,646	15,910	17,839	BW
Lavan Sands	22,773	16,502	13,991	15,824	16,683	17,155	
Eden Estuary	5,688	12,960	36,796	11,407	18,177	17,006	PG
Ythan Estuary	20,245	14,117	18,459	14,620	16,270	16,742	
Poole Harbour	15,975	15,759	17,879	15,064	16,984	16,332	AV,BW
Tay Estuary	18,462	18,199	14,440	14,368	13,971	15,888	
Fleet and Wey	13,772	13,053	14,314	15,682	22,545	15,873	MS
Inner Firth of Clyde	17,450	17,101	14,817	13,300	14,247	15,383	SZ
North West Solent	13,917	15,623	16,758	15,210	15,261	15,354	
Slains Lochs	11,408	17,604	19,700	14,748	11,782	15,048	PG
Cotswold Water Park (West)	12,195	12,530	13,361	17,434	14,156	13,935	
Middle Yare Marshes	12,711	18,657	13,817	11,605	12,433	13,845	
Mersehead RSPB Reserve	16,113	12,456	1,420	22,808	13,196	13,199	YS,PT
Blyth Estuary	13,433	19,188	14,092	10,024	8,223	12,992	
Portsmouth Harbour	14,275	14,019	14,035	12,172	9,549	12,810	DB
Taw-Torridge Estuary	13,155	10,240	16,373	12,231	11,191	12,638	
Southampton Water	11,467	11,360	11,170	11,680	14,397	12,015	
Arun Valley	13,791	11,964	10,838	9,595	11,783	11,594	
Dyfi Estuary	13,123	12,331	12,814	9,607	9,781	11,531	
WWT Caerlaverock (Inland)	14,199	13,933	10,545	6,224	12,712	11,523	WS,YS
Nosterfield Gravel Pits	12,290	11,485	9,741	14,646	8,808	11,394	
Ouse Fen and Pits	12,948	8,729	13,248	8,406	7,957	10,258	
Pitsford Reservoir	11,472	8,405	7,888	10,891	12,357	10,203	GA
West Freugh	.	.	.	17,657	2,352	10,005	PG,NW
Outer Ards Shoreline	12,293	9,674	9,734	8,545	8,993	9,848	QN
Loch of Lintrathen	10,936	11,155	13,133	5,641	7,480	9,669	PG
Loch of Harray	12,639	7,252	7,676	10,205	9,042	9,363	JI
Dundrum Inner Bay	6,566	13,582	8,634	9,269	6,478	8,906	QN
Lee Valley Gravel Pits	7,477	9,073	9,022	8,635	9,861	8,814	GA
R.Avon: R'wood-Christchurch	12,900	9,306	4,749	9,631	7,190	8,755	BW
R.Avon: F'bridge-Ringwood	8,636	8,238	7,809	8,126	9,975	8,557	GA,BW
Carlingford Lough	9,693	10,705	10,289	5,671	5,520	8,376	QN
Kilconquhar Loch	1,187	7,620	14,883	10,469	7,388	8,309	PG
Upper Lough Erne	8,785	7,460	6,455	6,043	8,514	7,451	MS,WS
Loch Fleet Complex	7,141	7,753	4,804	7,745	8,428	7,174	JI
Hule Moss	2,649	7,092	6,570	10,251	8,485	7,009	PG
Wedholme Flow	1,295	2,531	8,270	12,846	8,378	6,664	PG

Site	06/07	07/08	08/09	09/10	10/11	Average	Int.Imp.Species
Loch of Tankerness	.	.	7,731	2,480	8,198	6,136	JI
Dupplin Lochs	1,450	2,100	.	18,608	870	5,757	PG
Loch of Stenness	6,040	5,992	4,961	5,043	5,692	5,546	JI
Lochhill	1,814	5,506	7,516	7,000	.	5,459	PG
Horsey Mere	5,430	.	.	.	5,125	5,278	PG
Fala Flow	2,170	3,650	1,510	13,190	5,665	5,237	PG
North Uist	4,437	5,924	6,176	4,880	4,696	5,223	YN
Dee Flood Meadows	5,975	3,831	2,692	6,458	7,059	5,203	PT
Biggar Moss	638	7,442	7,375	.	.	5,152	PG
R.Nith: Keltonbank - Nunholm	8,115	.	4,282	7,563	478	5,110	YS
Loch of Boardhouse	5,983	4,939	5,200	4,607	2,754	4,697	JI
Orchardton and Auchencairn	4,167	2,799	5,017	5,221	4,446	4,330	YS
Loch Watten	2,964	2,827	3,864	7,611	2,975	4,048	JI
Overcote Marina	7,828	.	6,055	2,006	202	4,023	BW
Loch of Isbister	4,326	3,491	2,759	7,013	2,427	4,003	JI
Loch Bee (South Uist)	3,906	3,673	3,708	.	3,423	3,678	MS,JH
Water Sound	2,040	1,667	3,077	3,696	7,329	3,562	JI
Tweed Estuary	3,675	2,784	2,982	3,416	3,552	3,282	MS
Loch Heilen	2,568	4,899	492	7,980	280	3,244	JI
Martham Broad	1,059	1,198	10,932	1,180	992	3,072	PG
Loch of Swannay	3,073	3,729	3,259	3,130	2,149	3,068	JI
Loch of Skaill	2,542	2,785	2,619	4,712	2,670	3,066	JI
Broubster Leans	2,979	.	.	.	.	2,979	JI
Tiree	5,297	4,196	979	787	.	2,815	NW,YN
Loch Eye	1,086	1,667	2,001	5,708	3,560	2,804	WS
Warton Floods	.	3,049	3,137	1,691	2,489	2,592	BW
Lower Lough Erne	3,139	3,282	1,065	1,143	2,110	2,148	MS
Machrihanish	1,831	1,432	1,494	2,180	.	1,734	NW
Isle of Coll	3,143	1,245	341	323	.	1,263	NW,YN
Colonsay/Oronsay	.	1,200	.	.	.	1,200	YN
Sound of Gigha	105	194	1,462	1,983	1,940	1,137	NW,ND
Rhunahaorine	940	1,451	879	1,017	.	1,072	NW
Newmains Ponds	.	.	.	1,782	134	958	YS
Upper Quoile River	1,177	653	.	.	.	915	MS
Rova Head to Wadbister Ness	.	502	929	1,177	933	885	ND
Stranraer Lochs	1,105	877	273	490	.	686	NW
Whiteness to Skelda Ness	359	521	.	658	513	513	EF,SZ
Keills Peninsula and Danna	300	913	239	214	.	417	NW

Table 6. Other sites in the UK holding internationally important numbers of waterbirds in 2010/11 which are not routinely monitored by standard WeBS surveys. (Species codes are provided in Table 7.)

Site	Int.Imp.species	Site	Int.Imp.species
Berney Marshes	PG	North Norfolk Coast	PG
Bute	JI	Burnham Overy Saltmarsh	PG
Caithness Lochs	JI	Holkham Bay	PG
Colonsay/Oronsay	YN	Holme and Thornham	PG
Cromarty Firth	PG	Norton Marsh	PG
Nigg Bay	PG	Scolt Head	PG
Forth Estuary	PG	Wells-next-the-Sea	PG
Aberlady Bay	PG	North Uist	YN
Forth Grangemouth to Kincardine	PG	Balranald, Clettraval & Tigharry	YN
Hule Moss (West)	PG	Berneray	YN
Humber Estuary	PG	Malaclate To Grenitote	YN
Read`s Island Flats	PG	Orkney	JI, YN
Inner Moray and Inverness Firth	PG,JI	South Ronaldsay	JI
Beauly Firth	PG,JI	South Walls (Hoy)	YN
Findhorn Bay	PG	Simonswood Peat Moss	PG
Islay	NW,YN	Solway Firth	YS, PG
Isle of Oronsay	YN	Southwest Lancashire	PG
Isle of Lismore	NW	Strathearn (West)	PG JI
Loch Fleet	JI	Tay and Isla Valley	PG,JI
Lune Estuary	PG	Tayinloan	NW
Martin Mere and Ribble Estuary	WS	The Wash	PG
Middlemuir (New Pitsligo)	PG	Snettisham	PG
Morecambe Bay	PG	Winter Loch, St Fergus Gas Term.	PG
Wyre to Cockerham	PG		
Wyre Estuary	PG		

Table 7. Species codes for species listed in Tables 5., 6. and 8.

AV	Avocet	JE/JH	British/Irish Greylag Goose	RH	Red-throated Diver
BA	Bar-tailed Godwit	JI	Greylag Goose	RK	Redshank
BS	Bewick's Swan		(Icelandic population)	RM	Red-breasted Merganser
BV	Black-throated Diver	KN	Knot	RP	Ringed Plover
BW	Black-tailed Godwit	L.	Lapwing	RU	Ruff
CA	Cormorant	LG	Little Grebe	SP	Scaup
CO	Coot	MA	Mallard	SS	Sanderling
CU	Curlew	MS	Mute Swan	SU	Shelduck
CX	Common Scoter	ND	Great Northern Diver	SV	Shoveler
DB	Dark-bellied Brent Goose	NW	Greenland White-fronted Goose	SZ	Slavonian Grebe
DN	Dunlin	OC	Oystercatcher	T.	Teal
E.	Eider	PG	Pink-footed Goose	TT	Turnstone
EW	European White-fronted Goose	PO	Pochard	WN	Wigeon
GA	Gadwall	PS	Purple Sandpiper	WS	Whooper Swan
GG	Great Crested Grebe	PT	Pintail	YN	Barnacle Goose
GK	Greenshank	QN	Light-bellied Brent Goose		(Nearctic population)
GP	Golden Plover		(Nearctic population)		
GV	Grey Plover	QS	Light-bellied Brent Goose		
			(Svalbard population)		

WeBS Low Tide Counts

AIMS

Estuarine sites in the UK provide the most important habitat for non-breeding waterbirds, acting as wintering grounds for many migrants but also as stopover feeding locations for other waterbirds passing along the East Atlantic Flyway. Core Counts on estuaries tend to quantify birds present at high tide roosts. Although important, knowledge of roost sites provides only part of the picture, and does not elucidate the use that waterbirds make of a site for feeding.

The WeBS Low Tide Counts scheme has flourished since its inception in the winter of 1992/93, with most of the major estuaries covered. The scheme aims principally to monitor, assess and regularly update information on the relative importance of inter-tidal feeding areas of UK estuaries for wintering waterbirds and thus to complement the information gathered by WeBS Core Counts.

The data gathered contribute greatly to the conservation of waterbirds by providing supporting information for the establishment and management of UK Ramsar sites and Special Protection Areas (SPAs), other site designations and whole estuary conservation plans. In addition, WeBS Low Tide Counts enhance our knowledge of the low water distribution of waterbirds and provide data that highlight regional variations in habitat use, whilst also informing protection of the important foraging areas identified. WeBS Low Tide Counts provide valuable information needed to gauge the potential effects on waterbirds of a variety of human activities which affect the extent or value of inter-tidal habitats, such as proposals for dock developments, recreational activities, tidal power barrages, marinas and housing schemes. Designing mitigation or compensation for such activities can be assisted using data collected under the scheme. Furthermore, the effects on bird distributions of climate change and sea level rise can be assessed.

METHODS

The scheme provides information on the numbers of waterbirds feeding on subdivisions of the inter-tidal habitat within estuaries. Given the extra work that Low Tide Counts entail, often by the same counters that carry out the Core Counts, WeBS aims to cover most individual estuaries about once every six years, although on some sites more frequent counts are made. Co-ordinated counts of waterbirds are made by volunteers each month between November and February on pre-established subdivisions of the inter-tidal habitat in the period two hours either side of low tide.

DATA PRESENTATION

Tabulated Statistics

Tables 8 and 9 present three statistics for 18 of the more numerous waterbird species present on 21 estuaries covered during the 2010/11 winter: the peak number of a species over the whole site counted in any one month (with checks for count synchronicity made from assessing proximity of count dates and consultation with Local Organisers); an estimate of the mean number present over the winter for the whole site (obtained by summing the mean counts of each species for each count section) and the mean density over the site (in birds per hectare), which is the mean number divided by the total area surveyed (in hectares). The area value used for these calculations is the sum of the inter-tidal and non-tidal components of each count section but omits the sub-tidal areas (*i.e.* those parts of the count section which are under water on a mean low tide).

Dot Density Maps

WeBS Low Tide Count data are presented as dot density maps, with subdivision of count sections into basic habitat elements. The reason for such a subdivision is to ensure species are plotted on appropriate habitat areas and to improve the accuracy of density estimates. Each section for which a count has been made is divided into a maximum of three different habitat components:

Inter-tidal: Areas that lie between mean high water and mean low water.
Sub-tidal: Areas that lie below mean low water. In more 'open-coast'-type situations, a sub-tidal zone reaching 500 m out from the inter-tidal sections has been created arbitrarily, indicating the approximate extent of visibility offshore from land-based counts.
Non-tidal: Areas that lie above mean high water (usually saltmarsh although some grazing marshes are also covered).

The mean count for the sector is then divided amongst a varying number of the different components, dependent on the usual habitat preferences of the species involved. For example, Dunlin dots are plotted exclusively on inter-tidal sections whereas Wigeon dots are spread across inter-tidal, sub-tidal and non-tidal areas (in proportion to the relative areas of these three components).

Currently, throughout all WeBS Low Tide Count analyses, mean low tide and mean high tide are taken from the most recent Ordnance Survey 1:25000 maps (in Scotland, the lines on the OS maps are mean low water springs and mean high water springs instead). It is recognised, unfortunately, that these maps represent the current real shape of the mudflats, water channels and saltmarshes to varying degrees of accuracy. However, in the interests of uniformity across the UK, the Ordnance Survey outlines are adhered to throughout the analyses.

The maps display the average number of birds in each count section as dots spread randomly across habitat components of count sections, thus providing an indication of both numbers and density. It is important to note that individual dots do not represent the precise position of individual birds; dots have been assigned to habitat components proportionally and are then randomly placed within those areas. No information about the distribution of birds at a finer scale than the count sector level should be inferred from the dot density maps. For all maps in the present report, one dot is equivalent to one bird, except where stated. The size of

individual dots has no relevance other than for clarity.

As most estuaries have now been covered more than once at low tide, density maps show the relative distributions of species in the winter of 2010/11 compared to an earlier winter of survey. It is hoped that comparative dot density distributions will lead to an easier and fuller appreciation of low tide estuarine waterbird distribution, and changes therein. The following colour conventions apply to density maps: red dots = 2010/11 winter; blue dots = earlier winter; pale blue = water; yellow = inter-tidal habitat (e.g. mudflat, sandflat); pale green = non-tidal habitat (e.g. saltmarsh, reedbed); grey = not covered in one survey winter. More detailed information concerning analysis and presentation of WeBS Low Tide Counts can be obtained from the Low Tide Counts National Organiser, or from *Estuarine Waterbirds at Low Tide* (Musgrove *et al.* 2003)

ESTUARY ACCOUNTS
The main estuaries counted at low tide in the winter of 2010/11 are discussed. WeBS Low Tide Counts were carried out on 21 different sites, with estuary accounts encompassing 4 of these. To allow space in this report for these sites which have not been counted for many years, dot density distribution maps for all sites included in the 2010/11 Low Tide Counts are available on our website at www.bto.org/webs/low-tide-results or from the WeBS office. Other counts, usually on limited numbers of sectors or only in one month, were made in the winter of 2010/11 on Adur Estuary, Langstone Harbour, Loch Indaal, Fal Complex and Moray Firth. For all other sites, data were collected during the period November to February. Assessment of national and international importance is based on five- year peak mean counts from the main species accounts in this volume of *Waterbirds in the UK*. Fig. 66 shows the location of sites covered in 2010/11, and a site description is presented for each estuary. Distribution maps are presented for selected species; where possible, for species present in national or internationally important numbers, or which are known to be undergoing site-level changes. General bird distribution is described for winter 2010/11.

Figure 66. Map showing estuaries covered at low tide in the winter of 2010/11.
1: Loch Fleet; 2: Moray Firth; 3: Breydon Water; 4: Alde Estuary; 5: Orwell Estuary;6: Stour Estuary;7: Crouch-Roach Estuary; 8: Adur Estuary; 9 Chichester Harbour; 10: Langstone Harbour; 11: Beaulieu Estuary; 12: Northwest Solent; 13:Fal Complex; 14: Hayle Estuary; 15: Burry Inlet; 16: Carmarthen Bay; 17: Traeth Lafan; 18: Solway Estuary; 19: Loch Indaal; 20: Belfast Lough; 21: Strangford Lough.

Table 8. Sites covered by Low Tide Counts in 2010/11 and important bird numbers held. Numbers in parentheses refer to the location in Figure 66. For species codes see Table 7.

	International Importance	*National Importance*
Adur Estuary (8)	None	None
Alde Estuary (4)	AV, BW, RK	DN, PT, SU, SV, T., WN
Belfast Lough (20)	BW	SU, SV, SP, E., GN, RM, RH, BV, GG, OC, RP, PS, RK, TT
Beaulieu Estuary (11)	None	DB, GV
Bembridge Harbour	None	None
Breydon Water (3)	PG, WN, SV, AV, GP, L., BW, CN	BS, EW, T., PT, RU, RK
Burry Inlet (15)	PT, OC	SV, DN, CU, GK, KN, BW
Carmarthen Bay (16)	CX, SS, OC	GP, BW, GK, KN, RM
Chichester Harbour (9)	DB, DN, BW	BA, CU, GV, RK, SS, SU
Crouch-Roach Est. (7)	DB, BW	DN, GP, GV, L., RP, SU, SV
Fal Complex (13)	None	QN
Hayle Estuary (14)	None	None
Langstone Harbour (10)	DB	RM, GV, DN, BW
Loch Fleet (1)	JI	None
Loch Indaal (19)	None	QN, SZ, SP
Northwest Solent (12)	None	DB, PT, GV, BW
Orwell Estuary (5)	BW	DB, GA, AV, KN, BW, RK
Solway Estuary (18)	YS, KN, OC, PG, PT, SP, RK, RP	WS, BA, CU, DN, GP, SS, SU, T.
Stour Estuary (6)	MS, BW, KN	DB, SU, PT, AV, GV, DN, RU, RK, RM, TT
Strangford Lough (21)	MS, WS, QN, SU, KN, GV, L., RK	T., RM, BV, GG, CO, RP, GP, GV, WN, MA, PT, SV, E., GN, DN, CU, GK, BW, BA
Treath Lafan (17)	None	CU, OC, QN, RK, RM

Table 9. Peak, mean counts and mean density (birds per ha) of 18 species across 21 estuaries covered by WeBS Low Tide Counts in 2010/11. "+" indicates densities of <0.01 birds per ha.

	Adur Estuary			Alde Complex			Beaulieu Estuary		
Species	Peak No.	Mean No.	Mean Dns.	Peak No.	Mean No.	Mean Dns.	Peak No.	Mean No.	Mean Dns.
Brent Goose	0	0	0	479	215	0.05	660	481	0.83
Shelduck	1	0	+	906	723	0.17	116	68	0.12
Wigeon	0	0	0	6,374	5,243	1.23	984	776	1.34
Teal	238	103	1.37	3,391	3,201	0.75	877	643	1.11
Mallard	4	2	0.03	744	523	0.12	186	150	0.26
Pintail	0	0	0	142	149	0.04	34	10	0.02
Oystercatcher	2	2	0.03	214	93	0.02	63	52	0.09
Ringed Plover	61	23	0.31	222	77	0.02	11	7	0.01
Golden Plover	1	0	+	1,054	448	0.11	0	0	0
Grey Plover	12	7	0.09	64	65	0.02	66	34	0.06
Lapwing	352	165	2.2	3,490	3,197	0.75	605	328	0.57
Knot	0	0	0	72	48	0.01	336	128	0.22
Dunlin	238	183	2.44	2,185	2,640	0.62	347	183	0.32
Black-tailed Godwit	0	0	0	1,305	852	0.2	170	90	0.16
Bar-tailed Godwit	0	0	0	27	8	+	18	10	0.02
Curlew	0	0	0	922	909	0.21	213	186	0.32
Redshank	38	32	0.43	2,022	2,139	0.5	43	29	0.05
Turnstone	15	7	0.09	30	35	0.01	29	21	0.04

Table 9. cont.

Species	Belfast Lough Peak No.	Mean No.	Mean Dns.	Bembridge Harbour Peak No.	Mean No.	Mean Dns.	Breydon Water Peak No.	Mean No.	Mean Dns.
Brent Goose	88	62	0.14	370	223	1.59	0	0	0
Shelduck	206	165	0.36	25	16	0.11	54	26	0.06
Wigeon	147	119	0.26	1	0	+	29,370	12,112	30.13
Teal	704	532	1.17	193	84	0.6	884	489	1.22
Mallard	297	237	0.52	51	28	0.2	203	142	0.35
Pintail	0	0	0	0	0	0	86	33	0.08
Oystercatcher	3,374	2,929	6.42	25	21	0.15	34	10	0.02
Ringed Plover	160	132	0.29	12	5	0.04	24	12	0.03
Golden Plover	0	0	0	2	1	0.01	9,490	6,461	16.07
Grey Plover	2	0	+	21	9	0.06	37	19	0.05
Lapwing	510	366	0.8	182	55	0.39	16,955	7,384	18.37
Knot	134	65	0.14	0	0	0	100	58	0.14
Dunlin	1,344	1,007	2.21	93	54	0.39	5,407	3,675	9.14
Black-tailed Godwit	481	326	0.71	35	29	0.21	1,140	776	1.93
Bar-tailed Godwit	95	89	0.2	4	2	0.01	15	5	0.01
Curlew	280	185	0.41	17	15	0.11	672	299	0.74
Redshank	1,016	826	1.81	26	21	0.15	1,194	750	1.87
Turnstone	375	329	0.72	1	0	+	3	1	+

Species	Burry Inlet Peak No.	Mean No.	Mean Dns.	Carmarthen Bay Peak No.	Mean No.	Mean Dns.	Chichester Harbour Peak No.	Mean No.	Mean Dns.
Brent Goose	747	633	0.11	15	13	0.01	7,184	6,865	2.73
Shelduck	712	466	0.08	138	99	0.06	1,015	716	0.28
Wigeon	480	186	0.03	172	88	0.05	2,404	1,690	0.67
Teal	245	105	0.02	490	329	0.18	931	698	0.28
Mallard	15	7	+	0	119	0.07	351	310	0.12
Pintail	973	793	0.14	148	119	0.07	306	144	0.06
Oystercatcher	9,966	7,297	1.32	10,613	9,330	5.21	977	959	0.38
Ringed Plover	0	0	0	15	8	+	146	83	0.03
Golden Plover	112	37	0.01	0	0	0	967	538	0.21
Grey Plover	345	189	0.03	2	1	+	645	461	0.18
Lapwing	2,488	1,347	0.24	284	237	0.13	1,512	1,021	0.41
Knot	1,100	813	0.15	2,500	1,596	0.89	8,197	3,584	1.42
Dunlin	3,310	1,787	0.32	2,081	1,448	0.81	30,075	16,522	6.56
Black-tailed Godwit	703	474	0.09	96	68	0.04	572	347	0.14
Bar-tailed Godwit	25	8	+	20	14	0.01	1,628	987	0.39
Curlew	1,052	572	0.1	118	117	0.07	465	473	0.19
Redshank	451	390	0.07	281	213	0.12	687	589	0.23
Turnstone	0	0	0	42	15	0.01	102	87	0.03

Species	Crouch-Roach Estuary Peak No.	Mean No.	Mean Dns.	Fal Complex Peak No.	Mean No.	Mean Dns.	Hayle Estuary Peak No.	Mean No.	Mean Dns.
Brent Goose	4,368	2,685	1.56	0	0	0	0	0	0
Shelduck	2,115	1,438	0.83	0	0	0	49	36	0.34
Wigeon	5,932	3,168	1.84	3	1	0.05	1,675	790	7.52
Teal	4,403	3,029	1.76	0	0	0	1,423	735	7
Mallard	287	220	0.13	26	13	0.43	0	0	0
Pintail	356	133	0.08	0	0	0	0	0	0
Oystercatcher	468	268	0.16	4	2	0.08	20	17	0.16
Ringed Plover	126	72	0.04	0	0	0	17	9	0.09
Golden Plover	4,018	1,638	0.95	0	0	0	0	0	0
Grey Plover	364	173	0.1	1	1	0.02	5	2	0.02
Lapwing	5,857	4,172	2.42	0	0	0	290	77	0.73
Knot	418	108	0.06	0	0	0	0	0	0
Dunlin	6,433	2,558	1.48	1	1	0.02	375	155	1.48
Black-tailed Godwit	774	455	0.26	0	0	0	2	0	+
Bar-tailed Godwit	8	4	+	1	1	0.02	12	8	0.08
Curlew	510	396	0.23	4	2	0.07	469	129	1.23
Redshank	2,780	2,563	1.49	12	6	0.26	41	17	0.16
Turnstone	43	25	0.01	4	2	0.08	8	2	0.02

Table 9. cont.

Species	Langstone Harbour Peak No.	Mean No.	Mean Dns.	Loch Fleet Peak No.	Mean No.	Mean Dns.	Loch Indaal Peak No.	Mean No.	Mean Dns.
Brent Goose	1,972	1,902	4.71	0	0	0	29	25	0.07
Shelduck	215	143	0.35	175	90	0.16	25	28	0.07
Wigeon	932	881	2.18	996	687	1.18	313	261	0.69
Teal	153	73	0.18	144	126	0.22	145	127	0.34
Mallard	23	13	0.03	323	205	0.35	159	151	0.4
Pintail	98	55	0.14	0	0	0	5	6	0.02
Oystercatcher	417	352	0.87	1,089	923	1.59	198	230	0.61
Ringed Plover	60	46	0.11	8	3	0.01	216	206	0.55
Golden Plover	1	0	+	0	0	0	583	311	0.82
Grey Plover	177	118	0.29	0	0	0	11	16	0.04
Lapwing	55	29	0.07	0	0	0	180	108	0.29
Knot	22	12	0.03	56	14	0.02	70	50	0.13
Dunlin	5,078	3,320	8.22	392	188	0.32	313	286	0.76
Black-tailed Godwit	77	47	0.12	0	0	0	0	0	0
Bar-tailed Godwit	61	25	0.06	131	41	0.07	89	114	0.3
Curlew	201	164	0.41	300	257	0.44	360	261	0.69
Redshank	132	123	0.3	378	239	0.41	19	18	0.05
Turnstone	40	29	0.07	0	0	0	52	45	0.12

Species	Northwest Solent Peak No.	Mean No.	Mean Dns.	Orwell Estuary Peak No.	Mean No.	Mean Dns.	Solway Firth Peak No.	Mean No.	Mean Dns.
Brent Goose	2,653	2,114	2.81	1,547	790	0.64	0	0	0
Shelduck	282	207	0.27	1,130	825	0.67	766	954	0.06
Wigeon	1,351	971	1.29	1,809	1,346	1.1	1,922	2,094	0.13
Teal	717	408	0.54	1,344	747	0.61	599	515	0.03
Mallard	39	21	0.03	373	267	0.22	702	772	0.05
Pintail	180	68	0.09	202	175	0.14	3,929	2,246	0.13
Oystercatcher	104	93	0.12	1,743	1,506	1.23	15,306	19,902	1.19
Ringed Plover	73	29	0.04	152	72	0.06	103	111	0.01
Golden Plover	62	22	0.03	792	213	0.17	3,313	1,489	0.09
Grey Plover	194	142	0.19	451	259	0.21	370	237	0.01
Lapwing	67	39	0.05	1,200	813	0.66	1,603	1,571	0.09
Knot	171	99	0.13	2,771	1,120	0.91	2,685	2,398	0.14
Dunlin	3,980	3,313	4.4	4,292	2,512	2.05	7,307	10,464	0.63
Black-tailed Godwit	446	329	0.44	546	378	0.31	5	2	+
Bar-tailed Godwit	27	17	0.02	45	15	0.01	907	1,160	0.07
Curlew	156	121	0.16	584	542	0.44	2,830	3,355	0.2
Redshank	121	83	0.11	1,594	1,415	1.15	1,625	1,355	0.08
Turnstone	99	79	0.1	126	90	0.07	81	66	+

Species	Stour Estuary Peak No.	Mean No.	Mean Dns.	Strangford Lough Peak No.	Mean No.	Mean Dns.	Traeth Lafan Peak No.	Mean No.	Mean Dns.
Brent Goose	1,851	1,474	0.91	2,522	2,072	0.57	24	18	0.01
Shelduck	1,776	1,560	0.96	3,101	2,322	0.64	556	306	0.09
Wigeon	3,524	2,355	1.45	1,049	637	0.17	420	287	0.09
Teal	1,224	893	0.55	2,104	1,484	0.41	51	23	0.01
Mallard	269	214	0.13	326	296	0.08	284	217	0.07
Pintail	290	245	0.15	218	92	0.03	157	127	0.04
Oystercatcher	1,190	1,058	0.65	5,420	4,475	1.23	5,212	4,627	1.44
Ringed Plover	135	102	0.06	137	110	0.03	55	30	0.01
Golden Plover	493	172	0.11	1,819	1,321	0.36	0	0	0
Grey Plover	978	862	0.53	40	21	0.01	2	0	+
Lapwing	1,875	1,043	0.64	3,068	1,876	0.51	180	45	0.01
Knot	10,735	6,047	3.72	2,807	1,401	0.38	152	53	0.02
Dunlin	16,180	13,312	8.18	4,384	3,114	0.85	2,573	734	0.23
Black-tailed Godwit	1,644	857	0.53	313	238	0.07	0	0	0
Bar-tailed Godwit	144	121	0.07	737	588	0.16	43	11	+
Curlew	977	884	0.54	1,129	1,045	0.29	952	708	0.22
Redshank	1,755	1,435	0.88	2,018	1,900	0.52	714	599	0.19
Turnstone	538	462	0.28	144	126	0.03	115	58	0.02

ALDE COMPLEX

Site description

The Alde Complex is separated from the sea by the large shingle spit of Orfordness, and the estuary is comprised of three rivers – the Alde, Butley and Ore. The spit has been extending southwards since 1530, with the consequent effect of pushing the mouth of the River Ore progressively further to the southwest. Havergate Island lies at the confluence of the Rivers Ore and Butley, and supports the largest breeding colony of Avocets in Britain. The River Alde is relatively wide and shallow with mudflats in the upper reaches and saltmarsh including some *Spartina* exposed at low tide along both banks. The Butley River has extensive areas of mudflat, grading into saltmarsh and reedbed along its length. The River Ore has very little mudflat and is largely entrained by seawalls.

Industrial operations are virtually absent and water quality is excellent, however, a wide range of recreational activities takes place. Sailing occurs throughout (with moorings at Aldeburgh and Orford) and windsurfing, canoeing and water-skiing are permitted in the lower zones. Leisure use of the beach occurs around the mouth and wildfowling takes place over parts of the Alde, Butley and Orfordness. Other activities include oyster cultivation, fish trawling, eel netting, reed cutting and bait digging.

General bird distribution 2010/11

Area covered 5,807 ha; Mean total birds 23,502; Mean bird density 4.05 birds per ha.

The Alde Estuary supports high numbers of many waterbirds, with 57 species recorded during Low Tide Counts. These included two Spoonbills and one Bittern. Wigeon and Teal were the most numerous wildfowl species present, and were both found throughout the site with the Butley River, Havergate Island and the Snape Maltings used by marked concentrations. The extensive marshes on the site supported good numbers of other wildfowl, including three-figure counts of Shoveler, Gadwall, Pintail and Tufted Ducks, with Orfordness, Havergate Island, Oxley Marshes and Gedgrave Marshes being especially favoured. Up to 550 European White-fronted Geese were present at Aldeburgh & Sudbourne Marshes. This is a species infrequently recorded during Low Tide WeBS counts (as are Tundra Bean Geese and Smew, which were also noted at Alde Complex in 2010/11). Despite the lack of wide mudflats, the site held four-figure counts of several wader species, including Avocet, Dunlin and Redshank, whilst the presence of up to 38 Spotted Redshank in November was noteworthy.

Comparative bird distribution (Fig. 67)

Pintail are found on the Alde Complex in nationally important numbers though numbers counted during Core counts have fallen in keeping with the national index. Numbers counted during Low Tide counts have also decreased, declining from a mean count of 434 birds (0.08 birds per ha) in 2001/02 to 141 (0.02 birds per ha) in 2010/11. Havergate Island, the landward side of Orfordness and between Hazelwood Marshes and Snape Maltings were favoured by Pintail in both years. The Lantern Marshes and the seaward side of Orfordness were the main areas where birds were more apparent in 2001/02 than in 2010/11.

In keeping with the trends at many other east coast estuaries, numbers of Black-tailed Godwit on the Alde Complex have increased dramatically in the last ten years and the species is now present in internationally important numbers. Low Tide Counts reflect this increase, with the mean count in 2010/11 of 852 (0.20 birds per ha) significantly higher than the 39 (0.01 birds per ha) in 2001/02. The main concentrations of Black-tailed Godwits in 2010/11 were on the north side of the River Alde between Hazlewood Marshes and Snape Maltings, (where there was a mean count of 336 birds) and along the south side of Iken Marshes (where there was a mean count of 252 birds). The north end of the Butley River was the main area in 2001/02 and this area was also favoured in 2010/11 along with Sudbourne Marshes.

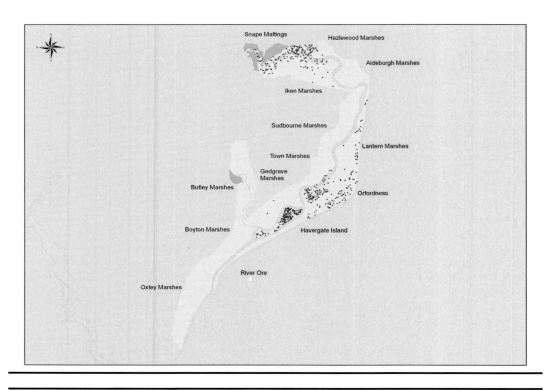

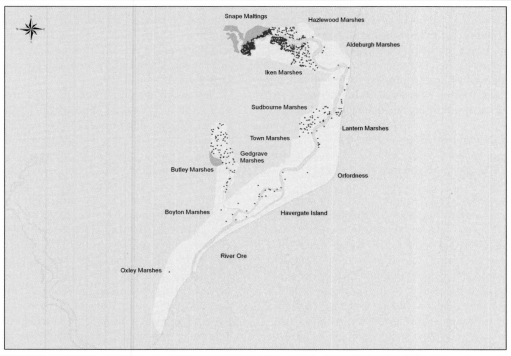

Figure 67. Low Tide distribution of Pintail (above) and Black-tailed Godwit (below) for the winters of 2001/02 (blue) and 2010/11 (red) on the Alde Complex. Yellow = intertidal; pale green = non-tidal; blue = subtidal. Grey areas were not counted in 2010/11.

CHICHESTER HARBOUR

Site description

Chichester Harbour is a large and complex estuary, situated between Chichester and Havant. It is connected to Langstone Harbour to the west by a channel along the north side of Hayling Island.

The Harbour is a land-locked area of deep salt-water channels; bounded by mud banks which are covered twice daily by tides flowing through the narrow entrance. There are sandbanks and shingle near the entrance and much of the shore at the high-tide mark is shingle. The river channels are muddy, whereas the intertidal areas south of Thorney Island are much sandier and support extensive areas of eelgrass and algae. Chichester Harbour is covered by international legislation, being designated as a Ramsar site and (combined with neighbouring Langstone Harbour) as an SPA. It also has national protection as a SSSI. The estuary is extremely popular with watersports enthusiasts, so although the majority of the shoreline is undeveloped with restricted access, the areas with public access tend to be heavily used.

General bird distribution 2010/11

Area covered 3,136 ha; Mean total birds 36,918; Mean bird density 11.8 birds per ha.

With 55 species recorded during the Low Tide Counts, Chichester Harbour held the highest number of the sites counted. Four-figure counts were recorded for Shelduck and Wigeon, whilst, Teal, Pintail Mallard, Tufted Duck and Red-breasted Mergansers were all recorded in three-figure numbers. The Great Deeps, traditionally a favoured area for many wildfowl, were not counted in 2010/11; this will have affected the overall totals of these species. Single Black Brant, Smew, Red-throated Diver, two Slavonian Grebes and 26 European White-fronted Geese were more unusual visitors to Chichester Harbour in 2010/11.

Dunlin was the most numerous wader, with a mean site count of nearly 16,500 birds. Knot, Bar-tailed Godwit and Lapwing were also present in four-figure numbers, with the extensive mudflats on the south side of

Thorney Island being favoured by these species. An additional eight species (Oystercatcher, Golden Plover, Grey Plover, Sanderling, Black-tailed Godwit, Curlew, Redshank and Turnstone) were recorded in three-figure numbers.

Comparative bird distribution (Fig. 68)

Dark-bellied Brent Geese are found in internationally important numbers in Chichester Harbour, it being the third most important site for the species. It was by far the most numerous wildfowl species present in 2010/11, with a peak count of over 7,100 birds. Despite the Great Deeps not having been counted in 2010/11, the mean density was still almost double that of 2001/02, being 6,753 birds (2.15 birds per ha) compared with 3,626 birds (1.17 birds per ha). Dark-bellied Brent Geese are found throughout the site, with the top end of Bosham Channel and around Thorney Island used by distinct concentrations in both years.

Although Knot numbers on the Chichester and Langstone Harbours SPA have been stable over the course of the last 25 years, in the last ten years they have seen a medium decline (*http://www.bto.org/webs/alerts/*). Low Tide Counts at Chichester Harbour do not reflect this decrease, however, with a mean site count of 3,569 (1.43 birds per ha) in 2010/11 compared to 580 (0.24 birds per ha) in 2001/02. The main concentration of Knots in 2010/11 was at the south end of Thorney Island where there was a mean count of 3,178 birds (7.93 birds per ha) compared with just 37 birds (0.09 birds per ha) in 2001/02. Another favoured area in 2010/11 was near Mengham on Hayling Island. In 2001/02, the main concentration was on the east side of Thorney Island with a mean of 264 birds (7.33 birds per ha), however despite the increased number of birds counted on the site in the recent winter this area was not widely used, with a mean of just eight birds (0.21 birds per ha).

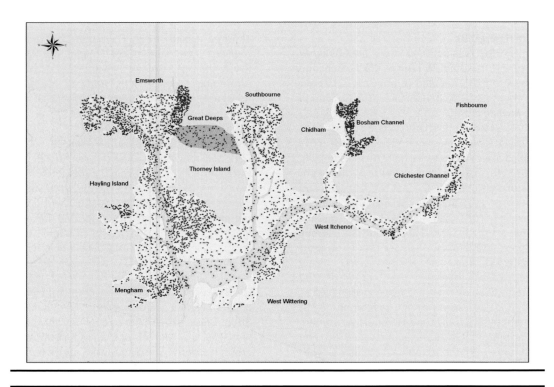

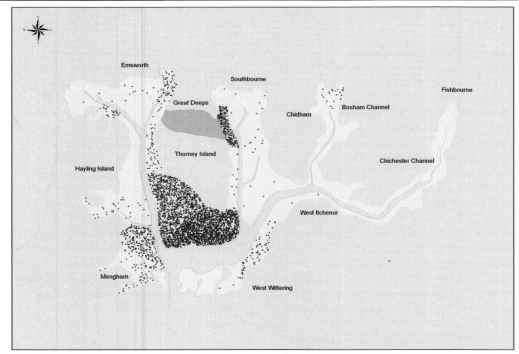

Figure 68. Low Tide distribution of Dark-bellied Brent Goose (above) and Knot (below) for the winters of 2001/02 (blue) and 20010/11 (red) at Chichester Harbour. Yellow = intertidal; pale green = non-tidal; blue = subtidal. Grey areas were not counted in 2010/11.

CROUCH-ROACH ESTUARY

Site description

The Crouch Estuary is traditionally considered together with its tributary, the Roach; the two converge on the coast of south Essex in eastern England. The River Crouch carves a shallow valley between two ridges of London Clay, whilst the River Roach is set predominantly between areas of brick earth and loams with patches of sand and gravel. Both rivers form dendritic creeks and low-lying riverine islands.

The surrounding habitat is almost exclusively lowland farmland and grazing marsh, with few urban developments. The intertidal zone along the rivers is 'squeezed' between the sea walls along both banks and the river channel, leaving a thin strip of tidal mud. The Crouch & Roach Estuary is an integral component of the phased Mid-Essex Coast SPA.

Threats to this SPA and environs are posed by disturbance caused by air activities, the development of a wharf, sea defences, homes and shops, car parks, marinas, holiday parks and an airport, and saltmarsh loss caused by sea-level rise. Seventy-five percent of the site is deemed by Natural England to be in unfavourable declining condition due mainly to saltmarsh erosion.

General bird distribution 2010/11

Area covered 2,896 ha; Mean total birds 23,913; Mean bird density 8.3 birds per ha.

With very little open mudflat habitat, numbers of wading birds are generally much lower on the Crouch-Roach than on other estuaries. Dunlin were the most abundant wader, present throughout the site and peaking at over 6,000 birds. Lapwing and Golden Plover were present in four-figure numbers, both favouring Bridgemarsh Island, Shelford Creek and the newly created managed realignment site on Wallasea Island. Redshank, typically, were numerous along the many creeks.

The narrow creeks also supported good numbers of Little Grebes with a peak count of 157 in December. Other wildfowl were present throughout the site, with Wigeon, Dark-bellied Brent Goose, Teal and Shelduck being the most numerous. As with the waders, Bridgemarsh Island and Shelford Creek were favoured areas for many wildfowl species along with Clementsgreen Creek and the bottom end of Paglesham Reach.

Comparative bird distribution (Fig. 69)

Teal occur on the Crouch-Roach Estuary in large numbers, though just fall short of the national important threshold. Numbers here have risen steadily in the last few years and this increase has been reflected in the Low Tide Counts. The mean total for the site has gone up from 2,218 (0.72 birds per ha) in 2004/05 to 3,023 (1.04 birds per ha) in 2010/11. With its narrow creeks, the Crouch-Roach is ideal habitat for Teal. Present throughout much of the site, particular concentrations in both years were found at Clementsgreen Creek, along Paglesham Reach, Shelford Creek and at Great Wakering. The areas around Bridgemarsh Island and along Paglesham Creek were also favoured in 2010/11 which only held a few birds in 2004/05, whilst the managed realignment site on Wallasea Island held the highest densities with a mean density of 7.87 birds per ha, which may also account for the increase in the overall mean total.

The Crouch-Roach, along with many east coast sites has seen a steady rise in the number of wintering Avocets over the past decade. Even between the most recent sets of Low Tide counts, this increase is apparent, with the mean site total increasing from 251 (0.26 birds per ha) in 2004/05 to 328 (0.32 birds per ha) in 2010/11. In both years, the favoured areas were along Paglesham Reach and along the east side of Potton Island. In 2010/11, birds were also recorded along the seafront area of Burnham-on-Crouch, an area not used extensively in 2004/05.

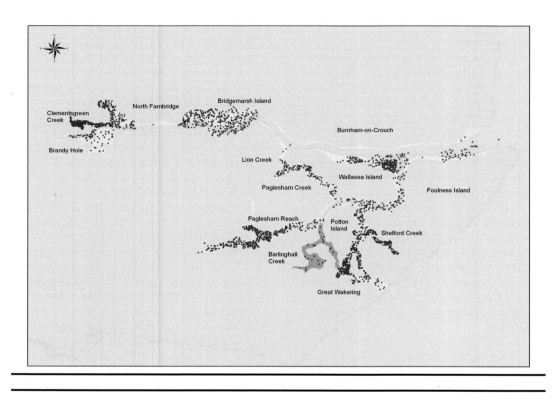

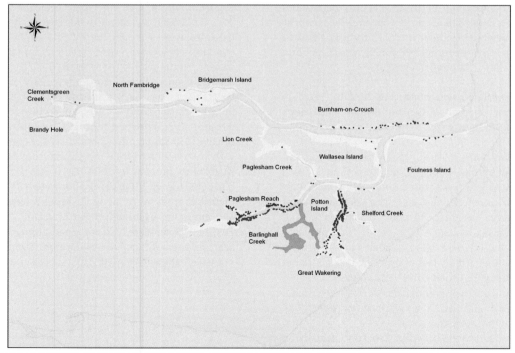

Figure 69. Low Tide distribution of Teal (above) and Avocet (below) for the winters of 2004/05 (blue) and 2010/11 (red) on Crouch-Roach Estuary. Yellow = intertidal; pale green = non-tidal; blue = subtidal. Grey areas were not counted in 2010/11.

TRAETH LAFAN (LAVAN SANDS)

Site description

Traeth Lafan is an extensive intertidal area situated at the northern end of the Menai Strait, between Bangor and Llanfairfechan. Three freshwater streams flow across the flats at low tide. There are a variety of habitats including both exposed and sheltered areas of sand, mudflats with an area of shingle, and mussel beds near Bangor. Some relatively small areas of saltmarsh have developed along the shore, particularly at the mouth of the Rhaeadrfawr and south-west of Llanfairfechan. The intertidal flats support an abundance of invertebrate fauna, which in turn attract large numbers of waterbirds. Industrial activity is limited, however, recreational and leisure use occurs. Boating, sailing and windsurfing take place in the channel, whilst walkers and dogs can cause disturbance to high tide roosts along the mainland coastline. Wildfowling, along with commercial and small-scale cockle gathering is another feature. Potential threats include oil pollution and the establishment of cord-grass in a small area of the site.

General bird distribution 2010/11

Area covered 4,654 ha; Mean total birds 7,939; Mean bird density 1.7 birds per ha.

With its large open mudflats, Traeth Lafan supports high numbers of many species. However, the mean totals were not as high as may have been expected owing to the fact that many birds shelter within inaccessible gullies at low tide, and so can only be seen when they are flushed (R. Pritchard pers. comm.). Only Oystercatcher and Dunlin were recorded in four figure numbers. Lapwing, Knot, Curlew, Redshank and Turnstone were all recorded in three figures with the Bangor Flats close to Bangor and opposite Beaumaris being the most favoured areas. Single Jack Snipe and Whimbrel represented more unusual records for the WeBS Low Tide count scheme. Whilst many waders typically favoured the open flats, many of the wildfowl species were much closer to shore on the Bangor Flats, at Abergwyngregyn and Llanfairfechan. Wigeon was the most numerous duck, peaking at 420 birds, whilst

Mallard and Pintail were also recorded in three figure counts. Little Egret numbers peaked at 22 birds in November, with birds present on the Bangor Flats and along the Menai Straits towards the Menai Bridge.

Comparative bird distribution (Fig. 70)

Numbers of Shelduck in Britain have shown a steady decline in the last ten years, as the population may have experienced a slight eastward shift across the North Sea into The Netherlands (Holt *et al.* 2011). Low Tide Counts at Traeth Lafan during this period have also mirrored this, with the mean site count of 439 (0.09 birds per ha) falling to 305 (0.07 birds per ha) in 2010/11. The favoured area for Shelduck within Traeth Lafan is on the sheltered Bangor Flats around Bangor. In 2010/11, fewer birds were seen on the more open flats towards Abergwyngregyn than in 2002/03, possibly in response to a colder winter. Birds were also present along the Anglesey coast between Beaumaris and Fryars Road. Oystercatchers are present at Traeth Lafan in nationally important numbers, with a five-year mean of 6,606 birds based on Core counts (p. 102 this report). Numbers of Oystercatchers have increased over the past 25 years and are stable during the last ten years (see *http://www.bto.org/webs/alerts/*). Low Tide Counts have shown a slight decline between 2002/03 and 2010/11, falling from a mean site count of 5,609 (1.74 birds per ha) to 4,626 (1.43 birds per ha). In both years, Oystercatchers were found in high densities off Llanfairfechan, though in 2002/03 the mean density here was 3.73 birds per ha (mean count of 932 birds) compared with 2.26 birds per ha (mean count of 566 birds) in 2010/11. In 2002/03, the other favoured area was north of Aber Ogwen, but in 2010/11 the main concentration was further to the west on Bangor Flats and on the Anglesey coast south of Beaumaris. Dutchman Bank was also used much more extensively by Oystercatchers in 2010/11 than in 2002/03.

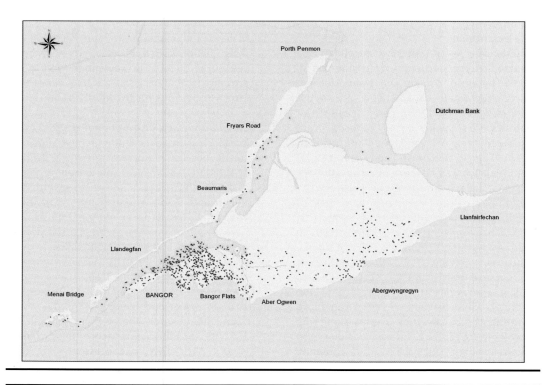

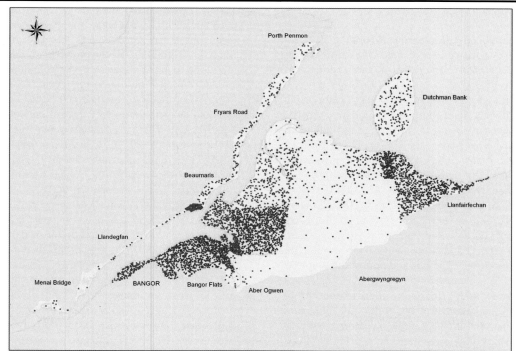

Figure 70. Low Tide distribution of Shelduck (above) and Oystercatcher (1 dot = 2 birds) (below) for the winters of 2002/03 (blue) and 2010/11 (red) at Traeth Lafan. Yellow = intertidal; blue = subtidal.

ACKNOWLEDGEMENTS

We are very grateful to the following people and organisations that contributed to the WeBS Low Tide Count scheme in the winter of 2010/11. Apologies to anyone omitted accidentally from the list.

Organisers: Hugh Thurgate, George Henderson, Chris Tyas, Rick Vonk, Mick Wright, Jim Rowe, Mark Smart, Chris Cockburn, Bob Howells, Ed Wiseman, Dave Hughes, Russell Wood, Ian Castle, Ed Rowsell, Rhion Pritchard Graham Johnstone, Simon Taylor, John Armitage, Michael Carrier, Andy Riches.

Other counters: Alastair Flannagan, Colin Peake, James Gloyn, Ralph Loughlin, Barry Collins, Brian Fellows, Stephen Gilbert, Horace Lee, John and Kay Shillitoe, Christopher Vine, Richard Williamson, C Woodburn, Ken Wright, Jeremy High, Andy Johnson, Owen Parker, Richard Black, Georgia Siddle, M Evans, Sophie Flax, John Arnott, Chris Lewis, Martin Smith, Paul Charlton, Peter Davidson, Jeff Delve, John Green, Tim Lawrence, Peter Mason, Nick Robson, Jillian Taylor, Steven Swaby, Leslie Pomphrett, Suzanne Grimwood, D Bruce, Mike Andrews, N Green, Jason Cook, Anne de Potier, Pete Potts, David Ellis, Geoff Gibbs, Gareth Howells, Gareth Jones, Buckley Jones, John Small, E.Rees, Stuart Graham, Bob Davison, Stephanie Elliot, Kate Horsfall, Dave Fairlamb, Norman Holton, Dave Shackleton, Frank Mawby, Anna White, Malcolm Ginns, Peter Jeavons, Anthony Bowman, Ian Enlander, Niall McCutcheon, James McNair, Paddy Mackie, Kerry Mackie, Jim Wilson, Dot Blakeley, Jon Lees, Kevin Mawhinney, Margaret Magre, Seamus Magouran, Andrew Upton, Jo Whatmough, Craig McCoy, Terry Paton, David Thompson, Liane Hamill, Frances Donan, Philip Johnston, Tamsin Roberts, Cal James, Alan Silcock, Andrew Crory, Rachael Bain, Richard Weyl, Bryan Pinchen, John Coit, Reg Etheridge, Rodney West, Dave Crawshaw, John Davies, Norman Lloyd, James McLeod, Michael Pratt, Dudley Sheppard, Barry Moss, Kieren Alexander, Aaron Howe, Terry Bugg, and Suffolk Wildlife Trust.

We would also like to acknowledge Harwich Haven Authority for their part in funding the Stour and Orwell counts.

Robert Gillmor

References

Atkinson, P.W., Maclean, I.M.D. & Clark, N.A. 2010. Impacts of shellfisheries and nutrient inputs on waterbird communities in the Wash, England. *Journal of Applied Ecology* 47: 191-199.

Austin, G.E., Collier, M.P. & Rehfisch, M.M. 2007. Non-estuarine Coastal Waterbird Survey: Population estimates and broad comparisons with previous surveys. *BTO Research Report* 501. BTO, Thetford.

Austin, G.E. & Rehfisch, M.M. 2005. Shifting nonbreeding distributions of migratory fauna in relation to climate change. *Global Change Biology* 11: 31-38.

Baillie, S.R., Marchant, J.H., Leech, D.I., Renwick, A.R., Eglington, S.M., Joys, A.C., Noble, D.G., Barimore, C., Conway, G., Downie, I.S., Risely, K. & Robinson, R.A. 2012. BirdTrends 2011. *BTO Research Report* 609. BTO, Thetford.

Banks, A.N., Burton, N.H.K., Calladine, J.R. & Austin, G.E. 2009. Indexing winter gull numbers in Great Britain using data from 1953 to 2004 Winter Gull Roost Surveys. *Bird Study* 56: 103-119.

Birdlife International. 2012. The IUCN Red List for birds. Downloaded from www.birdlife.org - 20 August 2012.

Boland, H. & Crowe, O. 2012. *Irish wetland bird survey: waterbird status and distribution 2001/02 - 2008/09*. BirdWatch Ireland, Kilcoole, Co. Wicklow.

Brown, S., Gilbert, G. & Wotton, S. 2012. Bitterns and Bittern Conservation in the UK. *British Birds* 105: 58-87.

Calbrade, N.A., Holt, C.A., Austin, G.E., Mellan, H.J., Hearn, R.D., Stroud, D.A. & Musgrove, A.J. 2010. *Waterbirds in the UK 2008/09: The Wetland Bird Survey*. BTO/RSPB/JNCC, Thetford.

Conway, G.J., Burton, N.H.K., Handschuh, M. & Austin, G.E. 2008. UK population estimates from the 2007 Breeding Little Ringed Plover and Ringed Plover surveys. *BTO Research Report* 510.

Coulson, J.C. 2010. A long-term study of the population dynamics of Common Eiders *Somateria mollissima*: why do several parameters fluctuate markedly? *Bird Study* 75: 1-18.

Crowe, O., Austin, G.E., Colhoun, K., Cranswick, P.A., Kershaw, M., & Musgrove, A.J. 2008. Estimates and trends of waterbird numbers wintering in Ireland, 1994/95 to 2003/04. *Bird Study* 55: 66-77.

D'Alba, L., Monaghan, P. & Nager, R.G. 2010. Advances in laying date and increasing population size suggest positive responses to climate change in Common Eiders *Somateria mollissima* in Iceland. *Ibis* 152: 19-28.

Dalby, L., Fox, A.D., Petersen, I.K., Delany, S. & Svenning, J-C. 2012. Temperature does not dictate the wintering distributions of European dabbling duck species. *Ibis* online early: doi: 10.1111/j.1474-919X.2012.01257.x

Daunt, F., Afanasyev, V., Silk, J.R.D. & Wanless, S. 2006. Extrinsic and intrinsic determinants of winter foraging and breeding phenology in a temperate seabird. *Behavioural Ecology & Sociobiology* 59: 381-388.

Davis, A.H. & Vinicombe, K.E. 2011. The probable breeding of Ferruginous Ducks in Avon. *British Birds* 104: 77-83.

Delany, S., Scott, D., Dodman, T. & Stroud, D. (Eds). 2009. An Atlas of Wader Populations in Africa and Western Eurasia. Wetlands International, Wageningen, The Netherlands.

Dillon, I.A., Smith, T.D., Williams, S.J., Haysom, S. & Eaton, M.A. 2009. Status of Red-throated Divers *Gavia stellata* in Britain in 2006. *Bird Study* 56: 147-157.

Eaton, M.A., Brown, A.F., Noble, D.G., Musgrove, A.J., Hearn, R.D., Aebisher, N.J., Gibbons, D.W., Evans, A. & Gregory, R.D. 2009. Birds of Conservation Concern 3: the population status of birds in the United Kingdom, Channel Islands and Isle of Man. *British Birds* 102: 296–341.

Ekroos, J., Fox, A.D., Christensen, T.K., Petersen, I.K., Kilpi, M., Jonsson, J.E., Green, M., Laursen, K., Cervencl, A., de Boer, P., Nilsson, L., Meissner, W., Garthe, S. & Ost, M. 2012. Declines amongst breeding Eider *Somateria mollissima* numbers in the Baltic/Wadden Sea flyway. *Ornis Fennica* 89: 81-90.

Fox, A.D., Madsen, J., Boyd, H., Kuijken, E., Norriss, D.W., Tombre, I.M. & Stroud, D.A. 2005. Effects of agricultural change on abundance, fitness components, and distribution of two arctic-nesting goose populations. *Global Change Biology* 11: 881-893.

Fox, A.D., Francis, I. & Walsh, A. 2012. *Report of 2008/2009 international census of Greenland White-fronted Geese*. Greenland White-fronted Goose Study, Kalø & National Parks and Wildlife Service, Wexford.

Furness, R.W., Mable, B., Savory, F., Griffiths, K., Baillie, S.R. & Heubeck, M. 2010. Subspecies status of common eiders *Somateria mollissima* in Shetland based on morphology and DNA. *Bird Study* 57: 330-335.

Gill, J.A., Watkinson, A.R., Sutherland, W.J. 1996. The impact of sugar beet farming practice on wintering pink-footed goose populations. *Biological Conservation* 76: 95-100.

Gotland University. 2012. Research in Sea Ducks in the Baltic Sea. Gotland University, Sweden.

Grant, M. 2002. Whimbrel. The Migration Atlas: Movements of the Birds of Britain and Ireland, T. & A.D. Poyser, London, 329-331.

Grebmeier, J.M., Overland, J.E., Moore, S.E., Farley, E.V., Carmack, E.C., Cooper, L.W., Frey, K.E., Helle, J.H., McLaughlin, F.A. & McNutt, S.L. 2006. A major ecosystem shift in the Northern Bering Sea. *Science* 311: 1461-1464.

Green, G. 2004. *The Birds of Dorset*. Phoenix Offset/Hanway Press Ltd.

Griffin, L. 2011. Svalbard Barnacle Goose monitoring in 2010/11. *GooseNews* 10: 21.

Guillemain, M., Sadoul, N. & Simon, G. 2005. European flyway permeability and migration in Teal (*Anas crecca*), an analysis based on ring recoveries. *Ibis* 147: 688–696.

Heubeck, M. & Mellor, M. 2012. SOTEAG Ornithological Monitoring Programme 2011 Summary Report. SOTEAG, Aberdeen.

Hall, C., Glanville, J.R, Boland, H., Einarsson, O., McElwaine, G., Holt, C.A., Spray, C.J. & Rees, E.C. (in press). Population size and breeding success of Icelandic Whooper Swans *Cygnus cygnus*: results of the 2010 international census.

Harvey, P.V. & Heubeck, M. (in prep.). Changes in the wintering population and distribution of Slavonian Grebes in Shetland.

Holling, M. & the Rare Breeding Birds Panel. 2012. Rare breeding birds in the United Kingdom in 2010. *British Birds* 105: 352-416.

Holt, C.A., Austin, G.E., Calbrade, N.A., Mellan, H.J, Mitchell, C., Stroud, D.A., Wotton, S.R. & Musgrove, A.J. 2011. *Waterbirds in the UK 2009/10: The Wetland Bird Survey*. BTO/RSPB/JNCC, Thetford.

Hornman, M., Hustings, F., Koffijberg, K., Kleefstra, R., Klaassen, O. & van Winden, E. SOVON Ganzen- en Zwanenwerkgroep & Soldaat L. 2012. *Watervogels in Nederland in 2009/10. SOVON-monitoringrapport 2012/02, Waterdienst-rapport BM 12.06*. SOVON Vogelonderzoek Nederland, Nijmegen.

Hornman, M., Hustings, F., Koffijberg, K. & van Winden, E., & SOVON Ganzen- en Zwanenwerkgroep 2011. *Watervogels in Nederland in 2008/09. SOVON-monitoringrapport 2011/03, Waterdienst-rapport BM 10.24*. SOVON Vogelonderzoek Nederland, Nijmegen.

JNCC. 2011. Seabird population trends: 2011 http://www.jncc.gov.uk/page-3201. JNCC. Accessed 12 July 2012.

Keller, V. 2000. Winter distribution and population change of Red-crested Pochard *Netta rufina* in southwestern and central Europe. *Bird Study* 47: 176-185.

Keller, V. 2009. Within-winter movements: a common phenomenon in the Common Pochard *Aythya ferina. J. of Ornithology* 150:483-494.

Keller, V. & Burkhardt, M. 2011 Monitoring hivernal des oiseaux d'eau: Résultats des recensements des oiseaux d'eau 2009/10 en Suisse. Stn. ornithologique suisse, Sempach.

Keller, V. & Müller, C. 2012. Monitoring hivernal des oiseaux d'eau: Résultats des recensements des oiseaux d'eau 2010/11 en Suisse. Stn. ornithologique suisse, Sempach.

Kendall, M.A., Burrowes, M.T., Southward, A.J. & Hawkins, S.J. 2004. Predicting the effects of marine climate change on the invertebrate prey of the birds of rocky shores. *Ibis* 146: 40-47.

Lehikoinen, A., Jaatinen, K., Vahatalo, A., Clausen, P., Crowe, O., Deceuninck, B., Hearn, R.D., Holt, C.A., Hornman, M., Keller, V., Nilsson, L., Langendoen, T., Wahl, J. & Fox, A.D. (in prep.). Rapid climate-driven shifts in wintering distribution of waterfowl.

Lehikoinen, A., Kilpi, M. & Ost, M. 2006. Winter climate affects subsequent breeding success of eiders. *Global Change Biology* 12: 1355-1365.

Lourenço, P.M. & Piersma, T. 2008. Changes in the non-breeding distribution of Continental Black-tailed Godwits *Limosa limosa limosa* over 50 years: a synthesis of surveys. *Wader Study Group Bulletin* 115: 91-97.

Maclean, I.M.D., Burton, N.H.K. & Austin, G.E. 2006. *Declines in over-wintering diving ducks at Lough Neagh and Lough Beg: comparisons of within site, regional, national and European trends.* BTO Research Report 432. BTO, Thetford.

Maclean, I.M.D., Austin, G.E., Rehfisch, M.M., Blew, J., Crowe, O., Delany, S., Devos, K., Deceuninck, B., Gunther, K., Laursen, K., van Roomen, M. & Wahl, J. 2008. Climate change causes rapid changes in the distribution and site abundance of birds in winter. *Global Change Biology* 14: 2489-2500.

Mitchell, C., Fox, A.D., Harradine, J. & Clausager, I. 2008. Measures of annual breeding success amongst Eurasian Wigeon *Anas penelope. Bird Study* 55: 43-51.

Mitchell, C., Coulhoun, K., Fox, A., Griffin, L., Hall, C., Hearn, R., Holt, C. & Walsh, A. 2010. Trends in goose numbers wintering in Britain and Ireland, 1995 to 2008. *Ornis svecica* 20: 128-143.

Mitchell, C. 2011a. *Status and distribution of Icelandic-breeding geese: results of the 2010 international census.* WWT Report, Slimbridge.

Mitchell, C. 2011b. Latest monitoring of British Greylag Geese in Northwest Scotland. *GooseNews* 10:17.

Mitchell, C. 2011c. Greenland Barnacle Goose counts, 2010/11. *GooseNews* 10:20.

Mitchell, C., Hearn, R. & Stroud, D. 2012. The merging of populations of Greylag Geese breeding in Britain. *British Birds* 105: 498-505.

Musgrove, A.J., Langston, R.H.W., Baker, H. & Ward, R.M. 2003. *Estuarine Waterbirds at Low Tide: the WeBS Low Tide Counts 1992/93 to 1998/99.* WSG/BTO/WWT/RSPB/JNCC, Thetford.

Musgrove, A.J., Austin, G.E., Hearn, R.D., Holt, C.A., Stroud, D.A. & Wotton, S.R. 2011. Overwinter population estimates of British waterbirds. *British Birds* 104: 364-397.

Newth, J. 2011a. Breeding success of Bewick's Swans wintering in Britain in 2010/11. *GooseNews* 10: 12-13.

Newth, J. 2011b. Breeding success of Iceland Whooper Swans wintering in Britain and Ireland in 2010/11. *GooseNews* 10: 13-14.

Nilsson, L. 2008. Changes in number and distribution of wintering waterfowl in Sweden during 40 years. *Ornis Svecica* 18: 135-226.

O'Brien, S.H., Wilson, L.J., Webb, A. & Cranswick, P.A. 2008. Revised estimate of numbers of wintering Red-throated Divers Gavia stellata in Great Britain. *Bird Study* 55: 152-160.

Pennington, M., Osborn, K., Harvey, P., Riddington, R., Okill, D., Ellis, P. & Heubeck, M. 2004. *The Birds of Shetland*. Helm, London.

Reay, P. & Kent, P. 2011. How many Avocets now winter on the Tamar. *Devon Birds* 64: 32-35.

Reed, J. 2011a. Taiga Bean Geese in Britain in 2010/11. *GooseNews* 10:16.

Reed, J. 2011b. Breeding success of European White-fronted Geese in 2010. *GooseNews* 10:19.

Reed, J. 2011c. Breeding success in Dark-bellied Brent Geese in 2010/11. *GooseNews* 10:23.

Rees, E.C. & Beekman, J.H. 2010. Northwest European Bewick's Swans: a population in decline. *British Birds* 103: 640-650.

Rehfisch, M.M, Austin, G.E., Freeman, S.N., Armitage, M.J.S. & Burton, N.H.K. 2004. The possible impact of climate change on the future distribution and numbers of waders on Britain's non-estuarine coast. *Ibis* 146: 70-81.

Reneerkens, J., Behoussa, A., Boland, H., Collier, M., Grond, K., Gunther, K., Hallgrimson, G.T., Hansen, J., Meissner, W., de Meulenaar, B., Ntiamoa-Baidu, Y., Piersma, T., Poot, M., van Roomen, M., Summers, R.W., Tomkovich, P.S. & Underhill, L.G. 2009. Sanderlings using African-Eurasian flyways: a review of current knowledge. *Wader Study Group Bulletin* 116: 2-20.

Rose, P.M. & Stroud, D.A. 1994. Estimating international waterfowl populations: current activity and future directions. *Wader Study Group Bulletin* 73: 19-26.

Sauter, A., Korner-Nievergelt, F. & Jenni, L. 2010. Evidence of climate change effects on within-winter movements of European Mallards *Anas platyrhynchos*. *Ibis* 152: 600-609.

Scott, D.A. & Rose, P.M. 1996. *Atlas of Anatidae populations in Africa and western Eurasia*. Wetlands International Publ. 41, Wageningen.

Skov, H., Heinänen, S., Žydelis, R, Bellebaum, J., Bzoma, S., Dagys, M., Durinck, J., Garthe, S., Grishanov, G., Hario, M., Kieckbusch, J.J., Kube, J., Kuresoo, A., Larsson, K., Luigujoe, L., Meissner, W., Nehls, H.W., Nilsson, L., Petersen, I.K., Roos, M.M., Pihl, S., Sonntag, N., Stock, A., Stipniece, A. & Wahl, J. 2011. *Waterbird Populations and Pressures in the Baltic Sea*.

TemaNord 2011: 550. Nordic Council of Ministers, Copenhagen.

Soloviev, M. & Tomkovich, P. (Eds.). 2011. *Arctic birds: an international breeding conditions survey*. Online DB: http://www.arcticbirds.ru/ Accessed 9 May 2012.

Thaxter, C.B., Sansom, A., Thewlis, R.M., Calbrade, N.A., Ross-Smith, V.H., Bailey, S., Mellan, H.J. & Austin, G.E. 2010. Wetland Bird Survey Alerts 2006/07: Changes in numbers of wintering waterbirds in the Constituent Countries of the United Kingdom, SPAs and SSSIs. *BTO Research Report* 506. BTO, Thetford.

Tomkanova, I., Reid, N., Boland, H. & Fox, A.D. (in prep.). Are declines in the diving water bird guild at Lough Neagh Special Protection Area due to flyway causes?

Trinder, M.N,., Rowcliffe, J.M., Pettifor, R.A. & Rees, E.C. 2005. Information paper: Status and population viability of the pink-footed goose in the UK. Institute of Zoology/WWT, 18 pp.

Trinder, M., Mitchell, C., Swann, R.L. & Urquhart, C. 2010. Status and population viability of Icelandic Greylag Geese *Anser anser* in Scotland. *Wildfowl* 60: 64-84.

Wernham, C.V., Toms, M.P., Marchant, J.H., Clark, J.A., Siriwardena, G.M. & Baillie, S.R. (Eds). 2002. *The Migration Atlas: movements of birds of Britain & Ireland*. T & AD Poyser, London.

Wetlands International. 2012. *"Waterbird Population Estimates"*. Retrieved from wpe.wetlands.org – 20 August 2012.

Wotton, S., Grantham, M., Moran, N. & Gilbert, G. 2011. Bittern distribution and abundance in the UK during the 2009/10 winter. *British Birds* 104: 636-641.

Zipkin, E.F., Gardner, B., Gilbert, A.T., O'Connell, A.F., Royle, J.A. & Silverman, E.D. 2010. Distribution patterns of sea ducks in relation to the North Atlantic Oscillation and environmental characteristics. *Oecologia* 163: 893-902.

Glossary

The terms listed below are generally restricted to those that have been adopted specifically for use within WeBS or more widely for monitoring.

1% criterion The criterion identifies sites as being of *international importance* if at least 1% of the *waterbirds* of a particular migratory flyway or population regularly make use of a site during their annual cycle. The term thus relates to the proportion (1%) that is used as a criterion of site selection. First used in the Ramsar Convention, the 1% criterion is used widely in assessment of site importance.

1% threshold This logically derives from the *1% criterion* and relates to the number of birds that are used as the nominal 1% of the population for the purposes of site selection. Thus, an international population of 82,000 Oystercatcher has a derived 1% threshold of 8,200.

African-Eurasian Migratory Waterbird Agreement (AEWA) An independent international treaty developed under the Convention on the Conservation of Migratory Species of Wild Animals (*'Bonn Convention'*). Parties to the Agreement are called upon to engage in a wide range of conservation actions addressing key issues such as species and habitat conservation, management of human activities, research and monitoring, education and information, and implementation. www.unep-aewa.org

All-Ireland Comprises the whole island of Ireland (Northern Ireland and the Republic of Ireland).

British Trust for Ornithology (BTO) The BTO is a well-respected organisation, combining the skills of professional scientists and volunteer birdwatchers to carry out research on birds in all habitats and throughout the year. Data collected by the various surveys form the basis of extensive and unique databases, which enable the BTO to objectively advise conservation bodies, government agencies, planners and scientists on a diverse range of issues involving birds. www.bto.org

Complex site A *WeBS site* that consists of two or more *WeBS sectors*.

Core Counts The fundamental WeBS counts that monitor all types of wetlands throughout the UK once per month on, or as near as possible to, pre-selected *priority dates*. Used to determine population estimates and trends and identify important sites.

Great Britain The countries of England Scotland and Wales (excludes the Channel Isles and the Isle of Man).

Incomplete counts When presenting counts of an individual species, a large proportion of the number of birds was suspected to have been missed, *e.g.* due to part coverage of the site or poor counting conditions, or when presenting the total number of birds of all species on the site, a significant proportion of the total number was missed.

I-WeBS An independent but complementary scheme operating in the Republic of Ireland to monitor non-breeding *waterbirds*, organised by BirdWatch Ireland, the National Parks and Wildlife Service (Ireland) and The *Wildfowl & Wetlands Trust*. http://www.birdwatchireland.ie/Default.aspx?tabid=111

Joint Nature Conservation Committee (JNCC) JNCC is the statutory body constituted by the Environmental Protection Act 1990 to be responsible for research and advice on nature conservation at both UK and international levels. The committee is established by Natural England, Scottish Natural Heritage and the Countryside Council for Wales, together with independent representatives from the Countryside Commission and Northern Ireland, and is supported by specialist staff. www.jncc.gov.uk

Local Organiser Person responsible for coordinating counters and counts at a local level, normally a county or large estuary, and the usual point of contact with the *WeBS office*.

Low Tide Counts (LTC) WeBS counts made at low tide to assess the relative importance of different parts of individual estuaries as feeding areas for intertidal *waterbirds*.

Nordic Waterbirds and Climate Network (NOWAC) A research group investigating distribution of waterbirds in Nordic countries with particular reference to climate change.

Priority date Pre-determined dates published by the *WeBS Office* to aid coordination of surveys. Counters are asked to count on, or as near as possible to, priority dates to minimise the risk of missing birds or double counting.

Royal Society for the Protection of Birds (RSPB) The RSPB is the charity that takes action for wild birds and the environment in the UK. The RSPB is the national BirdLife partner in the UK. www.rspb.org.uk

United Kingdom *Great Britain* and Northern Ireland (excludes the Channel Isles and the Isle of Man).

Waterbirds WeBS follows the definition adopted by *Wetlands International*. This includes a large number of families, those occurring regularly in the UK being divers, grebes, cormorants, herons, storks, ibises and spoonbills, wildfowl, cranes, rails, waders, gulls and terns.

WeBS count unit The area/boundary within which a count is made. The generic term for *WeBS sites, WeBS sub-sites* and *WeBS sectors*.

WeBS Office Main administrative centre for the day-to-day running of WeBS and main point of contact for information or data pertaining to WeBS (webs@bto.org).

WeBS Online The online database for the submission and retrieval of WeBS Core Count, Low Tide Count and supplementary data. www.bto.org/webs

WeBS sector The unit of division of large *sites* into areas that can be counted by one person in a reasonable time period. They are often demarcated by geographic features to facilitate recognition of the boundary by counters. The finest level at which data are recorded.

WeBS site A biologically meaningful area that represents a discrete area used by *waterbirds* such that birds regularly move within but only occasionally between sites. The highest level at which count data are stored.

WeBS sub-site A grouping of *sectors* within a *site* to facilitate coordination. In most cases, sub-sites also relate to biologically meaningful units for describing *waterbird* distribution.

WeBS-Year Defined as July to June inclusive, the WeBS-Year is centred on the time when most *waterbird* species are present in largest numbers, during *winter*. Counts during *autumn* passage and *spring* passage the following calendar year are logically associated with the intervening *winter*.

Wetlands International A leading global non-profit organisation whose mission is to sustain and restore wetlands, their resources and biodiversity for future generations through research, information exchange and conservation activities, worldwide. www.wetlands.org

Wildfowl & Wetlands Trust (WWT) Founded in 1946, WWT is the largest international wetland conservation charity in the UK. WWT works to conserve wetlands and their biodiversity, focusing on waterbirds and their habitats. It seeks to raise awareness of the value of wetlands, the threats they face and the actions needed to save them. www.wwt.org.uk

Appendices

APPENDIX 1. INTERNATIONAL & NATIONAL IMPORTANCE

Any site recognised as being of international ornithological importance is considered for classification as a Special Protection Area (SPA) under the EC Directive on the Conservation of Wild Birds (EC/79/409), whilst a site recognised as an internationally important wetland qualifies for designation as a Ramsar site under the Convention on Wetlands of International Importance especially as Waterfowl Habitat. Criteria for assessing the international importance of wetlands have been agreed by the Contracting Parties to the Ramsar Convention on Wetlands of International Importance (Ramsar Convention Bureau 1988). Under criterion 6, a wetland is considered internationally important if it regularly holds at least 1% of the individuals in a population of one species or subspecies of waterbird, while criterion 5 states that any site regularly supporting 20,000 or more waterbirds also qualifies. Britain and Ireland's wildfowl belong, in most cases, to the northwest European population and the waders to the east Atlantic flyway population (Wetlands International 2006).

A wetland in Britain is considered nationally important if it regularly holds 1% or more of the estimated British population of one species or subspecies of waterbird, and in Northern Ireland important in an all-Ireland context if it holds 1% or more of the estimated all-Ireland population.

The 1% thresholds for British, all-Ireland and international waterbird populations, where known, are listed in Table A1. Thus, any site regularly supporting at least this number of birds potentially qualifies for designation under national legislation, or the EC Birds Directive or Ramsar Convention. The international population for each species and subspecies is also specified in the table. However, it should be noted that, where 1% of the national population is less than 50 birds, 50 is normally used as a minimum qualifying threshold for the designation of sites of national or international importance.

It was agreed at the meeting of the Ramsar Convention in Brisbane that population estimates will be reviewed by Wetlands International every three years and 1% thresholds revised every nine years (Rose & Stroud 1994; Ramsar Resolution VI.4). 1% thresholds have not been derived for introduced species since protected sites would not be identified for these birds.

Sources of qualifying levels represent the most up-to-date figures following recent reviews: for wildfowl and waders in Britain see Musgrove et al. (2011); for gulls in Britain see Banks et al. (2007); for all-Ireland importance see Crowe et al. (2008). International criteria follow the revised population estimates of Wetlands International (2012).

It should be noted that for some populations, where the British total is the international total, the precise figure given for the estimates may differ because of different rounding conventions applied in the relevant publications.

Table A1. 1% thresholds for national and international importance

	Great Britain	all-Ireland	International	Subspecies/Population
Mute Swan: *British*	740	n/a	320	Britain
Irish	n/a	110	100	Ireland
Bewick's Swan	70	*20	220	*bewickii*, NW Europe (non-br)
Whooper Swan	110	130	270	Iceland (br)
Bean Goose: *Taiga*	*4	+	420	*fabalis*
Bean Goose: *Tundra*	*3	+	5,500	*rossicus*
Pink-footed Goose	3,600	+	3,500	Greenland, Iceland (br)
European White-fronted Goose	*24	+	12,000	*albifrons*, Baltic-North Sea
Greenland White-fronted Goose	130	110	240	*flavirostris*
Greylag Goose: *Iceland*	850	50	980	*anser*, Iceland (br)
British/Irish	1,400	?	?	*anser*, Britain/Ireland
Barnacle Goose: *Greenland*	580	90	710	E Greenland (br)
Svalbard	330	+	300	Svalbard (br)

	Great Britain	all-Ireland	International	Subspecies/Population
Dark-bellied Brent Goose	910	+	2,400	*Bernicla,* W Siberia (br)
Light-bellied Brent Goose: *Canada*	*7	220	400	*hrota,* Ireland (non-br)
Svalbard	*34	+	75	*hrota,* Svalbard, N Greenland (br)
Shelduck	610	150	3,000	NW Europe (br)
Wigeon	4,400	820	15,000	NW Europe (non-br)
Gadwall	250	20	600	*strepera,* NW Europe (br)
Teal	2,100	450	5,000	NW Europe (non-br)
Mallard	6,800	380	**20,000	*platyrhynchos,* NW Europe (non-br)
Pintail	290	20	600	NW Europe (non-br)
Garganey	+	+	**20,000	W Africa (non-br)
Shoveler	180	25	400	NW & C Europe (non-br)
Red-crested Pochard	+	+	500	C Europe & W Mediterranean
Pochard	380	400	3,000	NE & NW Europe (non-br)
Tufted Duck	1,100	370	12,000	NW Europe (non-br)
Scaup	52	*45	3,100	*marila,* W Europe (non-br)
Eider	550	*30	10,300	*mollissima,* NW Europe[1]
Eider: *Shetland*	55	+	85	*faeroensis,* NW Europe[1]
Long-tailed Duck	110	+	16,000	W Siberia, N Europe (br)
Common Scoter	1,000	230	5,500	*nigra*
Velvet Scoter	*25	+	4,500	*fusca,* Baltic, W Europe (non-br)
Goldeneye	200	95	11,400	*clangula,* NW & Central Europe (non-br)
Smew	*2	+	400	NW & C Europe (non-br)
Red-breasted Merganser	84	*35	1,700	NW & C Europe (non-br)
Goosander	120	+	2,700	*merganser,* NW Europe[2]
Red-throated Diver	170	*20	2,600	NW Europe (br)
Black-throated Diver	*6	*1	3,500	*arctica*
Great Northern Diver	*25	?	50	NW Europe (non-br)
Little Grebe	160	25	3,900	*ruficollis*
Great Crested Grebe	190	50	3,500	*cristatus*
Red-necked Grebe	*1	?	500	*grisegena,* NW Europe (non-br)
Slavonian Grebe	*11	?	55	*auritus,* NW Europe (large billed)
Black-necked Grebe	*1	?	2,100	*nigricollis,* Europe, N Africa
Cormorant	350	140	1,200	*carbo,* NW Europe
Shag	1,100	?	2,000	*aristotelis*
Little Egret	45	?	1,300	*garzetta,* W Europe, NW Africa
Grey Heron	610	30	2,700	*cinerea,* W Europe, NW Africa (br)
Moorhen	3,200	?	**20,000	*chloropus,* Europe, N Africa (br)
Coot	1,800	330	17,500	*atra,* NW Europe (non-br)
Oystercatcher	3,200	680	8,200	*ostralegus,* Europe, NW Africa
Avocet	75	+	730	W Europe (br)
Ringed Plover	340	150	730	*hiaticula,* Europe & N Africa (non-br)
Golden Plover	4,000	1,700	9,300	*altifrons,* Iceland & Faeroes, E Atlantic[3]
Grey Plover	430	65	2,500	E Atlantic (non-br)
Lapwing	6,200	2,100	**20,000	Europe (br)
Knot	3,200	190	4,500	*islandica*
Sanderling	160	65	1,200	E Atlantic, W & S Africa (non-br)
Purple Sandpiper	130	*35	710	*maritima,* E Atlantic
Dunlin	3,500	880	13,300	*alpina,* W Europe (non-br)[4]
Ruff	*8	+	12,200	W Africa (non-br)
Jack Snipe	1,000	250	20,000	NE Europe (br)
Snipe	10,000	?	**20,000	*gallinago,* Europe (br)
Woodcock	14,000	?	**20,000	Europe (br)
Black-tailed Godwit	430	140	610	*islandica*
Bar-tailed Godwit	380	160	1,200	*lapponica*
Whimbrel	*1	+	6,700	*islandicus*
Curlew	1,400	550	8,400	*arquata*
Spotted Redshank	*1	+	850	Europe (br)
Redshank	1,200	310	2,400	*robusta*[5]
Greenshank	*6	*20	2,300	Europe (br)
Green Sandpiper	*9	?	15,500	Europe (br)
Common Sandpiper	*1	?	17,300	N, W & C Europe (br)
Turnstone	480	120	1,400	*interpres,* NE Canada, Greenland (br)

Table A1. continued

	Great Britain	all-Ireland	International	Subspecies/Population
Little Gull	?	?	1,100	N, C & E Europe (br)
Black-headed Gull	22,000	?	**20,000	N & C Europe (br)
Common Gull	7,000	?	16,400	*canus*
Lesser Black-backed Gull	1,200	?	5,500	*graellsii*
Herring Gull	7,300	?	10,200	*argenteus*[6]
Great Black-backed Gull	760	?	4,200	NE Atlantic
Kittiwake	?	?	**20,000	*tridactyla*, E Atlantic (br)
Sandwich Tern	?	?	1,700	*sandvicensis*, W Europe (br)
Common Tern	?	?	1,800	*hirundo*, S, W Europe (br)
Little Tern	?	?	190	*albifrons*, W Europe (br)
Black Tern	?	?	7,500	*niger*

?   *Population size not accurately known.*
+   *Population too small for meaningful figure to be obtained.*
*   *Where 1% of the British or all-Ireland wintering population is less than 50 birds, 50 is normally used as a minimum qualifying level for national or all-Ireland importance respectively.*
**   *A site regularly holding more than 20,000 waterbirds qualifies as internationally important by virtue of absolute numbers.*

1   Following the recommendations of Scott & Rose (1996) and Furness *et al.* (2010), Common Eiders *Somateria mollissima* on Shetland are treated as a separate population from those elsewhere in Britain, and are now treated as such by Wetlands International (2012).

2   Wetlands International (2012) considers Goosanders breeding in Scotland, northern England and Wales to be a discrete population. However, a review of available data by DEFRA's SPA and Ramsar Scientific Working Group found limited evidence to support this conclusion, and recommended that for site-selection purposes, British Goosanders continue to be considered as a component of the NW and C European population of Goosander, with an international 1% threshold of 2,700.

3   Three populations of Golden Plover listed by Wetlands International (2012) overlap in the UK in winter. Draft guidelines from Ramsar suggest that the largest of the three thresholds (*i.e.* that for *altifrons,* Iceland & Faeroes, E Atlantic) should be used for site-selection purposes.

4   Whilst several populations of Dunlin occur in the UK at different times of the year, most wintering birds are referable to the listed population.

5   Three populations of Redshank listed by Wetlands International (2012) overlap in the UK in winter: *totanus* E Atlantic (non-br), *robusta* and *brittanica*. Most *totanus* winter outside the UK but the other populations are known to occur widely. Draft guidelines from Ramsar suggest that the larger of the two thresholds (*i.e.* that for *brittanica*) should be used for site-selection purposes.

6   Two populations of Herring Gull overlap in the winter in the UK; *argentatus* and *argenteus*. Whilst substantial numbers of *argentatus* appear to winter in the UK, the largest proportion of Herring Gulls in winter is probably of *argenteus*. Following Ramsar guidance and given the conservation status of British-breeding Herring Gulls, the threshold for *argenteus* is used in this report for site-selection purposes.

Table A2 provides details of principal WeBS sites mentioned in the Principal Sites table (Table 6.). Sites are listed alphabetically with details of the central Ordnance Survey 1-km square. Numbers following Principal Core Count sites refer to the sites' location in Figure A1. Details of all WeBS sites are available from www.bto.org/webs or the WeBS Office (see *CONTACTS*).

Table A2. Details for Principal Sites mentioned in Table 6. Numbers refer to the sites' location in figure A1.

Site	1-km sq	
Abberton Reservoir	TL9618	111
Alde Complex	TM4257	104
Alt Estuary	SD2903	85
Arun Valley	TQ0314	120
Baleshare	NF7862	18
Balnakeil Bay	NC3869	9
Balranald Nat. Res.	NF7169	15
Beaulieu Estuary	SZ4297	126
Belfast Lough	IJ3983	73
Blackwater Estuary	TL9307	110
Breydon Water & Berney Marshes	TG4706	99
Broubster Leans	ND0361	10
Burry Inlet	SS5096	138
Cameron Reservoir	NO4611	40
Carlingford Lough	IJ1814	77
Carmarthen Bay	SN2501	139
Carsebreck and Rhynd Lochs	NN8609	45
Chew Valley Lake	ST5659	135
Chichester Harbour	SU7700	122
Cleddau Estuary	SN0005	140
Colne Estuary	TM0614	109
Cotswold Water Park (West)	SU0595	136
Cromarty Firth	NH7771	26
Crouch-Roach Est.	TQ9895	105
Dalreoch	NN9917	46
Deben Estuary	TM2942	106
Dee Estuary England and Wales	SJ2675	89
Dee Flood Meadows	SJ4059	90
Dengie Flats	TM0302	112
Dornoch Firth	NH7384	29
Duddon Estuary	SD2081	80
Dungeness GPs	TR0619	119
Dyfi Estuary	SN6394	141
Eden Estuary	NO4619	39
Exe Estuary	SX9883	132
Fleet and Wey	SY6976	131
Forth Estuary	NT2080	48
Gadloch	NS6471	52
Hamford Water	TM2225	103
Hickling Broad	TG4221	96
Holburn Moss	NU0536	61
Hornsea Mere	TA1846	83
Hule Moss	NT7149	59
Humber Estuary	TA2020	84
Inner Firth of Clyde	NS3576	50
Inner Moray and Inverness Firth	NH6752	28
Island of Egilsay	HY4831	1
Isle of Coll	NM2055	24
Kentra Moss and Lower Loch Shiel	NM7168	25
Kilconquhar Loch	NO4801	42
Lake of Menteith	NN5700	49
Langstone Harbour	SU6902	123
Lavan Sands	SH6474	142
Lee Valley GPs	TL3807	102
Lindisfarne	NU1041	62
Loch An Eilein	NL9843	22
Loch Bee	NF7743	17
Loch Bhasapoll	NL9746	21
Loch Eye	NH8379	30
Loch Fleet Complex	NH7896	27
Loch Garten	NH9718	36
Loch Gorm	NR2365	55
Loch Gruinart Floods	NR2766	56
Loch Hempriggs	ND3447	12
Loch Ken	NX6672	64
Loch Leven	NO1501	43
Loch Lomond	NS3599	51
Loch Paible	NF7168	14
Loch Riaghain	NM0347	23
Loch Sandary	NF7368	16
Loch Scarmclate	ND1859	11
Loch Slapin	NG5516	19
Loch Spynie	NJ2366	31
Loch Tullybelton	NO0034	47
Loch a`Phuill	NL9541	20
Loch of Boardhouse	HY2625	4
Loch of Harray	HY2915	7
Loch of Hundland	HY2926	3
Loch of Lintrathen	NO2754	38
Loch of Skaill	HY2418	5
Loch of Skene	NJ7807	35
Loch of Stenness	HY2813	8
Loch of Strathbeg	NK0660	32
Loch of Swannay	HY3128	2
Lough Foyle	IC5925	71
Loughs Neagh& Beg	IJ0475	72
Lower Derwent Ings	SE6939	82
Lower Lough Erne	IH0960	79
Lower Teviot Valley	NT6725	58
Medway Estuary	TQ8471	114
Mersehead RSPB	NX9255	66
Mersey Estuary	SJ4578	88
Middle Yare Marshes	TG3504	98
Milldam & Balfour Mains Pools	HY4817	6
Moine Mhor & Add Estuary	NR8293	53
Montrose Basin	NO7057	37
Morecambe Bay	SD4070	81
Nene Washes	TF3300	92
North Norfolk Coast	TF8546	95
North West Solent	SZ3395	127
Orchardton and Auchencairn Bays	NX8151	65
Orwell Estuary	TM2238	107
Ouse Washes	TL5394	93
Outer Ards Shoreline	IJ6660	76
Outer Loch Indaal	NR2353	54
Pagham Harbour	SZ8796	121
Pegwell Bay	TR3561	116
Pitsford Reservoir	SP7870	100
Poole Harbour	SY9988	130
Portsmouth Harbour	SU6204	124
R Clyde: Carstairs to Thankerton	NS9841	57
Ribble Estuary	SD3825	87
R.Avon: Fordingbr'- Ringwood	SU1410	128
R.Avon: Ringwood- Christchurch	SZ1499	129
R.Nith: Keltonbank – Nunholm	NX9774	67
R.Tay: Haughs of Kercock	NO1339	44
Rutland Water	SK9307	91
Rye Harbour and Pett Level	TQ9418	117
Severn Estuary	ST5084	137
Slains Lochs (Meikle, Sand & Cotehill)	NK0230	33
Solway Estuary	NY1060	69
Somerset Levels	ST4137	134
Southampton Water	SU4507	125
St Benet's Levels	TG3815	97
Stour Estuary	TM1732	108
Strangford Lough	IJ5460	74
Swale Estuary	TQ9765	115
Taw-Torridge Est.	SS4731	133
Tay Estuary	NO4828	41
Tees Estuary	NZ5528	70
Thames Estuary	TQ7880	113
The Wash	TF5540	94
Traigh Luskentyre	NG0599	13
Tring Reservoirs	SP9113	101
Tweed Estuary	NU0052	60
Upper Lough Erne	IH3131	78
Upper Quoile River	IJ4745	75
Walland Marsh	TQ9923	118
Wigtown Bay	NX4456	63
WWT Caerlaverock	NY0565	68
WWT Martin Mere	SD4214	86
Ythan Estuary	NK0026	34

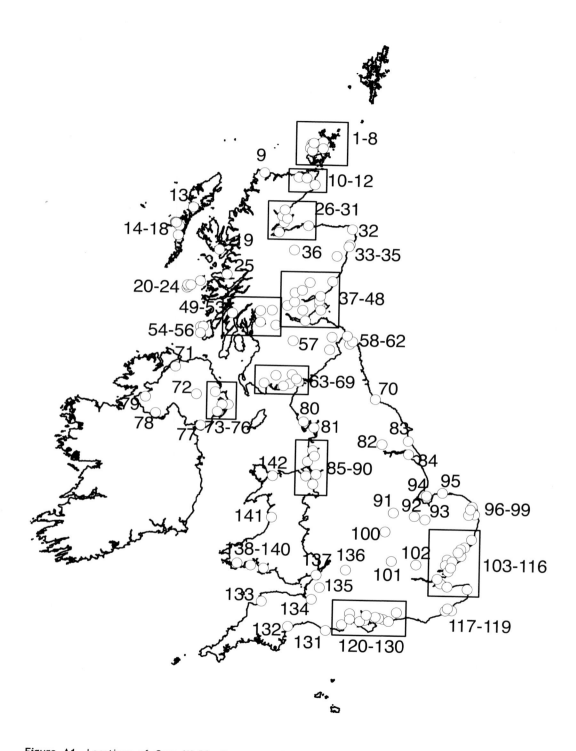

Figure A1. Locations of Core WeBS sites supporting more than 10,000 waterbirds or which support internationally important numbers of one or more waterbird species (see *PRINCIPAL SITES*). Numbers refer to sites listed in Table A2.